published by Duke University Press

positions east asia cultures critique

volume 6   number 3   winter 1998

empires of hygiene

T. Watanabe

Contents

Guest Editors' Introduction

Following the example set decades ago by Foucault, critical studies of medicine, health, and disease have become important subfields in history, anthropology, and the humanities. But these incursions into the domain previously monopolized by biomedical research have opened and occupied a contested and unstable ground. Perhaps the moral freight attaching to medical positivism—the widely held view that only scientifically verifiable knowledge is an ethical foundation for clinical intervention—has led to especially intense anxieties about the power of history, anthropology, and textual criticism to relativize contemporary truths. New visions of the medical past and respectful accounts of nonbiomedical healing traditions have, for some, threatened to undermine confidence in the march of science toward truth, as well as encouraged those needing sound medical care into the pathways of error and mysticism.

However, with the growth of social and critical studies of science over the

positions 6:3 © 1998 by Duke University Press.

last two decades and an attendant decline in the popular prestige of American and European health-care delivery systems, it has proven impossible to contain the scandal of critical study of medicine, disease, and health-care institutions. There have been numerous approaches to opening "medicine" — that diverse and overflowing category — to scholarly examination. Ethnographic strategies have attempted to remove nonbiomedical healing methods from the realm of the exotic — which can be seen as harmless at best — while treating sites at the heart of the bioscience enterprise as "other cultures." Historical approaches have uncovered debates that reveal the arbitrary and contingent roots of scientific method, as well as events that demonstrate the complicity of scientific practice with forms of domination and exclusion. Some of these approaches have brought together the methods of anthropology and history in studies of colonial medicine and disease. Such studies of European expansion have gone beyond demonstrating that medicine has often been a tool of empire to show that events and institutions also dominate materially, transforming bodily life. As a consequence, historical change in many domains ramifies into developments in the worlds of medicine (and vice versa, of course). A narrow history of medicine — seen as an autonomous domain with its own developmental trajectory — has become unjustifiable.

Research in the humanities has been innovative as well, undertaking new readings of canonical texts to show how writing on illness and representations of medical treatment work as alibis for other, more profound disruptions and dominations. Scholars have also turned to new bodies of literature, finding interpretive riches in the life histories of patients and health-care workers that unsettle both bland narratives of objectivity and overwrought tales of heroism and salvation. Even philosophers have begun to expand their traditional interest in the ethical issues raised by medical practice, turning to a consideration of ways in which medicine in practice challenges the assumptions of ethical theory itself.

Taken together, critical research in the human sciences on medicine, health, and disease has opened a window on the social (and the "naturalized") that has begun to overcome classical divides between subjective humans and objective facts, historical error and contemporary verities, scientific empiricism and humanistic interpretation, metropolitan expertise and peripheral backwardness. The recent volume of essays *Framing Disease: Studies in Cultural History*, edited by Charles Rosenberg and Janet Golden, is one example of this research trend, showing that disease can be a subject of cultural histories in Europe and the United States. The present collection of essays both benefits from these exciting trends and contributes to them with carefully theorized empirical studies of medicine and disease in Asia.

Borrowing from Michael Bourdaghs's essay, we have titled this issue "Empires of Hygiene." The essays that are included, which draw on and advance the projects referred to above, show that ultimately the empirical cannot be separated from the imperial; in other words, fact cannot be separated from rule. And medicine, the worldwide craft of healing, is always in some sense a hygiene, that is, an effort to discipline the unruly forces of nature and culture into the pathways of the—presumed to be—proper, orderly, and normative.

Not one but several empires are at issue in this collection: two studies of medical imperialism—by Philippa Levine and Warwick Anderson—are the most obvious examples. These essays directly tackle empire by documenting respectively the disciplinary health work the British colonial administration undertook in Hong Kong and the Straits Settlements in the latter half of the nineteenth century, and the U.S. government's colonial project carried out in the Philippines in the first two decades of the twentieth century. Both authors draw on a number of important works in the expanding domain of colonial and postcolonial studies for their analyses of imperial hygiene; they simultaneously shift the focus away from India and Africa to the Pacific Rim, where such scholarship has just begun to emerge.

Thomas Lamarre's study of Mori Rintarō's writing subtly examines the early development of imperial themes in Japan. Lamarre considers Mori's science and strategy, poetry and patriotism, in a nonreductionist discussion that links Meiji state building with such seemingly mundane biomedical issues as the nutritive properties of rice. In his counterreading of the novelist Shimazaki Tōson's *Broken Commandment*, Michael Bourdaghs adopts a more deconstructive method to explore the kind of bodily management that accompanies and is presupposed by the novelist's own imperial nationalism. The earliest study we have included, that of Marta Hanson, examines the process through which a broad medical innovation was assembled in nineteenth-century imperial China; she shows how physicians in the Jiangnan region contentiously promoted local knowledge and even imagined local bodies and thus implicitly made claims against the state-sanctioned universal orthodoxy of the Qing intellectual empire. Hugh Shapiro's investigation of spermatorrhea in Republican China, by contrast, depicts a disintegrating empire with parallel anxieties over personal sovereignty and the forms of discipline (or consumption) that might remedy a faltering self-rule.

Nathan Sivin's commentary does not address questions of political empire but rather reviews the contours of medical history; by arguing that several modes of historical research are converging in the history of medicine in Europe and in China, he suggests that the disciplinary rule that is characteristic of each is bound to change—he envisions, if not upheavals of empire, at least a revolution in the empirical.

All of these essays are ambitious. As historical studies, they seek expanded frontiers of both topic and method, transgressing and supplementing not only the standard categories of disciplines, politics, and nations but also the more naturalized notions of disease and the body. The concepts of disease that are developed here link individuals to society, colonizers to the colonized, and the empirical to the imperial along a spectrum from the disease that is somatically suffered to that which is culturally codified. Anderson and Levine, for example, turn their attention to leprosy and STDs, diseases that have specific cultural histories and biomedical identities in Western settings but which emerge in these studies as inseparable from certain colonial regimes. Hanson and Shapiro, by contrast, attend to indigenous Chinese disease categories—warm-factor disorders (*wenbing*) and spermatorrhea (*yijing*)—that cannot be easily reduced to a biomedical disease or diagnosis but which illuminate specific intersections between the individual, the environment, and the imperial formation or nation-state. In their innovative rereadings of well-known works of modern Japanese literature, Bourdaghs and Lamarre expand the notion of disease from the biomedical and cultural to the political and theoretical. Bourdaghs sees Japanese nationalism and imperialism as a kind of disease as he examines why the novelist Tōson associated modern hygiene with warfare, and tuberculosis with the marginalized *burakumin* social group. Through Mori Rintarō's writing, Lamarre pushes the term further by exploring both the analogy between, and the simultaneous creation of, bacterial cultures and linguistic colonies. His tracing of a natural-cultural network that links theories of language; Koch's bacterial cultures; Meiji military science; nutritional research on rice; Japanese imperial policies in China, Taiwan, and Korea; and various poems and novels brings to our attention a new, disseminated "body" that is afflicted with a much broader form of disease.

The other essays also reexamine the taken-for-granted body. Levine, in her study of contagious diseases ordinances and the debates surrounding them, describes nothing less than "the codification of female sexuality in the British colonial context"; she links questions of sexuality with those of race in ways that colonial studies have illuminated in other contexts. Anderson's nuanced untangling of the imagination of the modern citizen in an American-administered leper colony in the Philippines similarly reveals the arrogance of government in colonial peripheries as lepers on a barren island are trained in "civic responsibility" to become model citizens while they are simultaneously recast as medical subjects of a treatment that now seems barbaric. It involves little intellectual effort simply to add "disease stigma" to the litany of race, class, gender, and sexual orientation when speaking of systems of domination. But both the Anderson and Levine essays go further by also taking up the more fundamental question (for medical cultural studies) of collaborations between the unassailable norms of modern hygiene and the forms of violence that are typical of colonial governance and which tend to be performed on the bodies of the governed.

Oddly, it has been harder to sustain the insight that modern healing involves "some powerfully coercive mechanisms for negating [individual] liberty in practice" (Levine) than to admit the collusion of colonialism with (hetero)sexism and racism. Studies such as these make this point unequivocally and in fascinating historical detail; by doing so, they begin to interrogate the foundations of all modern authority in specifically disciplined bodies (see especially Anderson's conclusion).

Marta Hanson's meticulous study of the emergence of a new school of thought in nineteenth-century Jiangnan is a fine example of China-centered history (Paul Cohen's term). Like the best of this now established genre, it demonstrates the liveliness and complexity of intellectual politics in the Qing. She shows not only that history is full of contention but that much of that contention is over historiography. Thus, her focus on prefaces to medical works supports her argument that it was in these prefaces themselves that one of the most important schools of medicine in the Qing (whose diagnostic methods and therapies are still practiced today) came into being. But she goes further than this, subtly drawing out not just a local intellectual tradition but local bodies, not just a historiography but what might be called a specific physiography of China and the Chinese. Far from supporting recent assertions about Chinese "racism," Hanson's pioneering work demands that "local biologies" (Margaret Lock's term) be investigated with sensitivity to the debates within which the substance of embodiment is brought into question.

Just as Hanson has turned intellectual and social history into a study of a specific and embodied sense of place, Hugh Shapiro analyzes the masculine-gendered and embodied experience of a particular historical moment. Shapiro's study captures the male body suffering from loss of control over reproductive capacity—the disease of spermatorrhea—at the same time that the Chinese Republic (1912–1949) is in disarray. Shapiro argues that understanding spermatorrhea requires imagining how people experienced illness in early China. Tracing yijing to late antiquity, he shows that it erupted in the wake of exhausting lapses of self-possession. He insightfully links the disorder—and the attendant loss of self-control—to ideas that were prominent in the imagination of the late imperial era, such as sexual violation by demons. To explain the prevalence of this age-old disorder in the twentieth century, he untangles a complex skein of influences: the rise of the pharmaceutical industry, competing medical frameworks, sexually transmitted diseases, and the transformation by imperialism of fundamental aspects of self-understanding. By mapping the changing epidemiology of spermatorrhea, Shapiro illuminates two important trends of the period: the lived experience of downward mobility in a context of fierce economic competition and the rise of the discourse of nerves in Chinese medicine.

The "body" is important even in the most "literary" of these studies, Michael Bourdaghs's reading of *Broken Commandment*. Insofar as writers and readers share the common ground of a situated style of embodiment, representations of hygiene can be read for the mundane disciplines that are both taken for granted and advocated in fictional works. Like the tropes of time and space that have been more extensively studied in literary criticism, the disciplined body forms one of the conditions that make modern writing and reading possible.

All of these historical studies, then, exemplify the ease with which cultural history moves across domains to develop productive juxtapositions and newly useful comparisons. This fluidity of motion across boundaries is perhaps best figured in both the work of Mori Rintarō and Lamarre's Latourian reading of his corpus. Latour's research on modern science and technology upsets the usual conceptions of modernity by challenging the contested boundary between normal sciences and all other forms of knowledge. Lamarre's reading of Mori, in turn, disrupts a certain nationalist account of Japanese modernity that sees it in terms of an insular national subjectivity that is opposed to the West and offers in its stead a logic of hybridity. As Bourdaghs also shows, hybridization may not only better explain modernity but also be one of the unacknowledged means through which empire establishes its reality.

Taken together, these essays not only problematize healing and the body for Asian studies, they challenge commonsense assumptions about the natural fixity of disease and the universality of medical knowledge. As scholarship turns both to the historical topics and sources Nathan Sivin discusses at length in this issue's commentary, and to imaginative representations of hygiene and suffering in literary and artistic texts, the old—can one call them modernist?—boundaries of medicine and disease are shifting both epistemologically and institutionally. The essays in this issue help to put such broad national and global changes in a perspective that may not be comforting but surely is exhilarating.

Judith Farquhar and Marta Hanson, Guest Editors

Robust Northerners and Delicate Southerners: The Nineteenth-Century Invention of a Southern Medical Tradition

Marta Hanson

In what ways did the Chinese conceptualize human diversity before the twentieth century? During the past decade, scholars have increasingly addressed this question by studying constructions of ethnicity during the Qing dynasty (1644–1912). The foreign Manchu rulers, for example, systematically codified cultural, linguistic, and ethnic difference to reinforce their ideology of universal emperorship over all peoples within the empire.[1] Despite assimilation between Manchus, Mongols, and Chinese Bannermen, however, there were limits to complete sinification.[2] Several scholars have studied how the Manchus and other ethnic groups within and along China's frontiers formed ethnic identities; one historian has even argued that the Qing state promoted a discourse on race as early as the Qianlong reign (1736–1795).[3]

Two problems arise related to this academic discussion on ethnicity and race. First, the Chinese did not think about human difference in the biolog-

positions 6:3 © 1998 by Duke University Press.

ical, essentialist, and evolutionary terms of the modern conception of race until Western influence became dominant after the turn of the century. Before 1895, the year when Darwin's views on evolution first influenced the political writings of the Chinese scholar Yan Fu (嚴復), the modern biological—and still at times evolutionary—conception of race can do nothing to illuminate pre-twentieth-century history when retrospectively projected as a catchall category onto indigenous Chinese discourses regarding human variation.[4] Second, scholars have not systematically examined indigenous naturalistic conceptions of difference. Chinese explained human diversity in cultural and ecological rather than biological terms by employing an ancient concept of resonant and not deterministic local *qi* (*diqi* 地氣 or *tuqi* 土氣).[5] Physicians, in particular, used this conception of local qi to explain regional differences between peoples living within China's borders and the different therapies local practitioners recommended to treat them.

This article discusses medical explanations of regional body types, which I believe have broad implications for how to approach Chinese explanations of difference between themselves, as well as their conceptions of the other and, later, of race. I approach these implications somewhat indirectly by giving an account of the invention of one of the most recent and important branches of Chinese medicine still practiced. This new medical tradition focused on acute fevers the Chinese called warm-factor disorders (*wenbing* 溫病).[6] First some background.

A Brief History of Chinese Medicine

The Chinese regard for classical precedent has often prompted a picture of medicine as a static art, its doctrines perfected early and merely elaborated later. Actually, Chinese medical doctrines changed regularly, perhaps more so than those of premodern Europe. Up to the end of the Ming dynasty (1368–1644), two canonical medical texts from the Han dynasty (221 B.C.E.–220 C.E.) established the foundation for all later developments: *The Inner Canon of the Yellow Emperor: Basic Questions and Divine Pivot* [*Huangdi neijing: Suwen, lingshu* 黃帝內經素問·靈樞, prob. first century B.C.E.] and *The Treatise on Cold Damage and Miscellaneous Disorders* [*Shanghan zabing lun* 傷寒雜病論, 196–220 C.E.]. Traditionally, the Chinese have considered

bones (*gusuan*) as a symptom of jing decrement.[23] Zhang Ji, in the late second century, observes that head chills (*touhan*) and hair loss (*faluo*) are signs of seminal loss.[24] Because the head is the most *yang* part of the body, it cools with the loss of jing. Loose teeth and buzzing in the ears (*erming*) are other common symptoms of shen depletion. Volition rises from the shen,[25] which might pertain to postcoital exhaustion.[26] The signs of sexual excess are first seen in the shen. Its association with sexuality in modern times is captured by an exchange in 1933 between an American neuropsychiatrist and a Chinese patient: Physician: "Is your disease connected with sex?" Patient: "Of course. My kidney (shen) is weak."[27] In Joseph Needham's words, the shen is "as much sexual as excretory."[28]

To summarize, understanding yijing requires imagining how people got sick in early China: it erupted in the wake of exhausting lapses in self-control.

Modern Formulations

By the fourteenth century, the medical shape of yijing had nearly crystallized into the form it would retain until the early twentieth century. Its most influential articulation is found in the writings of Zhu Zhenheng (1281–1358), one of the "major theorists of the last millennium."[29] Zhu Zhenheng, known also as Danxi, names four sources of the disorder, which have been cited for centuries.[30] The first, "excessive mental exertion" (*yongxin guodu*), which causes "seminal emission" (*shijing*), draws, I suspect, on the *Suwen*'s "longing without end," but it is a notion with a fundamentally different nuance. The second cause, "unsatisfied lascivious thought" (*si seyu busui*), which causes "the jing to leak out" (*jing er chu*), reads similarly to the *Suwen*'s "that which one seeks is unattainable." The third source, "too much sex" (*yu taiguo*), which causes "the semen to flow uninterrupted" (*huaxie bu jin*), reminds us of excessive venery. The fourth cause, "abstinence when in life's prime" (*niangao qisheng jiuwu seyu*), is novel: it causes "the *jingqi* to overflow" (*jingqi manxie*).[31] This last cause—sexual deprivation—is important, for it suggests that sexuality itself was not inherently anathema to physical well-being. And from the late Song period (twelfth century), doctors observed that sex in moderation was not necessarily damaging.[32] However, that the other sources of yijing would be influenced by the *Suwen* makes sense, for Danxi lived in an era of intensive analysis of classical texts.[33] But there is a profound difference in his conceptualization: the psychological origins of the sickness are given much broader significance. In brief, sixiang becomes the dominant image of the disease.

"The illness is in the heart," writes Danxi; it "arises from sixiang."[34] Sixiang retains much of its early sense of longing; more than two hundred years later, a young man dies from *sixiang*, that is, from longing, in the legendary novel *The Golden Lotus* [*Jin ping mei*].[35] But Danxi's use of the notion hints at a broader trend in Chinese medicine. During the late twelfth and early thirteenth century, there was a growing emphasis on the emotions as a source of illness. Linked to this trend was the rise of the discourse of Fire (*huo*), a concept that becomes ubiquitous, along with Water, in the medicine of the late imperial era.[36] In one sense the mechanism of Fire is physiological; the dynamic of yijing's eruption provides a good example of this sense. In what can be described as a classic sequence, strenuous mental work (*yongxin guodu*) —from too much study, for example—strains the cardiac envelope, the *xinbao*, which is associated with mental activity. Overheated in this way, the xinbao ignites a pathological Fire, generating a heat differential between the visceral systems, one that scorches the shen. As the renal system heats up, the jing liquefies and flows from the body. Ultimately, the Fire destroys the seminal essence.

Fire is also a medium through which the emotions move about the body. Wild emotions—burning anger, for example—assume material form as the pathogen *huoxie*, which roams and settles in the body. The discourse of Fire, the emphasis on emotions, and yijing become interconnected with another important phenomenon in Chinese medicine: dreams (*meng*). Danxi gives dreams special prominence by calling the disorder *mengyi*, or "dream emissions."[37] Li Ting (fl. 1570), the renowned Ming physician, explains mengyi this way: "That which the heart longs for during the day will be emitted at night during dreams."[38] Dreams come to be understood as one origin of the pathogen Fire. Upsetting dreams disturb the soul (*ganhun*), which generates the Fire, causing unwilled emission. Dreams thus cleave yijing into two distinct maladies that afflict different parts of the body and call for different treatments. Yijing occurring in the absence of dreams (*yijing wumeng*) calls for the fortification (*bu*) of the depleted renal system. Yijing occurring with dreams (*yijing youmeng*), on the other hand, requires the dispersal of this fire (*qinghuo*), which is first stirred up by a disturbed soul.[39]

Dreams have too complex a genealogy in Chinese medicine to be dealt with here. Let me simply emphasize one aspect of dreams that is germane to the changing social identity of the yijing sufferer. In the late imperial period, from roughly 1500 to 1850, the disorder came to be associated with people bearing heavy psychological or mental burdens, such as scholar-officials or busy merchants, for this reason: dreams beset the overstimulated mind. Harmful dreams were the product of restless sleep, and uneasy sleep afflicted the person with overactive thoughts. While the person apparently slumbered, the feverish mind kept working. Danxi's yongxin guodu came to describe the mental exhaustion afflicting the person who read too much or delved too deeply into thorny problems. Usually it was the clever and shrewd who experienced the disorder; rarely the rustic and ignorant. This was the conclusion of the celebrated late Ming physician Zhang Jiebing in the seventeenth century.[40]

But there is a pejorative aspect of the restless mind that produces dreams: lack of focus. Not only is this person overstimulated, he is devoid of resolve. Lacking discipline, his thoughts wander too freely in the realm of the imagination. In the 1680s, Chen Shiduo, the early Qing physician, profiled mengyi sufferers as "those restless youth" who:

lose themselves in desultory reading, or ponder sexuality, or gratify themselves by manually loosening their seed, or abandon themselves to the reveries of writing with no thought for the consequences, or tossing and turning in bed, go out into the night trawling for women and, losing their sense of chastity, surrender to lust, until their urethra will not close . . . and the seminal essence spills out until they are dead.[41]

This passage describes a floating world of bookish swains—unserious, unattached, adrift without purpose. Aimless in life, those youth who would die from mengyi are muddled; they lose track of the basic distinctions that keep people both healthy and civilized. Day blurs into night until all sense of regimen is lost. Reading should be directed and not include bawdy novels.

Writing should be constructive, not pornographic. Everything is mixed up. Here the dream is metaphoric. The phrase *zuisheng mengsi* (drunk in life, dying in a dream) describes exactly this aimlessness that dulls acuity, confuses the mind, squanders vitality. This profile of the unvigilant person with dispersed concentration is related to another theme in late imperial medicine: visitation by demons, a phenomenon also intertwined with spermatorrhea.

Danxi observes that the popular locution for spermatorrhea is "sexual intercourse with demons in dreams" (*yemeng guijiao*).[42] Wang Kentang (1549–1613), one of the foremost medical writers of the late Ming, devotes an entire chapter to treatments for victims of sexual intercourse with demons.[43] One way to think about this phenomenon is in terms of susceptibility. Just as some people are susceptible to hypnosis, it was often the mentally hazy, or the unguarded, who fell prey to sexual violation by demons. Predation by demons was especially damaging because the ejaculations, as in yijing, were unwilled and uncontrolled, something that since the Tang (618–907) has been understood as profoundly more damaging than normal emissions.[44] The theft of qi by sexual vampires was dangerous for the same reason. Though distinct from yemeng guijiao, qi theft occurred under similar circumstances: it was the unwary, the cloudy-minded, or the drugged who fell for the wiles of qi-thieving mystagogues. Victims of these misfortunes—of yemeng guijiao, qi theft, and yijing—shared in common a loss of self-awareness. The masterworks of late imperial fiction provide vivid illustrations.

Four chapters of the Ming novel *Yesou puyan*, by Xia Jingqu, are devoted to a Taoist's scheme for stealing qi from unwitting donors.[45] Li, a benign qi vampire, selects as his prey a traveler with no strict destination. Li lures the traveler into his home and instructs his concubines to ply him with wine, potency drugs, and sexual favors. The concubines work up the victim by taking turns licking his penis. When the hostage is sufficiently aroused, they prop him up to a wall, alert the master, and fit the man's jade stalk through a hole in the wall. On the other side waits Master Li, who envelopes the traveler's yang member in his mouth and inhales. "The sperm ducts open immediately and the sperm gushes out." Li "finishes sucking the sperm of the torpid victim" and orders the concubines "to arouse him and induce him to generate more for further consumption."[46] The use of wine and drugs to break down resistance recalls the *Suwen*'s advice against entering the bedchamber intoxicated. The theme is resonant: the loss of self-control is catastrophic. I can think of no clearer presentation of this idea than in the sexual gluttony of the *Jin ping mei*'s Ximen Qing.

Ximen Qing devotes himself to sex singlemindedly. Yet he remains relatively healthy. Only when he is exhausted, asleep, and an overdose of aphrodisiac is forced down his throat (making him unconscious, yet erect) and a starved Pan Jinlian mounts him insatiably, does he ejaculate to death. After his violently spurting semen runs dry, the body's final reservoir of vitality—blood—opens and seeps away.[47] He is wholly depleted. His penis, however, remains grotesquely frozen in an erection, which "kept on squirting nothing but cold air until the ejaculatory motion stopped."[48] His destruction illustrates, too, the body's hierarchy of energetics and its transmutation of raw energy into spirit: air ⇒ food ⇒ saliva ⇒ blood ⇒ semen (jing) ⇒ qi ⇒ spirit (*shen*).[49] The extraordinary abuse of his body that reversed this process, breaking down and liquefying his constituent parts, occurred only during an episode of drugged exhaustion, when Ximen Qing was devoid of self-consciousness and vulnerable.

Jia Rui, too, was delirious, "mistaking the false for the real," when he ejaculated to death in the monumental eighteenth-century novel *The Story of the Stone* [*Honglou meng*].[50] In contrast to the anesthetized Ximen Qing, a skein of pressures reduced Jia Rui's defenses: sexual deprivation, a night of exposure, the suspicion of pederasty, a drubbing by his grandfather, ten days' worth of study being crammed into one, being doused with excrement, insomnia from humiliation, anxiety over debt, self-abuse, and heartbreak. Having fallen ill, Jia Rui sank into a delirium. It was in those helpless moments that a Taoist manipulated him into an erotic hallucination. Jia Rui probably would have survived had he retained some sense of self and held back a bit. But desperately ill and starved for physical affection, he completely lost control. Abandoning himself to the vision, Jia Rui died in a cold puddle of his own semen.[51]

The epic novels were integral to the social life of the period. Those who did not read the great novels grew up hearing their plots from storytellers, seeing them performed on the operatic stage, or worshiping deities inspired by their characters.[52] Still, some will ask, despite the evidence of these literary masterworks and the writings of respected physicians, did people in late imperial China truly believe that a person could die from the spontaneous emission of semen, as was said to have happened to Ximen Qing and Jia Rui? To answer this question, we turn to the most famous case of yijing in the twentieth century, which involved China's last adult emperor, Guangxu, who died in 1907.

Spermatorrhea killed Guangxu, not assassins. So suggest the emperor's medical records, which are held in the First Historical Archives in Beijing.[53] Although these documents do not absolve those excoriated figures so often associated with Guangxu's death—the dowager, the eunuchs, Yuan Shikai—they do provide an archetypal case history of yijing, circa 1900. According to the "Records of the Pulse," a sickly childhood predisposed the emperor to illness. The informal histories (*yeshi*) add that promiscuity in youth further weakened his constitution. In adulthood, full-blown yijing ravaged the frail emperor.[54] During his last year alive, Guangxu pondered his decrepit frame: "Over the last twenty years of my illness with spermatorrhea, attacks occurred more than ten times a month. . . ." Winter aggravated the affliction, and then it "erupted spontaneously in the absence of dreams."[55] Foreign physicians summoned from the Legation Quarter, such as the French doctor Detheve, confirmed the Chinese physicians' diagnosis of spermatorrhea.[56] (This was a diagnosis that also reflected the concerns of European medicine.)[57] Court intrigue aside, spermatorrhea was familiar enough to be recorded as the official cause of death. Yet yijing was not an imperial disease. Throughout the Qing period (1644–1911), physicians wrote about spermatorrhea in the same proportion as they wrote about other diseases.[58] On the eve of the Republic, quite simply, yijing was recognized as a widespread and dangerous affliction.

Women's bodies also contained the vital essence jing, and as with men, it was regulated by the shen and could be enhanced or diminished. But women fade from the medical discussions of these disorders early on, except as their source—that is, as the depleting object of man's uncontrolled desire and expenditure. Sex, however, was but one cause. Anxiety, physical labor, irregular regimen, sexual deprivation, losing oneself in art, mental over-stimulation, aimless imaginings, pining away for a desired object, and dis-

Figure 3 From *Shenbao*, 3 February 1933, 19.

turbing dreams were other types of experience that provoked the disorder. Rooted in thinking about the relation of vitality to hygiene, the disorder revealed attitudes of how people should conduct themselves.

The Republic (1912–1949)

During the Republic, spermatorrhea became "perhaps the most obsessive theme of medical literature on sex."[59] The ubiquity of its image in the mainstream press is striking. The following drug promotions, published between 1933 and 1935, typify the pitch made for treating yijing and related illnesses from the 1920s to the late 1940s.[60]

"Do you lose precious semen just from sleeping?" asks an ad for Spermin. "Worry no more. This medicine controls nocturnal emissions by thickening the blood and constricting the spermaduct, which makes it difficult for the vital essence to leak out" (fig. 3). A skull and crossbones augurs the demise of those who would ignore the disorder. By contrast, the advertisement for medications to treat opium addiction depicts the addict as wearing a cangue but surviving.

The text of another Spermin ad is representative of the message:

> When weakness of any nature reaches an extreme point, just take a dose at night and you will slip into a deep sleep, enjoying peace of mind. Worry no more about losing your precious semen just from sleeping. Shesheng Ling specially controls yijing that occurs when dreaming or spontaneous emission in the absence of dreams. If you face this condition each time you sleep, then take a tablet. It generates strength in your body proportional to the amount taken. This medicine will not upset digestion nor arouse your energies in the slightest. Taken every four hours, this valuable product will never disappoint.

Showing off its French origin, the ad notes: "An explanation in Chinese is included."[61]

The man in figure 4 experiences erotic dreams. The ad queries: "Is seminal emission something that can be left to take its natural course?" Answer: "Failure to treat is fatal." To convey the morbidity of the disorder, it cites a report from the *Paris Health Journal*: in 1929 alone, 2,079 people died of yijing.

Lower-back pain (*beitong*) figures prominently in renal stress, for the lower back cradles the kidney. This explains in part the popularity of Doan's Backache Kidney Pills (fig. 5). Medical advertisements (*guanggao*) of this sort dominated the big dailies and stressed the expediency, privacy, and economy of self-therapy.[62]

In figure 6, Shou Er Kang (Longevity and Health), a German product, offers rescue from the death sentence of kidney disorder (*shenbing*). "Impotence (*yangwei*), premature ejaculation (*zaoxie*), spermatorrhea (*yijing*), and sore back (*yaotong*) all originate with renal deficiency (*shenkui*)!"[63] In addition to bracing up sexual function, Longevity and Health vows

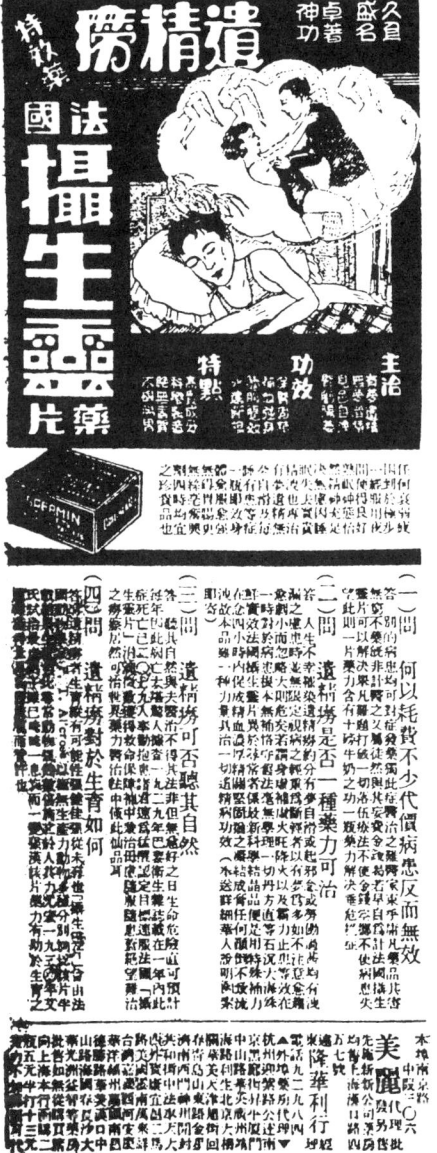

Figure 4 From *Shenbao*, 5 November 1934, 17.

Figure 5 From *Shibao*, 7 June 1924, 10.

to "nourish (bu) the blood, nourish the brain (*nao*), and nourish the renal system."

This last promise, of feeding the brain to enhance its health and power, is conspicuous. Unlike the brain-centered view of the body in the West, traditional Chinese physiology viewed the gray matter with relative disinterest. In the normal working of the body, the brain was judged a minor organ. The emergence of the brain as an object of therapy in modern China can be attributed in part to the influence of Western medicine and its anatomical visualization of the body. The dissected torso of figure 7 illustrates the trend. More critical for understanding changes in thinking about yijing, however, was the influence of Western medicine's analysis of seminal emission, which was distinctly encephalocentric. Excessive expenditure of bodily fluids caused the "whole brain" of the eighteenth-century sufferer to dry up until it was "heard to rattle in the pericranium." Or these people simply "go mad."[64] By the nineteenth century, spermatorrhea's influence "upon the

Figure 6 From *Shenbao*, 29 January 1935, 14.

brain is well attested,"[65] provoking a canvas of distress from "headaches" and "strange sensations at the top of the head"[66] to "insanity" and "mental derangement"[67] (though some argued that seminal emission was both cause and effect of nervous disease).[68]

Contemporary studies of what has been called spermatophobia[69] in the West generally trace the anxiety to Tissot's mid–eighteenth century *Onanism*[70] or to Lallemand's articulation of spermatorrhea in the first quarter of

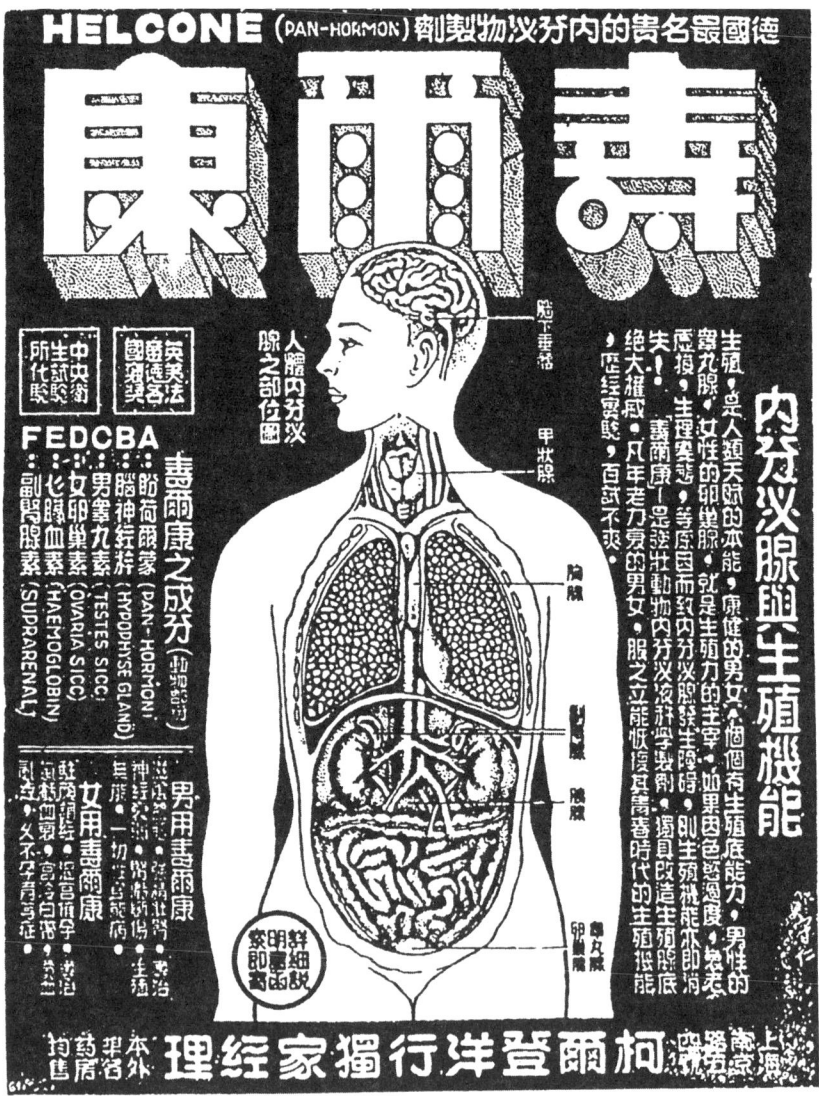

Figure 7 From *Shenbao*, 22 June 1934, 17.

the nineteenth century.[71] But the problem needs more careful explication, for this anxiety—and its connection to the brain—runs deep in the Western imagination, perhaps to the fourth century, when victims fell "stupidly silent" and became "dull,"[72] and maybe even earlier, to the Galenic corpus.[73]

However, and this is important, while the brain was peripheral to the concerns of traditional Chinese medicine, it has been important in pharmacology and sexology in China since the early imperial era. Here, I will only draw attention to "circulating the seminal essence and replenishing the brain" (*huanjing bunao*), a technique of qi transformation in which the brain performs a critical function.[74] In physiological alchemy, the adept experiences stimulation without emission (*dong er bu xie*).[75] The retained semen becomes an energized force that fuels an alchemical reaction in the body: the energized semen transmutes into qi which, circulating (*huan*) through the body, ascends to the brain, where it mingles with and expands the spirit (shen).[76] What is important to this discussion is the explicit association of the renal system, and qi, with the brain, the "ball of mud" (*niwan*) (see fig. 8).[77] This connection of the kidney to the brain is just one example of a traditional source for a modern synthesis, one suggesting that the introduction of Western biomedicine into China was not simply a question of technology transfer.

While certain Western ideas of hygiene that were imported into China resonated with traditional therapies, others were grafted onto preexisting concepts. The Chinese name for Spermin is a good example: *shesheng* refers to the *yangsheng baoyang* tradition of cultivating vitality.[78] The negotiated transfer of Western medicine into China is complex.[79] An important aspect of this transfer was the marketing of foreign drugs, as is illustrated by the ad for Shou Er Kang, or Helcone (Pan-Hormon), in figure 7. This ad promotes hormonal treatment for a spectrum of conditions: anemia, neurasthenia, renal deficiency in men, infertility in women. The ad's "Chart of the Body's Glands" indicates the sites where the ingested hormone would take action. Prior to synthesization, hormones were chemically isolated from glandular tissue. In early Western endocrine therapy, animal tissue, such as cow thyroid, was itself desiccated and consumed.[80] This seems to be the idea of Shou Er Kang. Those ingredients of the pan-hormone that are

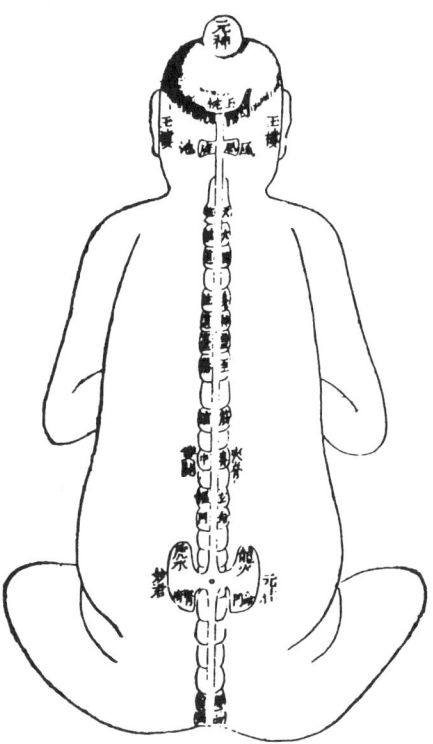

Figure 8 *Fanzhao tu*. From Yin Zhenren, *Xingming guizhi* [The gnomon of life] (1615).

"animal part" (*dongwu bufen*) are listed bilingually at the left of the ad, under the letters A to F. But the translations are ambiguous. They give the impression that the hormones have been extracted from human glands. For example, *nan gaowan su* (C) and *nü luanchao su* (D) refer plainly to human testes and human ovaries. ("Testes sicc," under [C], could refer to substances derived from either human or animal tissue). However, another reading of animal could be this: animal (including human) as opposed to botanical or synthetic. In that case, the pan-hormone was being marketed as a drug derived from human tissue. The ad would then be playing off the notion of the body as the best medicine, in which a specific body part is consumed to fortify that same part of the body.[81] To give the product a genuine feel, the ad utterly transforms the idea of this particular form of hormonal therapy.

Ads such as this clearly had an audience in mind. The contrast between the images of sexual reverie used to market a French product and those of science and anatomy used to sell a German one stands out and suggests one popular view of French and German culture in this period. To some urban-ites, these guanggao provided entertainment.[82] Others responded to their message. In 1909, the Imperial Post Office attributed a surge in mailed parcels to extensive medical advertising and the purchase of nostrums via the post.[83] This apparent dread of sickness can be explained concretely: debilitating illness pervaded life in early-twentieth-century China. Tuber-culosis, small pox, diphtheria, cholera, typhus, gastrointestinal disorders, and ascariasis was endemic, venereal infection was epidemic, and plague infested certain regions of the country. Despite this range of menacing dis-orders, yijing ranked among the most commonplace disorders discussed in the press and analyzed in the medical literature. Physicians not only diag-nosed and treated spermatorrhea, patients brought to hospitals their tribu-lations of failed treatment with injections, pills, washes, electric belts, and hypnosis.[84]

Our question thus becomes more complex: why, in an environment of contagion, did spermatorrhea emerge as a dominant image of disease? The first reason is profit.

Profitization of Medicine

In the infected metropolis, medicine was tremendously profitable.[85] Late Qing society, too, had invested significantly in "diet, medicines and health generally,"[86] but the scale of the Republican medical industry, and the inter-dependence of pharmaceutical houses, hospitals, practitioners, and newspa-pers, was unprecedented. Critics savaged the dailies as pandering to adver-tisers,[87] and one veteran reporter of the period dismissed the "medical supplement" as invented solely to inveigle readers (*pian ren*) into swallow-ing medicine.[88] Drug firms employed in-house doctors to prescribe company products,[89] and leading hospitals adopted questionable treatments to maintain market share.[90]

For an industry absorbed by profit, yijing provided a useful category of illness. Not least of all, the malady was familiar. Urbanites who were conversant in the language of traditional medicine recognized the graphic tales of spermatorrhea that were spun in the press or analyzed in medical handbooks.[91] Spermatorrhea was also symptomatically vague. Common sensations such as headache or back pain could fall under its expansive rubric. As a disorder, moreover, yijing flared up with little provocation, and once experienced, it was hard to uproot. Hence, the sickness required long-term attention and a steady consumption of medicine.

Without question, the web of interests that were dependent on the burgeoning patent-medicine industry exploited the latent concerns of a public acutely aware of the visible dangers of infectious disease and progressively aware of the invisible, microscopic world of contagion.[92] The rampant commercialization of medicine, however, is only part of the reason for spermatorrhea's apparent prevalence during the Republic. Though pharmaceutical companies cashed in on people's uneasiness over sickness, the industry, as much as it tried, had not invented these anxieties. Venereal infection in particular ranked high among urban anxieties, for by most estimations, venereal disorders plagued both city and countryside.[93]

Venereal Disease

Many of the cases understood as yijing were almost certainly incidences of gonorrhea. In traditional medicine, analyses of yijing have been grouped together with the emission (*lin*) ailments.[94] Keeping "substances that belong within the body from escaping" was perceived as "a single activity of the healthy body."[95] For this reason, both the involuntary loss of semen and urethral discharges of a bacterial source fell under the same heading. Nosological convention, therefore, depicted emission disorders to a certain degree as "treatable by the same methods regardless of the substance involved."[96] Those philters promising to cure the gamut of emission disorders thus conformed to this tradition of classification. Even fear-mongering ads presented gonorrhea, and syphilis, as among the "five emissions" (*wulin*).

Appealing to the fastidious consumer, of course, preoccupied the pharmaceutical houses. By deploying the language of emission, treatments for venereal infection put a socially tolerable face on disturbing disorders. While implicitly sexual in nature, spermatorrhea was not venereal per se. Although a serious disorder, it contaminated the victim with little of the polluting stigma of more troubling diseases. Nor was it contagious. Still, profit motive aside, the vocabulary of depletion applied generally both to yijing and to venereal infection. To physicians and patients of the period, gonorrhea was described as *linbing*, the affliction of emission. The acute awareness of yijing, moreover, influenced the actual experience of venereal infection. In 1932, a patient, born in 1891, was positively diagnosed with chronic gonorrhea. However, the man suffered the prototypal signs of vital-essence deficiency: ringing ears, sore bones, lower-back pain, uneasy sleep, exhaustion.[97] Ambiguities in diagnosis were complicated further by the competing medical systems of the period.

Competing Medical Frameworks

When patients described the symptoms of seminal depletion to foreign and foreign-trained Chinese doctors, the complaints were routinely traced to organic sources. In the absence of an organic source, these specialists, trained to recognize disorders formulated in Europe and North America, chose a neuropsychiatric label. As we know, patients suffering kidney disorders articulated a constellation of symptoms. However, if no material origin for the complaints could be discovered, patients were generally referred to neuropsychiatry. In rare cases, biased by the habitus, attitude, or class background of the patient, complaints such as sibilations in the head (*erming*) were interpreted as auditory hallucinations; this contributed to a diagnosis of schizophrenia.[98] More commonly, neuropsychiatry in China traced these complaints to patient regimen or hypochondria. I will give one example.

In 1935, at the Peking Union Medical College, then China's foremost institution of Western medicine, a twenty-one year-old man complained of chronic lethargy and listlessness, due, the patient stated, to uncontrolled seminal emissions.[99] Referred to neuropsychiatry, that department traced the complaint to undereating and devised a course of treatment to stimulate the young man's appetite. Over nine days, the patient was given fifty injections of insulin, for insulin lowers the blood sugar and can theoretically generate hunger. The patient was then discharged without incident. His spermatorrhea was only diagnosed three years later, in 1938, when he returned to the same hospital as an outpatient. At that time, a urologist prescribed for the patient's chronic disorder a common sedative, potassium bromide, to be taken at night before sleep.[100] As to why the outpatient staff of the PUMC diagnosed spermatorrhea, the record is silent. We do not know whether they merely conspired to satisfy an obstinate patient or whether urology was more in tune with a patient population that generally understood its symptoms as manifestation-type disorders within the traditional medical styles of diagnosis.

Yet this much is clear: this man's drawn-out bout with the disease points to a shift in the experience of yijing during the early twentieth century. The disease could be outlasted. While death remained a threat, it no longer dominated the concerns of the afflicted. Increasingly, in popular and medical discussions, the menace of spermatorrhea lay not in its power to kill but rather in its capacity to cripple. Anxiety regarding the disorder turned toward the unpredictable way that it weakened the body.

The Body Politic and the Biological Body

Such individual foreboding about the weakened body fit broader speculations regarding masculinity. The waning national strength that had permitted nearly a century of encroachment by Europeans, Japanese, Russians, and Americans was traced not merely to weakness but to the physical weakness of men in particular. One solution: fortify the sickly bodies. A 1918 piece in the May Fourth journal *New Youth*,[101] the most influential forum of the period, specifies the form of masculinity Chinese youth should fashion.[102] Whereas the old-style gentleman slouched, shook his head, and wore hoof-shaped sleeves, the new man strides in leather shoes. Instead of savoring Shaoxing's effeminate wines, the robust man smokes cigarettes, drinks whiskey, and wears a trenchcoat—hard symbols of the Western male. Too much study, some argued, had enfeebled China's youth, turning their hands "white and slender."[103] In short, foreign aggression had distorted the male self-image.

This brings me to my next point: the association of national vulnerability with the absence of a vigorous sexuality. "In our China," lamented Lu Xun, the most enduring art is "man transvesting as woman."[104] A female impersonator's "quest to acquire manliness" lay at the core of the 1941 best-selling serial in foreign-occupied Shanghai. Resolution comes only after the performer realizes that "men do not sing female roles."[105] Diffidence in sexuality preoccupied such writers as Lu Xun for, to his mind, sexual ambiguity enfeebled China's chance for survival in the ruthless arena of nations. His remedy: foster sexual aggressiveness. Similar views were popularized by Zhang Jingsheng, China's phenomenally successful sexologist of the 1920s, known to most urbanites at the time as "Dr. Sex." The basic problem, Dr. Sex asserted, was that the Chinese man was not masculine, Chinese sex organs were not fully developed, and the Chinese body itself was inadequate and required thorough reconstruction. The rebuilt "hypermasculine" male would be endowed with a large nose, broad shoulders, and sturdy genitalia.[106]

In Zhang Jingsheng's vision of brawny replicants we see a preoccupation with frailty that concerned not only the biological body but the body politic, a weakness that was at once physical and national. The West's violent humiliation of China provoked a deep sense of shame, and, now, public discussions of the era never seem entirely free from a nagging sense of inadequacy. The new anatomy fantasized by Dr. Sex was unmistakably a Western body. Advertisements for products such as Spermin and Longevity and Health strongly suggest that Western-made hormones were being sold to treat Chinese male anxieties and symptoms of inferiority vis-à-vis images of Western men. The ads thus hint at not only the transfer of Western biomedical ideas into China by grafting them onto similar indigenous ideas but also the material transfer of Western "male" hormones into the Chinese body. The weak Chinese male imbibes Western-made Spermin not only to secure his vitality and increase his virility but also to save his life and, by extension, that of the nation.

The notion that national weakness generated a degraded sense of self is not only found in the works of sexologists and writers, though authors wrote forcefully about this issue.[107] Medical case histories of the era also show the entanglement of sexual anxiety with political collapse. In 1937, a thirty-three-year-old engineer who worked at Japan's Manchoukuo Electric Company in China's occupied northeast sought treatment for insomnia, poor memory, and cloudy thinking.[108] Especially alarming were his frequent nocturnal emissions and confusing dreams associated with weakness in his lower extremities. The patient volunteered his own diagnosis: guilt for working in occupied territory and frustration at being unable to move his family from a part of China occupied by the Japanese army. He insisted that he was not a traitor.

Drug vendors had exploited the association of personal weakness with national crisis since the twilight of the Qing.[109] By the 1930s, Emperor Guangxu's reputed death by seminal depletion had worked its way into the pharmaceutical narrative. In large characters, a 1934 ad for Spermin announces: "The Former Qing Emperor Guangxu Expired from Yijing" (fig. 9). Reaching for the sacerdotal image of the imperial household, the ad insinuates that the health of the realm can be measured by a leader's potency.[110] It also plays off Guangxu's sexual excess in youth (his "sexual suicide"), alleged by the informal histories, casting Guangxu as the licentious ruler who indulged in private life at public expense and thus perished ignominiously.[111] But more than presenting Guangxu as the infirm leader of a withering state, the ad yokes together images that express the changing epidemiology of yijing.

At the center of the ad, askew, appears one page of classical prose, torn from the apocryphal *Yuwan xiongjin*. It opens by telling of Guangxu's illness and of rare treatments ministered by celebrated physicians. But nighttime ravaged the emperor, who failed "to evade the grip of the illness." The passage disposes of the emperor and moves on to the narrator's own search for an elixir—a journey that led him to Shanghai, a city "so vast that nothing is too odd to be found there." The narrator suspects his quest will be thwarted by rampant quackery: "Shanghai's pharmaceutical market has long lost credibility." But a trusted friend, after a prodigious hunt, discovers the French product Shesheng Ling. For one month, the grateful narrator swallowed "only" three bottles of Spermin, yet the drug's efficacy surpassed all expectation. He gained fifteen pounds, could walk ten *li* without tiring, and

Figure 9 From *Shenbao*, 16 March 1934, 19.

though working (*laodong*) day and night, outperformed all the rest. In the market economy of Chinese cities, in other words, Spermin was the stuff a person needed to survive. Most striking about this ad is its promise to counteract a specific type of debilitation engendered by yijing: the inability to work.

Living at the Margin

Yijing sapped energy that was perceived as indispensable for survival in a rapidly changing economy. During the 1920s and 1930s, the special circumstances of Beijing, the city for which we have the most detailed case histories of yijing, aggravated the economic uncertainty of life in the Republic. It is difficult to know whether Chinese society in the 1930s was more dangerous for the unprotected or more chronically miserable for the poor than, for instance, Chinese society in the 1860s. And I am not arguing that the adversities facing Beijing residents were more severe than in other cities. Yet Beijing does illustrate, starkly, the pressures on lower social groups, especially the keen competition for work, during this period of China's modern history.

First, Beijing was at the intersection of bitter rivalries between warring militarists.[112] From the city's hinterland, endemic warfare drove a shattered rural populace, defeated soldiers, and inflation into the city. Second, although the Qing state collapsed in 1911, many dependents of the empire had not been forced en masse into the market economy of the city until the early 1920s.[113] Third, the removal of the capital from Beijing to Nanjing by the new Nationalist Government in 1928 deprived the city (renamed "Beiping") of revenue and decimated the service trades. Fourth, Beijing's gender imbalance intensified the contest for work, for the city carried "a great preponderance of males."[114] Fifth, the invasion of China's northeast in 1931 by Japan's renegade Kwantung Army swelled Beijing with refugees.[115] Finally, the eruption of full-scale war between China and Japan in July 1937 accelerated the city's decline. The web of misery expanded beyond the normally vulnerable social groups; disaster ruined families that traditionally had been insulated from social chaos by walled compounds, personal connections, and material resources.[116]

This expansion of misery is discernible in the city's medical record. Rising TB rates in the mid-1920s were attributed to the declining fortunes of bannermen.[117] In the 1930s, practically for the first time, the city's affluent began showing up in the psychopathic hospital, driven there by destitution and other forces. The patient population of the city's psychopathic hospital was extremely complex and defies easy profiling. Yet one experience of the group stands out: economic calamity. Staff psychiatrists routinely identified the loss of money as the precipitating factor in mental disturbance.[118] People who had lost money, often small amounts —to pickpockets, gambling, cons, or bad loans—appeared to suffer the cumulative effects of living with meager resources in an environment of scarcity. Even more devastating than losing money was losing work. And the tragedy of unemployment, in complex ways, was tied up with the experience of spermatorrhea.

An exhausted man could not work, and an unemployable man lacked value. Men already living near the social margin complained conspicuously of yijing. For downwardly mobile men, stripped of all resources, yijing threatened to destroy their only remaining asset—literally, the seminal qi—which gave vitality to their bodies. For these men, the ability to work represented their most relevant connection to society. Labor surplus on top of material scarcity had created a demographic context in which people worked for less than subsistence wages.[119] Yijing undermined the ability to perform labor, and in an environment of intense competition, the disorder threatened to make these men redundant. An unemployed sufferer of spermatorrhea was asked by a doctor in 1934 what constituted happiness. The patient, stricken also with gonorrhea, responded: "A strong body."[120] To the twenty-nine-year-old, the future looked forbidding; maimed by yijing, he wondered aloud if he had enough strength to meet it.[121]

More generally, the commonness of yijing during the Republic might be linked to the precariousness of city life. According to medical records of the period, men who in some way had already been diminished experienced the disorder acutely. Men who had suffered humiliation, endured imprisonment, clashed with superiors, contracted disease, watched their families fall apart, suffered intimidation by coworkers, or been caught up in a riot, would present themselves at hospitals, describing the ruinous effects of yijing. To the unprotected, the city represented constant danger. Routine exposure to market forces, to the power of local authority, to organized or random violence, translated into incarceration, unemployment, debt, penury, hunger, death. The idea of yijing was one way to rationalize the anxiety and impotence of living vulnerably in this menacing environment every day.

The sheer insecurity of city life, I would argue, generated a specific symptomatology. Poverty produced its own delirium; powerlessness, debilitating humiliation; venomous political conflict, paranoia. The perception that the weakness engendered by yijing struck at a person's final reserve in a scramble for survival hints at the causality between environment and experience, or in Arthur Kleinman's words, the "dialectic between symptom and society."[122] For people near the margin, the 1930s were years of economic depression, civil war, foreign invasion, and political terror. In this setting, yijing became homologous with shrinking opportunity and the destruction of the self.

The Discourse of Nerves

Traditionally, spermatorrhea struck the educated and the comfortable. Beginning in the 1920s, however, people from these backgrounds began complaining less of the disorder while those from poorer backgrounds complained of it more. While yijing's association with sex remained—perhaps grew even more prominent—its relation to exertion changed fundamentally. Less and less was it associated with the overexertion of thinking or lifting heavy objects. Instead, it became a condition specifically inhibiting physical labor. In short, a new social identity of the disease had emerged.

The most obvious explanation for this shift is the changing practice of medicine. In China, as elsewhere, elite hospitals attempted to reach poorer groups; thus, a greater range of patients were picked up than in the traditional record. But this explanation is incomplete. To this, I would add the contiguity of yijing to the sexually transmitted diseases. This contaminating proximity, combined with the disorder's growing association with the socially marginal, contributed to an image of yijing that was more negative than anything witnessed in the traditional era. Growing distaste for the disorder could be interpreted as one index of changing identities among urban groups, especially a nascent middle class.[123] A 1995 conversation in a Shanghai pharmacy drove home the idea that this disorder remains associated with low social status. Looking through the array of treatments for yijing and related afflictions, I asked the pharmacist: who generally purchased the products? The pharmacist responded, a bit disgusted, "Only day workers, with their lousy bodies" [*Dagong de, shenti hen chade ren*].

But there was a more dramatic development during the Republic related to the changing identity of yijing: the rise of the discourse of nerves. Understood as a depletion disorder since late antiquity, medicine in China had come to describe spermatorrhea as a deep-seated constitutional disorder arising from weakened nerves. This shift is remarkable: the "nervous system," as such, only entered Chinese medical discourse in the last half of the nineteenth century. *Shenjing* (nerves) quite simply do not have antecedents in traditional Chinese medicine.[124] How do we explain the process whereby the nervous system became the new substrate for an age-old depletion disorder? How do we explain the transposition of a discourse of qi into the language of nerves? One answer lies in the enormous impact of the foreign disorder neurasthenia, which means debilitated nerves, or exhausted nervous force. Neurasthenia, without roots in Chinese society, found especially fertile soil in China. As in Japan and in the West, neurasthenia, translated as *shenjing shuairuo*, took hold among the educated. Concrete manifestations of its influence were seen in the coining of neologisms for yijing. In the early 1930s, physicians at the Shanghai Hospital for the Insane reworded yijing into neurasthenia's homophone: *shenjing shuairuo* (debilitation of the renal system).[125] In this same period, yijing was reformulated into the foreign category "sexual neurasthenia" (*xing shenjing shuairuo*).[126] Yet a larger question remains to be answered: whether neurasthenia in China represents a new disease or merely a different way of discussing the old depletion disorder yijing. This question is central to understanding the modern transformation of the Chinese body.

Glossary

baiyin	白淫
banchan louxia	半產漏下
beitong	背痛
bing zai xin	病在心
bu	補
Chen Shiduo	陳士鐸
dagongde shenti hen chade ren	打工的身體很差的人
Danxi	丹溪
dong er bu xie	動而不泄
dongwu bufen	動物部份
erming	耳鳴
faluo	髮落
fanzhao tu	反照圖
fawei jinwei	發為筋痿
ganhun	肝魂
guanggao	廣告
Guangxu	光緒
guijiao	鬼交
gusuan	骨痠
ha lo	哈囉
Honglou meng	紅樓夢
Huangfu Mi	皇甫謐
huanjing bunao	還精補腦
Hua Tuo	華佗
huaxie bujin	滑泄不禁
huo	火
huoxie	火邪
Jingyue quanshu	景岳全書
Jia Rui	賈瑞
jing	精
jing er chu	精而出
jingqi manxie	精氣滿泄
Jin ping mei	金瓶梅

jiwei baiyin	及為白淫
Kaitai shinsho	解體新書
lao	勞
lao	癆
laodong	勞動
laolin	勞淋
laoxin	勞心
lao zhi wei bing	勞之為病
linbing	淋病
Lingshu	靈樞
Li Ting	李梴
loujin tu	漏盡圖
Lu Xun	魯迅
meng	夢
mengyi	夢遺
nan gaowan su	男睪丸素
nao	腦
niangao qisheng jiuwu seyu	年高氣盛久無色欲
niwan	泥丸
nü luanchao su	女卵巢素
pian ren	騙人
Qianlong Yuyong Shengjing Dan	乾隆御用生精丹
qinghuo	清火
renzao zilai xue	人造自來血
rufang taishen	入房太甚
shen	腎
shen	神
Shenbao	申報
shenbing	腎病
shenkui	腎虧
shenjing	神經
shenjing shuairuo	神經衰弱
shenjing shuairuo	腎經衰弱
Shesheng Ling	攝生靈

shijing	失精
shishou	失守
Shou Er Kang	壽爾康
si	思
si seyu bu sui	思色慾不遂
sixiang chengbing	思想成病
sixiang wuqiong	思想無窮
Sugita Gempaku	杉田玄白
sui	髓
suoyuan bude	所願不得
Suwen	素問
Tang Zonghai	唐宗海
touhan	頭寒
Xiehe yiyuan	協和醫院
Ximen Qing	西門慶
xinbao	心包
xing shenjing shuairuo	性神經衰弱
Xin qingnian	新青年
Wang Kentang	王肯堂
wulin	五淋
wumeng zihua	無夢自滑
wuqi ze si	無氣則死
Xia Qingqu	夏敬渠
Xue Ji	薛己
yang	陽
yangsheng baoyang	養生保養
yangwei	陽痿
yaotong	腰痛
yemeng guijiao	夜夢鬼交
yeshi	野史
Yesou puyan	野叟曝言
Yibu quanshu	醫部全書
yijing	遺精
yijing lao	遺精癆
yijing wumeng	遺精無夢

yijing youmeng	遺精有夢
yin	淫
yiyin yuwai	意淫於外
yongli juzhong	用力舉重
yongxin guodu	用心過度
yu taiguo	慾太過
zang	藏
ze shang shen	則傷腎
Zhang Ji	張機
Zhang Jiebin	張介賓
Zhang Jingsheng	張兢生
Zhu Zhenheng	朱震亨
zaoxie	早泄
zongjin shizong	宗筋弛縱
zuisheng mengsi	醉生夢死

Notes

I thank Shigehisa Kuriyama for his expert and generous help in preparing this essay; Judith Farquhar and Marta Hanson for their critical reading and extremely valuable comments; Philip A. Kuhn for his very careful reading of an early version; and Robin D. S. Yates for his highly constructive discussion of the paper at the New England Conference of the Association for Asian Studies, where it was first presented. The excellent comments of the anonymous reviewer were also extremely helpful. I received financial support from the Harvard-Yenching Institute and the University of Nevada, Reno, while conducting this research.

Figures 2 and 8 in my essay are reprinted from Joseph Needham's *Science and Civilisation in China*, vol. 5, by permission of Cambridge University Press. (See list of abbreviations below for full bibliographical information.)

The following abbreviations appear in the text:

JHMAS	*Journal of the History of Medicine and Allied Sciences*
LS	*Huangdi neijing zhangju suoyin: Lingshu* (Taipei: Qiye Shuju, 1987)
SCC 5.5	Joseph Needham, *Science and Civilisation in China*, vol. 5, *Chemistry and Chemical Technology*, pt. 5, *Spagyrical Discovery and Invention: Physiological Alchemy* (Cambridge: Cambridge University Press, 1983).
SW	*Huangdi neijing zhangju suoyin: Suwen* (Taipei: Qiye Shuju, 1987)
XHYY	*Xiehe Yiyuan* (Peking Union Medical College [PUMC])

YBQS   *Gujin tushu jicheng, yibu quanshu* [Qianlong encyclopedia] (1726; reprint, Taipei: Yiwen Yinshuguan, 1977).

1 The full name of the drug was Spermin Testicle Tablets. A pivotal time in modern China, the Republican era (1912–1949) represents a dynamic, chaotic period between the collapse of the imperial system and the founding of the P.R.C.

2 Of the terms used to describe the unwilled emission of semen—for example, *baiyin*, *shijing*, *mengyi*—I settled on *yijing* because of its common use by physicians and drug houses from the 1920s through the 1940s. One of the earliest uses of the term *yijing* is found in Huangfu Mi's third-century-C.E. *Zhenjiu jiayi jing* (vol. 2, no. 1 (*shang*), p. 6b, reprinted in Kosoto Hiroshi et al., eds., *Toyo igaku zempon sosho*, vol. 7 [Osaka: Toyo Igaku Kenkyukai, 1981], 23 [3rd section]). Defining yijing as spermatorrhea is an approximation, for spermatorrhea is generally understood as semen loss without orgasm. Yijing involves a broader range of experience. The term *spermatorrhea* was coined by Francois Lallemand in *Des pertes seminales involontaires* (Paris: Bechet, 1836).

3 The Babylonian, Hippocratic, and Ayurvedic traditions record a similar syndrome. See Edward Podolsky, "An Assyro-Babylonian Treatise on Diseases of the Male Urinary and Genital Organs," *Annals of Medical History* 3 (1921): 62–63; *Hippocratic Writings*, Regimen 4, trans. J. Chadwick and W. N. Mann (New York: Penguin Books, 1983), 258; Alain Bottero, "Consumption by Semen Loss in India and Elsewhere," *Culture, Medicine, and Psychiatry* 15, no. 3 (September 1993): 303–320; and Lawrence Cohen, "The Epistemological Carnival: Meditations on Disciplinary Intentionality and Ayurveda," in *Knowledge and the Scholarly Medical Traditions*, ed. Don Bates (Cambridge: Cambridge University Press, 1995), 320–343.

4 On *qi* see Benjamin I. Schwartz, *The World of Thought in Ancient China* (Cambridge, Mass.: Harvard University Press, 1985), esp. 179–184, 269–275; Robin D. S. Yates, "Body, Space, Time, and Bureaucracy: Boundary Creation and Control Mechanisms in Early China," in *Boundaries in China*, ed. John Hay (London: Reaktion, 1994), 56–80; Nathan Sivin, *Traditional Medicine in Contemporary China* (Ann Arbor: University of Michigan Center for Chinese Studies, 1987), 237–240; and Onozawa Seiichi, ed., *Ki no shiso* [The idea of qi] (Tokyo: Tokyo University Press, 1981).

5 Charlotte Furth, "Rethinking Van Gulik: Sexuality and Reproduction in Traditional Chinese Medicine," in *Engendering China: Women, Culture, and the State*, ed. Christine K. Gilmartin, Gail Hershatter, Lisa Rofel, and Tyrene White (Cambridge, Mass.: Harvard University Press, 1994), 133.

6 "Without qi, then death" [*Wuqi ze si*]. (LS, *pian* 8, *zhang* 2). The *Yellow Emperor's Classic of Medicine* [*Huangdi neijing*] consists of two separate compilations, the *Suwen* [Basic questions] and the *Lingshu* [The celestial pivot]. These collections—compiled sometime between the first century B.C.E. and the early first century C.E.—draw together the work of many authors

and comprise the most influential writings of Chinese medicine. See Sivin, *Traditional Medicine*, 5 n3.

7 Shigehisa Kuriyama, "Interpreting the History of Bloodletting," JHMAS 50, no. 1 (January 1995): 33.

8 SW, *pian* 1, *zhang* 1.

9 Shigehisa Kuriyama, "Concepts of Disease in East Asia," in *The Cambridge World History of Human Disease*, ed. Kenneth F. Kiple (Cambridge: Cambridge University Press, 1993), 54.

10 This translation of the title is by Joseph Needham (SCC 5.5, 253).

11 "Yousuo yongli judong, ruo rufang guodu . . . ze shangshen" (LS, *pian* 4, *zhang* 1, *jie* 1). See also SW, *pian* 1, *zhang* 4: "Wai bu lao xing yu shi, nei wu sixiang zhi huan."

12 YBQS, 6433a–6433b.

13 Even by the third century B.C.E., *si* connotes a negative preoccupation; it suggests something that a person cannot stop thinking about almost obsessively. See for example, *Lushi chunqiu*, chap. 7, "Mengqiuji, jinsai," in *Lushi chunqiu suoyin* [A concordance to the Lushi chunqiu], ed. D. C. Lau, Chen Fong Ching (Hong Kong: Commercial Press, 1994), 35.

14 SW, *pian* 44, *zhang* 2.

15 The potential harm of *sixiang* is also associated in the *Suwen* with excessive physical exertion: "Wai bu lao xing yu shi, nei wu sixiang zhi huan" (SW, *pian* 1, *zhang* 4).

16 The modern use of *sixiang*—thought, ideology, thinking—contains little of the early sense of yearning or pining.

17 *Baiyin* comes also to represent the discharges of leucorrhea and albumen in the urine.

18 LS, *pian* 8, *zhang* 2.

19 YBQS, 6433a.

20 SCC 5.5, 22, note d. On the shen, see Nathan Sivin, "Physiology and Pathology of the Renal System," in Sivin, *Traditional Medicine*, 226–229.

21 LS, *pian* 8, *zhang* 2.

22 SW, *pian* 1, *zhang* 3.

23 LS, *pian* 8, *zhang* 2.

24 YBQS, 6432b.

25 SW, *pian* 23, *jie* 10.

26 Douglas Wile, *Art of the Bedchamber: The Chinese Sexual Yoga Classics including Women's Solo Meditation Texts* (Albany: State University of New York Press, 1992), 20. Fear, too, reaches the *shen*, this suggests why fright damages the *jing*. See LS, *pian* 8, *zhang* 2.

27 XHYY, case no. 46851, 23. This exchange suggests also the intercultural confusion between patient and doctor in foreign hospitals of the Republican era.

28 SCC 5.5, 22, note d.

29 Sivin, *Traditional Medicine*, 110.

30 YBQS, 6437b.

31. The notion of a healthy person's vitality naturally overflowing dates to late antiquity: for example, "Erba, shenqi sheng . . . jingqi yixie" [At age twenty-eight, when the *shenqi* is flourishing, the *jingqi* overflows] (SW, *pian* 1, *zhang* 3). Unlike Danxi, however, the *Suwen* does not suggest the lack of sex as a source of the condition.

32. But the very need to repeat this message reflects the deep-seated concerns about sexuality.

33. Another contrast: the *Suwen* presents the problem sequentially, as a narrative; Danxi breaks up the sequence into independent causes.

34. "Sixiang chengbing, bing zai xin" (YBQS, 6436b).

35. *Jin ping mei ci hua* (Hong Kong: Xianggang wenhai chuban she, 1963), chap. 32: "Sixiang chengbing . . . bujiu shenwang." See Anonymous, *The Plum in the Golden Vase, or Chin P'ing Mei*, vol. 1, *The Gathering* [*Jin ping mei*], trans. David Tod Roy (Princeton, N.J.: Princeton University Press, 1993), 27. Roy estimates that the novel was written during the years 1596 to 1618.

36. The link between emotions and the discourse of Fire was introduced to me by Shigehisa Kuriyama.

37. YBQS, 6438a.

38. YBQS, 6444b. In "Diseases" ["Jibing"] Pu Songling (1640–1715) observes the connection between yijing and dreams. See Lu Dahuang, ed., *Pu Songling ji* (Shanghai: Zhonghua Shuju, 1962), 747.

39. See, for example, Tang Zonghai, *Yixue jianneng* (Shanghai: Hechen Jushi, 1895), 31. Tang, a late-nineteenth-century physician, was renowned for integrating Chinese and Western medicine.

40. Zhang Jiebin, *Jingyue quanshu* [Collected works], ed. Zhao Lixun (reprint, Beijing: Renmin Weisheng Chubanshe, 1991), 29:634.

41. YBQS, 6458b–6459a.

42. YBQS, 6438a.

43. Victoria B. Cass, "Female Healers in the Ming and the Lodge of Ritual and Ceremony," *Journal of the American Oriental Society* 106, no. 1(1986): 237.

44. Wile, *Art of the Bedchamber*, 131.

45. See Joanna Ching-yuan Wu Kuriyama, "Confucianism in Fiction: A Study of Hsia Ching-ch'u's *Yeh-sou-p'u-yen*" (Ph.D. diss., Harvard University, 1993).

46. Ibid., 160–161; translation slightly modified. By placing a wall between the two men, this homoerotic scene is neutralized; it becomes one of jing consumption. Today, the criminal code of the P.R.C. prohibits *xijing fan*, the crime of imbibing seminal essence. Whether this reflects the state prohibition of homosexuality or is designed to prevent qi stealing is unclear.

47. Li Zhongzi (1588–1655), the influential Ming physician, held that emitting blood was the most catastrophic type of depletion. YBQS, 6448a.

48. C. T. Hsia, *The Classic Chinese Novel: A Critical Introduction* (New York: Columbia University Press, 1968), 199.

49. On the nourishing of the body's prenatal endowment of vitality by entities in the postnatal

environment see Sivin, *Traditional Medicine*, 237. The Later-Han-dynasty *Shuowen* [Words explained] emphasizes the rice (*mi*) component of the character *qi*, which is suggestive of the "nourishing vapors of boiling rice or grain" that "maintain life and human energy." See Schwartz, *World of Thought*, 180. The character *jing*, too, contains the rice radical.

50 Cao Xueqin, *Honglou meng*, Guben xiaoshuo congkan, vol. 1 (Beijing: Zhonghua Shuju, 1987), 1957–1966. For a superb rendering of this episode in English see David Hawkes, "The Golden Days, vol. 1, chap. 12 of *The Story of the Stone* (New York: Viking Penguin, 1973), 243–254.

51 Jia Rui's death raises the connection between yijing and possession. The Ming physician Jiang Guan records a case of yijing (c. 1522) in which a man fell ill after caressing at some length a statue of a young woman in a temple. A priest was dispatched to destroy the image. Upon smashing the sculpture, the priest discovered that its clay was damp; it had absorbed and apparently taken possession of the man's semen. See Li Jianmin, "*Suibing* yu 'changsuo': Chuantong yixue dui *suibing* de yizhong jieshi" [*Suibing* and "place": One explanation of *suibing* by traditional medicine], *Hanxue yanjiu* [Chinese studies] 12, no. 1 (June 1994): 129. On the body and possession see Philip A. Kuhn, *Soulstealers: The Chinese Sorcery Scare of 1768* (Cambridge, Mass.: Harvard University Press, 1990).

52 See David Johnson, "Actions Speak Louder Than Words: The Cultural Significance of Chinese Ritual Opera," in *Ritual Opera, Operatic Ritual: "Mu-lien Rescues His Mother" in Chinese Popular Culture*, ed. David Johnson (Berkeley, Calif.: Chinese Popular Culture Project, 1989), 1–45; and Meir Shahar, *Crazy Ji: Chinese Religion and Popular Literature*, Harvard-Yenching Institute Monographs, no. 48 (Cambridge, Mass.: Harvard University Press, 1998).

53 Fragments of Guangxu's medical records appear in Li Jingwei, ed., *Zhongguo gudai yishi tulu* [Illustrations of the history of medicine in early China] (Beijing: Renmin Weisheng Chubanshe, 1992), 106.

54 Zhu Jinfu, "Jiekai Guangxudi 'zu si' zhi mi" [Breaking open the mystery of Emperor Guangxu's death], in *Gugong yishi* [Miscellaneous history of the Forbidden City], ed. Zhou Yuehua (Shanghai: Shanghai Wenhua Chubanshe, 1984), 272.

55 Ibid.

56 Li, *Zhongguo gudai yishi*, 106. On Guangxu's death see Serge Franzini, "Le docteur Detheve appele en consultation par l'empereur Guangxu," *Etudes chinoises* 14 (1995): 95–129.

57 On the nineteenth-century French medical preoccupation with seminal emission see Theodore Tarczylo, *Sex et liberte au siecle des lumieres* (Paris: Presses de la Renaissance, 1983), esp. 297–298.

58 Qin Bowei, ed., *Qingdai mingyi yian qinghua* [Selected cases from celebrated physicians of the Qing dynasty] (Shanghai: Shanghai Kexue Jishu Chubanshe, 1981), 51, 148, 161, 189, 256, 331, 404, 468, for example.

59 Frank Dikötter, *Sex, Culture, and Modernity in China: Medical Science and the Construction of Sexual Identities in the Early Republican Period* (London: Hurst and Co., 1995), 166–167.

60 The Spermin ads call the disorder *yijing lao*. This formulation could be explained in several ways. First, this *lao* is an alternate reading of the *lao* of exhaustion, one of the most enduring images of the disorder, dating to Zhang Ji (late second century C.E.), who described seminal emission (shijing) as a "sickness arising from exhaustion" (*lao zhi wei bing*). See YBQS, 6432b. This *lao* contains some of the connotations of yijing: exhaustion arising from overexertion (*laoxin*) and its manifestation in emission (*laolin*). Second, since at least the Ming period, yijing has been identified as a symptom of the lao of consumption or the wasting diseases. See, for example, Xu Chunfu, *Gujin yitong daquan* [Complete ancient and modern medical compendium] (1556; reprint, Beijing: Renmin Weisheng Chubanshe, 1991), 1322. Finally, *lao* could play off the word for labor, *laodong*. For yijing's connection to labor see below.

61 *Shenbao*, 16 March 1934, 19.

62 Ge Gongzhen, *Zhongguo baoxue shi* [A history of China's newspapers] (Beijing: Sanlian Chubanshe, 1955), 216. See also Huang K'e-wu, "Cong Shenbao yiyao guanggao kan minchu Shanghai de yiliao wenhua yu shehui shenghuo, 1912–1926" [Examining early Republican Shanghai's medical culture and social life through Shenbao's medicinal advertisements, 1912–1926], *Zhongyang yanjiuyuan jindaishi yanjiusuo jikan* [Bulletin of the Institute of Modern History Academia Sinica] 17, no. 2 (December 1988): 141–194.

63 Today *shenkui* is a major category that includes an array of renal-urogenital distresses. Most commonly it is understood as impotence. The word *shenkui* appears as early as the sixteenth century in the work of Xue Ji (c. 1550) (see Zhang, *Jingyue quanshu*, 636). However, *shenkui* does not appear in major dictionaries such as the Morohashi, the *Hanyu da cidian*, or the *Zhongguo yixue da cidian*. During the Republic, products such as "Doan's Backache Kidney Pills" highlighted shenkui as the disorder requiring alleviation. On its contemporary meaning see Jung-kwang Wen and Ching-lun Wang, "Shen-k'uei Syndrome: A Culture-Specific Sexual Neurosis in Taiwan," in *Normal and Abnormal Behavior in Chinese Culture*, ed. Arthur Kleinman and Tsung-yi Li (Boston: D. Reidel Publishing Co., 1981), 357–369.

64 S. A. D. Tissot, *Onanism: A Treatise upon the Disorders Produced by Masturbation*; or, *The Dangerous Effects of Secret and Excessive Venery* (London: J. Pridden, 1766, reprinted in R. Trumbach, ed., *Marriage, Sex, and the Family in England, 1660–1800* (New York: Garland, 1985), 7–8.

65 Richard Dawson, *An Essay on Spermatorrhoea and Urinary Deposits, with Observations on the Nature, Causes, and Treatment of the Various Disorders of the Generative System, Illustrated by Numerous Cases*, 8th ed. (London: Aylott and Co., 1853), 15.

66 See, for example, G. H. Savage, *Insanity* (1886), cited in Havelock Ellis, *Studies in the Psychology of Sex*, vol. 1 (Philadelphia: F. A. Davis, 1897), 249.

67 Dawson, *Essay on Spermatorrhoea*, 15, 34–35.

68 "Anything that weakens the nervous system may bring on seminal emissions" yet emissions are "frequently the cause of nervous" diseases (George M. Beard, *Sexual Neurasthenia [Nervous Exhaustion], Its Hygiene, Causes, Symptoms and Treatment, with a chapter on Diet for the*

Nervous, *Fifth Edition*, *With Formulas* (New York: E. B. Treat and Co., 1898), 118–119. On American spermatorrhea see Gail Pat Parsons, "Equal Treatment for All: American Medical Remedies for Male Sexual Problems: 1850–1900," JHMAS 32, no.1 (January 1977): 55–71; on American technology for its control, see Hoag Levins, *American Sex Machines: The Hidden History of Sex at the U.S. Patent Office* (Holbrook, Mass., Adams Media Corporation, 1996), 11–42.

69 Edward Payson Hurd, "Syphilophobia and Spermatorrhea," *Medical Age* (Detroit) 7 (1889): 244–246.

70 Peter Gay traces Tissot's work to a fear-mongering piece on masturbation that coined the term "onanism" in the early sixteenth century, *Onania, or the Heinous Sin of Self-Pollution, And all the frightful Consequences, in both Sexes, Considered*, penned by an anonymous "clergyman dabbling in quackery." See Peter Gay, *The Bourgeois Experience, Victoria to Freud*, vol. 1, *Education of the Senses* (Oxford: Oxford University Press, 1984), 295–296.

71 See n. 2.

72 Clement of Alexandria, *The Pedagogue*, chap. 10, quoted in Michel Foucault, *History of Sexuality*, vol. 2, *The Use of Pleasure*, trans. Robert Hurley (New York: Vintage Books, 1985), 15.

73 Writing about *gonorrhoia*, the involuntary emission of seed, Galen observes in the second century that "[s]ince the discharge of sperm is involuntary," it is possible "to define it as independent of our will" ("Diseases of Viscera and Urogenital Tract," chap. 6, book 6, *Galen on the Affected Parts*, trans. Rudolph E. Siegel (Basel and New York: S. Karger, 1976), 192; 223 n. 40. (*Gone* = seed; *rhoia* = a flow; distinct from bacterial gonorrhea.) Risking caricature of a complex tradition, I hypothesize that Galen's observation of the unwilled aspect of the event foreshadows the perceived sympathy between the testes and the brain of modern times. In American and European discussions too, death struck those who spent too much semen. Yet the emphasis is provocative: the cost of careless or uncontrolled exudation is the loss of the will. Autonomy, the ability to act on one's own accord, lay near the core of Western thought. To lose this free will was perhaps more threatening than the loss of life itself.

74 The concept *huanjing bunao* appears in the *Baopuzi*, a fourth-century-C.E. compendium of Taoist arts that is noted for its alchemical content. The concept was part of the growing importance of sperm in health discourse.

75 The phrase *physiological alchemy* is from SCC 5.5. On the colossal body of writings on diet, exercise, and sex, which is loosely characterized as the cultivation of vitality (*yangsheng*) see Henri Maspero, "Les procedes de 'nourrir le principe vital' dans la Religion Taoiste Ancienne," *Journal Asiatique* 229 (July–September 1937): 177–252, 353–340; Robert H. Van Gulik, *Sexual Life in Ancient China: A Preliminary Survey of Chinese Sex and Society from ca. 1500 B.C. till 1644 A.D.* (Leiden: E. J. Brill, 1974); Joseph Needham, *Science and Civilisation in China*, vol. 2, *History of Scientific Thought* (Cambridge: Cambridge University Press, 1956), 146–152. SCC 5.5; Kristopher Schipper, *Le Corps Taoiste* (Paris: Fayard, 1982); Donald Harper, "The Sexual Arts of Ancient China As Described in a Manuscript of the Second

Century B.C.," *Harvard Journal of Asiatic Studies*, 47, no. 2 (1987): 539–593; and Wile, *Art of the Bedchamber*.

76 Wile challenges Maspero's reading of *huan* as "to return" (which Needham adopts), reworking it as "to circulate." See Wile, *Art of the Bedchamber*, 56–57.

77 SCC 5.5, 202.

78 *Shesheng* dates to the *Laozi*. See *Laozi*, *Guisheng*, no. 50; D. C. Lau, Chen Fong Ching, eds., *Laozi zhuzi suoyin* [A concordance to the *Laozi*] (Hong Kong: Commercial Press, 1996), 111.

79 For an analysis of this problem see the work of Bridie J. Andrews, esp. "Tuberculosis and the Assimilation of Germ Theory in China, 1895–1937," JHMAS 52, no. 1 (January 1997): 114–157.

80 With limited effect, for most of the endocrine entity was probably digested in the stomach.

81 William C. Cooper and Nathan Sivin, "Man as a Medicine: Pharmacological and Ritual Aspects of Traditional Therapy Using Drugs Derived from the Human Body," in *Chinese Science: Explorations of an Ancient Tradition*, ed. Shigeru Nakayama and Nathan Sivin, MIT East Asian Science Series, vol. 2 (Cambridge, Mass.: MIT Press, 1973), 203–272; Johann Frick, "How Blood Is Used in Magic and Medicine in Ch'inghai Province," *Anthropos* 46 (1951): 964–979.

82 One Republican-era newspaperman contends that *Xinwen bao* surpassed its nemesis *Shenbao* in circulation because it printed a larger quantity of torrid ads. See Wang Zhongwei, "You jingzheng you lianhe de 'Xin' 'Shen' liangbao" [In competition, in cooperation: *Xinwen bao* and *Shenbao*], in *Xinwen yanjiu ziliao* [Materials on media research] 2, no. 15 (1982): 83.

83 "Report on the Working of the Imperial Post Office for the First Year of Hsüan Tung [1909]," 5.

84 XHYY, case no. 64022, 17; case no. 69151, 7.

85 "Infected metropolis" is from Richard Horton, "The Infected Metropolis," *Lancet* 347, no. 8995 (20 January 1996): 134–135.

86 Mark Elvin, "Tales of *Shen* and *Xin*: Body-Person and Heart-Mind in China during the Last One-Hundred Fifty Years," in *Fragments for a History of the Human Body, Part Two*, ed. Michel Feher (New York: Zone, 1989), 277. On nineteenth-century medical advertisements see Jonathan D. Spence, "Aspects of the Western Medical Experience in China, 1850–1910," in *Medicine and Society in China*, ed. John Z. Bowers and Elizabeth F. Purcell (New York: Josiah Macy Jr. Foundation, 1974), 45–47.

87 The dailies depended on advertising to the point of "unreadability, degeneration, and prostitution," stated Lin Yutang ("Contemporary Chinese Periodical Literature," *T'ien Hsia Monthly* 2, no. 3 [March 1936]: 230). On the commercialization of the press in the 1930s see Stephen R. MacKinnon, "Toward a History of the Chinese Press in the Republican Period," *Modern China* 23, no. 1 (January 1997): 3–32, esp. 7–11.

88 Xu Zhucheng, interview by author, Shanghai, 1991. Xu Zhucheng was a reporter for the *Dagong bao* and an editor of the *Wenhui bao*.

89 "Quack Medicines" *China Medical Journal* 30, no. 3 (May 1916): 203. On the competition of

pharmaceuticals see James W. Bennett, "Pills of Ten Thousand Efficacies," *Asia* 30 (1930): 616.

90 Dr. Edward H. Hume, "Notes for the Hunan-Yale Medical Council, Growing out of Observations Made on a Recent Trip in North and East China, December 20, 1923, to January 13, 1924," Records of the Yale-China Association, series 2, box 34, folder 280, Sterling Memorial Library, Yale University.

91 See, for instance, Zhu Zhensheng, *Yijing ziliao fa* [Self-treatment for spermatorrhea] (Shanghai: Baibing Ziliao Congshu, n.d.).

92 On contagion see Shigehisa Kuriyama, "Epidemics, Weather, and Contagion in Traditional Chinese Medicine" (paper presented at the "Symposium on Contagion in Premodern Societies," Wellcome Institute for the History of Medicine, London, 1993).

93 For estimates of infection rates see Edgar T. H. Tsen, "The Prevalence of Syphilis in Peking, First Report," *National Medical Journal of China* 6 (1920): 159–166; and Harry S. Gear, "The Incidence of Venereal Diseases in Hospital Patients in China," *China Medical Journal* 49, no. 10 (October 1935): 1122–1135.

94 European and North American physicians up through the nineteenth century also organized these illnesses into a single group. See John L. Milton, *On the Pathology and Treatment of Gonorrhoea and Spermatorrhoea* (New York: Wood, 1887).

95 Sivin, *Traditional Medicine*, 229, 229 n. 15. Another explanation of the conceptual grouping of seminal emission with gonorrhea emphasizes the prominence of "self-discipline" and "the dominance of the mind over the body" leading to medical advocacy for "individual responsibility in the control over bodily fluids." See Dikötter, *Sex, Culture, and Modernity*, 167.

96 Sivin, *Traditional Medicine*, 229, 229 n. 15. Enuresis, too, was grouped with the lin ailments, traditionally and in this period.

97 XHYY, case no. 58930, 8, 17.

98 XHYY, case no. 45965, 34, 59.

99 XHYY, case no. 20603, 54, 59–62, 81–83. On the PUMC see Mary Brown Bullock, *An American Transplant*: *The Rockefeller Foundation and Peking Union Medical College*, (Berkeley and Los Angeles: University of California Press, 1980).

100 XHYY, case no. 20603, 101.

101 May Fourth refers to a pivotal era of modern Chinese life from roughly 1915 to 1923; it was an era that combined nationalist fervor with intense cultural scrutiny. See Chow Tse-tsung, *The May Fourth Movement*: *Intellectual Revolution in Modern China* (Cambridge, Mass.: Harvard University Press, 1960); and Vera Schwarcz, *The Chinese Enlightenment*: *Intellectuals and the Legacy of the May Fourth Movement of 1919* (Berkeley and Los Angeles: University of California Press, 1986).

102 Luo Jialun, "Qingnian xuesheng" [Student youth], *Xin qingnian* [New youth] 4, no. 1 (January 1918): 74.

103 Mao Zedong, "A Study of Physical Education" in Stuart R. Schram, *The Political Thought of Mao Tse-tung*, rev. and enl. (New York: Praeger, 1976), 152–153, 155, 160. This article was originally published in the April 1917 issue of *New Youth*.

104 Sun Lung-kee, "The Fin de Siècle Lu Xun" (paper presented at the thirty-second Association for Asian Studies, South-East Conference annual meeting, 15 January 1993, Hilton Head, S.C.), 6.

105 Ng Mau-sang, "Popular Fiction and the Culture of Everyday Life: A Cultural Analysis of Qin Shouou's *Qiuhaitang*," *Modern China* 20, no. 2 (April 1994): 135, 139.

106 Leo Ou-fan Lee, *The Romantic Generation of Modern Chinese Writers* (Cambridge, Mass.: Harvard University Press, 1973), 270. On hypermasculinity as a psychological response to foreign occupation, see Ashis Nandy, *The Intimate Enemy: Loss and Recovery of Self under Colonialism* (Delhi: Oxford University Press, 1983), esp. 10, 22, 29, 37–38, 52, 100.

107 In Yu Dafu's 1921 story "Sinking," a Chinese youth, feeling snubbed by two Japanese women, rages, "The girls must have known! They must have known that I am a Chinaman; otherwise why didn't they even look at me once?" (Yu Dafu, "Sinking" [Chenlun], trans. Joseph S. M. Lau and C. T. Hsia, in *Modern Chinese Stories and Novellas, 1919–1949*, ed. Joseph S. M. Lau, C. T. Hsia, and Leo Ou-fan Lee [New York: Columbia University Press, 1981], 128–129,140).

108 XHYY, case no. 57487.

109 A promotion for the gray-beard product "man-made blood supply" (*renzao zilai xue*) stated in 1909: "The conflict between the yellow and white people is reaching its climax. The waxing and waning of vitality (*xueqi*) determines a country's ascendence or decline, its strength or weakness. Our pharmacy has invented 'man-made blood supply' with the enlightened intent of strengthening the country and fortifying the people" *Shibao*, 1 November 1909.

110 Mussolini held out his vaunted sexual prowess as proof of the virility of the fascist system. See Victoria De Grazia, *How Fascism Ruled Women: Italy, 1922–1945* (Berkeley and Los Angeles: University of California Press, 1991), 43.

111 The counterexample to Guangxu would be the eighteenth-century Qianlong emperor, whose many offspring symbolized a robust empire. Today drug companies use his image; a Fujian company named its product Qianlong Yuyong Sheng Jing Dan (Qianlong Emperor Sperm Essence Pills).

112 On warlordism in Beijing see David Strand, "City People under Siege: The Impact of Warlordism," in *Rickshaw Beijing: City People and Politics in the 1920s* (Berkeley and Los Angeles: University of California Press, 1989), 198–221; James E. Sheridan, "The Warlord Era: Politics and Militarism under the Peking Government, 1916–1928," in *The Cambridge History of China*, vol. 12, *Republican China, 1912–1949*, pt. 1, ed. John K. Fairbank (Cambridge: Cambridge University Press, 1983), 284–321; and Andrew Nathan, *Peking Politics, 1918–1923: Factionalism and the Failure of Constitutionalism* (Berkeley and Los Angeles: University of California Press, 1976).

113 Until 1921, warlord governments had maintained payment of Manchu bannermen stipends. By the 1920s, bannermen made up about one-third of Beijing's population. See Strand, *Rickshaw Beijing*, 13.

114 In the early 1920s, about 64 percent of the city's population was male. See Sidney Gamble assisted by John S. Burgess, *Peking: A Social Survey* (New York: George H. Doran Co., 1921), 99.

115 The annexation of Manchuria created a double burden for Beijing. Not only did the uprooted take refuge in the former capital, those people who would have left Beijing seeking work in the northeast often remained in the city.

116 For the other Beijing—the one of leisure and reflection, above the lower depths—see Tim Weston, "Intellectuals in a Fading Capital: Living and Writing in Republican Beijing" (paper presented at the Association for Asian Studies annual meeting, Chicago, March 1997).

117 "The prevalence of tuberculosis," wrote a physician in 1925, appears "aggravated in recent years" by the "lowered economic conditions amongst the Manchus" (J. B. Grant, "Public Health and Medical Events during 1925," in *The China Year Book, 1926–1927*, ed. H. G. W. Woodhead [Tientsin: Tientsin Press, n.d], 725).

118 XHYY, case no. 46593, 43, for example.

119 For one formulation of this phenomenon see Mark Elvin, "High Level Equilibrium Trap," in *The Pattern of the Chinese Past* (Stanford, Calif.: Stanford University Press, 1973), 298–319.

120 XHYY, case no. 45489, 17.

121 In Lao She's 1937 novel *Luotuo Xiangzi*, the narrator says of the ailing rickshaw puller, "His body was the only thing he had confidence in" (Lao She, *Rickshaw: The Novel* Lo-to Hsiang Tzu, trans. Jean M. James [Honolulu: The University of Hawaii Press, 1979], 30). A phrase heard today, spoken by men with limited opportunities, is "my body is my capital" [*shenti shi wo benqian*].

122 Arthur Kleinman, *Social Origins of Distress and Disease: Depression, Neurasthenia, and Pain in Modern China* (New Haven, Conn.: Yale University Press, 1986), 2.

123 On emerging social identities in urban China see Yeh Wen-hsin, "Progressive Journalism and Shanghai's Petty Urbanites: Zou Taofen and the Shenghuo Enterprise, 1926–1945," in *Shanghai Sojourners*, ed. Frederic Wakeman Jr. and Yeh Wen-hsin, China Research Monograph, no. 40 (Berkeley and Los Angeles: University of California Press, 1992), 186–238.

124 The term *shenjing* was coined by Sugita Gempaku in 1774, in the first Japanese translation of a Western anatomical text. See Ogawa Teizo, "*Kaitai shinsho* no shinkeigaku" [The neurology of the *Kaitai shinsho*], *Juntendo igaku zasshi* [Juntendo medical journal] 15, no. 1 (1969): 29. The term gained popularity only in the late nineteenth century, during Meiji times.

125 See case no. 77 in Song Chengzhang et al., eds., *Shanghai fengdian zhuanmen yiyuan yuanwu gaiyao* [An outline of the administration of the Shanghai special hospital for the insane] (Shanghai: Shanghai Fengdian Zhuanmen Yiyuan, 1934), 21. *Shen* (kidney) and *shen* (of nerves) have different tones and thus are not exact homophones.

126   See Beard, *Sexual Neurasthenia*; Tu Qihua, *Xing shenjing shuairuo yu shenjing shuairuo* [Sexual neurasthenia and neurasthenia] (Shanghai, 1946); and Dikötter, *Sex, Culture, and Modernity*, 162–164.

Bacterial Cultures and Linguistic Colonies: Mori Rintarō's Experiments with History, Science, and Language

Thomas Lamarre

The Collected Works of Mori Ōgai (pseudonym of Mori Rintarō, 1862–1922) contains essays that discuss microbes, aesthetics, minerals, infirmaries, war strategies, water indices, character indices, nose rings, corsets, and Russian techniques for dealing with intense cold, as well as poems, novellas, and plays.[1] It is difficult, however, to speak of the relations between these diverse topics, modes, and interests, despite their historical and textual proximity. What do microbes have to do with novellas, novellas with microbes, or infirmaries with aesthetics? Such questions are made all the more difficult by a certain intellectual division of labor that is manifested in the organization of *The Collected Works*, in which the scientific writings are strictly separated from the literary texts. An unthinkable divide comes between Mori's science and his literature: even if one reads these texts in tandem, it is almost impossible to find a common logic or subjectivity.

To a certain extent, the life of Mori Rintarō invites stories about incommensurable differences and impossible divides. Born in 1862 in a small village on the Japan Sea, he followed in the footsteps of his father, a physician to the daimyo of Tsuwano, studying the Chinese classics as well as Dutch medicine. In 1872 the daimyo sent him to Tokyo, where he received further medical training. He also studied German, which was quickly replacing Dutch as the language of medical research in Japan. Upon completing medical school in 1881, Mori joined the army with the rank of lieutenant and, in 1884, traveled to Germany to study military hygiene. There, he became interested in the emergent science of microbes and participated in the debates around Koch and Pettenkoffer, as well as in military maneuvers and diplomatic missions. He also read widely in German literature and philosophy, taking to Goethe, Hartmann, Schopenhauer, and others and following the European debates on naturalism. In 1888, with the rank of captain, he returned to Tokyo to become a professor of physiology at the Army Medical School. In Tokyo, his education and experiences put him in a position to dominate scientific and literary circles. He took part in the debates on hygiene and nutrition in Japan, founded a literary magazine in which he translated Western writers and wrote essays, and taught anatomy at the Tokyo Academy of Fine Arts.

When Japan entered into war with China in 1894, Mori sailed for Korea, where he played a central role in the maintenance of military hygiene, reducing Japanese casualties and assuring victories on the continent. He returned to Tokyo, to become head of the Army Medical School; he also founded another literary journal. In 1899, the army transferred him to the small city of Kokura on the southern island of Kyūshū; this was apparently as a reprimand for his vociferous insistence on modern notions of science, which challenged certain military authorities. Reprieved in 1902, he returned to Tokyo, resumed his career as a military bureaucrat, and gained ever greater recognition as a translator, dramatist, novelist, poet, and critic. He served in the Russo-Japanese War (1904–1905), largely in Korea but also briefly in Manchuria. After his return, he became the director of the Bureau of Medical Affairs for the War Bureau in 1907 and continued his literary activities. Around 1911, toward the end of the Meiji era (1868–1912), Mori shifted his literary emphasis and began to reflect on history, turning to the composition of historical fiction (*shiden* and *rekishi shōsetsu*), which dominated his literary output till the time of his death in 1922.[2]

Nowadays, the career and works of Mori are for the most part the subject of literary inquiry. In *The Collected Works*, essays about hygiene, war, and nutrition are tacked onto the literary works, and their import is confined largely to the domain of historical or biographical background on the author. Biographies of the military doctor Mori Rintarō often sketch a portrait of a man impossibly divided in his impulses, a man bound to conflicting realms of experience and divided in his aesthetics and duties. This almost schizophrenic portrait suggests a parallel between the life of Mori Rintarō and the drama of Japanese modernization. The diversity and hybridity of his works often stand metonymically for the confusion and competing demands of the Meiji era, with which the notion of *wakon yosai*, or "Japanese spirit, Western techniques," is frequently associated. Mori's scientific, literary, and bureaucratic pursuits, deemed mutually incommensurable, ultimately stand for the turmoil of the era; the conflicts of Japanese modernity itself are crystallized in the divided figure of Mori Rintarō/Ōgai.

A number of dichotomies run through even this sketchy overview of the life of Mori Rintarō: city and countryside, "feudalism" and modernity, science and literature, art and army, empire and colony, and Japan and the West. While it is impossible to map any of these dichotomies consistently onto the others, all of them seem to be constitutive of Japanese modernity, emerging and functioning together. Usually, the opposition of Japan and the West—as in "Japanese spirit, Western techniques"—serves as a master trope and focuses attention on certain dichotomies at the expense of others. As James Fujii has pointed out about another important Meiji writer, Natsume Sōseki, scholars attend to Sōseki in England, not to Sōseki in Korea or Manchuria.[3] Similarly, it is common to devote a great deal of attention to Mori in Germany and thus to think of his works in terms of a struggle to reconcile East and West, or tradition and modernity. We don't say much about Mori in Korea and Manchuria. This silence begins with Mori's literature itself: the literary figure Mori Ōgai says little about this other nexus. There is a series of poems written during Mori's time on the front of the Russo-Japanese War, but these poems provide only fleeting allusions to the war or the colonies.[4] They speak of loss, bereavement, and recollection, as if the hardships of war were but an extension—or perhaps, an intensification —of personal sorrows and memories. Mori does not focus any attention specifically on the imperial theater. Germany, on the contrary, receives a great deal of attention, from both Mori Ōgai and his subsequent readers. Only in Mori Rintarō's texts on hygiene and nutrition do these other aspects of Japanese modernity come into consideration. It is precisely for this reason that this account centers on the scientific texts of Mori Rintarō rather than on the literary texts of Mori Ōgai. Ultimately, I have two interrelated goals: (1) to develop a strategy for reading between science and literature, and (2) to rethink the nexus of Japanese modernity, focusing on national expansion rather than on national consolidation (which is somewhat entrenched and tends to dwell on national isolation).

It is not easy, however, to read science in conjunction with social, historical, and rhetorical concerns. And it is not always possible to read science as a subset of a larger logic of knowledge without a complete loss of specificity. In fact, there are reasons to think it undesirable, if not impossible. In an interview, Michel Foucault claimed that it would be excessively complicated to pose the question of the relations obtaining between the "normal sciences" (such as theoretical physics or organic chemistry) and the political and economic structures of society. Therefore, he turned to the "dubious sciences" (such as psychiatry) and their relations to politics and society.[5] Because Foucault sets apart the normal sciences in the manner of Thomas Kuhn, he was able to turn to the vast middle ground that lies between power and knowledge and attend to a kind of discursive field that brings order to the gesture and the glance, and to the utterance and the gaze, around the dubious sciences.

Such a strategy is relevant to the study of Meiji science and Mori Rintarō/ Ōgai. The meditations of a critic such as Karatani Kōjin call attention to the new forms of seeing, speaking, and knowing that emerged in regard to Meiji art and literature—which Karatani relates to the formation of Japanese modernity and national subjectivity.[6] These new forms of seeing, speaking, and knowing could, in the manner of Foucault, be further localized and related to new criteria for clinical expertise in connection with the emergence of modern institutions with historically specific modes of observation, evaluation, incarceration, and so forth. In that case, the question of national identity or subjectivity would arise in another register, in relation to a series of modern discursive formations. In both Karatani and Foucault, however, it is difficult to discern certain forms of agency—microbes, chemicals, and so forth—for these remain the province of the normal sciences.

On the other hand, recent studies in the realm of the sociology and anthropology of science challenge the boundary that Foucault and Karatani leave implicitly intact—the boundary between the normal sciences and other forms of knowledge. By challenging this boundary, scholars such as Bruno Latour and Isabelle Stengers question the ways in which modernity is conceptualized: at stake is not only the delineation of the normal sciences but also the scientific criteria for modernity itself. Latour is particularly important in this account of Mori Rintarō for three reasons: First, since Latour deals with the emergence of bacteriology in his study of Pasteur, he provides an important historical overlap with the work of Mori Rintarō on military hygiene and nutrition. Second, he attempts to rethink the status of scientific modernity, with an emphasis on the intersection of scientific, textual, and social networks. Third, by looking at the production of "quasi-objects," he also enables an approach to the question of material agency.[7]

As with Foucault or Karatani, however, a note of caution is in order. In Latour's studies, it is possible to think about material agency and yet it becomes difficult to take into account certain forms of desire and subjectivity that are integral to nation, colony, or empire, and these invariably swarm into the field of analysis. Nevertheless, because Latour affords a way to reformulate the network of science and literature that informs the works of Mori Rintarō, his approach helps to disturb accounts of Japanese modernity that have become more and more conventional with respect to the emergence of national subjectivity. What emerges is a story of Meiji Japan and Japanese modernity that does not simply dwell on the formation of insular national subjectivity in opposition to the West. It becomes possible to explore a modern logic of hybridity that entails the incessant generation of unthinkable mixes of microbes, poems, foodstuffs, hygienic practices, novels, essays, water indices, character indices, and so forth, and to ask what subjectivity might attend this productive cascade of hybrids.

National and Scientific Victories

Mori Rintarō's name often arises in the context of the debate over what food would assure the vitality of Japanese subjects. Diet was one of the crucial issues for the modern nation at war: soldiers who marched into the enemy's territories died as soon from poor nutrition or infection as from enemy fire, and usually sooner. In Japan, as in Germany, France, and England, hygiene and nutrition became a central concern, not only to assure the health of national citizens but to enable the advance of national armies as well. This conflation of soldiers and citizens around the debates over Japanese food marked a milestone in the way in which national subjects were constructed in the modern nation. By introducing universal (male) conscription in Japan in 1873, the modern nation made its citizens into soldiers. Or rather, by exacting military loyalty as a feature of national belonging, the modern nation transformed sundry subjects (farmers, bureaucrats, artisans, etc.) into national subjects. Thus, when Mori wrote in response to debates on Japanese nutrition, he almost naturally conflated soldiers with citizens. Preparation for war, in the guise of national defense and under the aegis of science, had begun to permeate the nation.

In histories of Japanese science, Mori's contributions to the debates on Japanese food command scant attention. That his name appears at all is probably due to his status as a writer or to the fact that he was an important historical figure. As a result, analyses of his treatises on Japanese food have been performed primarily by literary scholars. Although these literary analyses largely confine themselves to a discussion of Mori's emotions even in his scientific writings, they address the problem of nationalism quite directly. A fairly recent article by Oya Yukiyo is a good example. Oya examines Mori's rather unconventional response to the debates on Japanese food. If Mori's response seemed (or seems) strange, it is because he did not follow the scientific trend that proclaimed the insufficiency of the Japanese dietary regime. Mori tried to establish scientific grounds for the adequacy of Japanese food: the title of an 1889 essay was "The Argument against Japanese Food May Soon Lose Its Foundation" ["Hi Nihon shoku ron wa masa ni sono konkyo wo ushinawan to su"]. Oya points out, quite rightly, that Mori was not writing against meat (that is, against scientific fact) but rather to counter the argument against Japanese food.[7]

Later in his career, in the somewhat autobiographical 1911 story "Day-dreams" ["Mōsō"], Mori Rintarō (as Ōgai) wrote about a scientist who returns from Germany to Japan and finds himself in the company of conservatives on issues of city planning, script reforms, and nutrition:

> There was also a debate over improving the Japanese diet. They wanted to stop people from eating rice and make them eat lots of meat instead. I advised them that it would be better to leave the Japanese diet as it had always been, because rice and fish were so easy to digest. Not that one would prevent anyone from raising cattle and eating meat as well. . . .
>
> So it turned out that whenever people tried to reform things, I advocated the status quo. I was thus driven into the company of conservatives.[9]

Oya relates this passage to "The Argument against Japanese Food May Soon Lose Its Foundation." He asks whether the anger that Mori expresses in his defense of Japanese food can be attributed simply to an ultranationalist or conservative position. Oya himself doesn't feel that Mori can be explained so simply. Is there not a trace of sadness behind Mori's anger? While Oya demurs that his might be "too literary" an interpretation, he suggests that it derives from Mori's "sadness as a Japanese."[10]

It is significant that Oya's initial impulse is to distinguish between conservative nationalism and "sadness as a Japanese." His "literary" interpretation distinguishes cultural nationalism—a sense of nationness—from political nationalism, ultranationalism, conservativism, and so forth. His interpretation of Mori's science is part of that culturalist project. Oya writes that "of course, as an expert in hygiene, his conclusions have scientific foundation, but at bottom, is there not something else?" At bottom Oya finds nationalism: he avows that Mori is a nationalist but "not a simple nationalist."[11]

Another question follows quickly in the wake of this issue of nationalism. If Mori's defense of Japanese food derives from his sadness as a Japanese, what is the status of his science? The narrator of Mori's "Daydreams" implies that he conducted research in an attempt to prove his opinions—a bias that hardly upholds the scientific ideal of objectivity; rather, national sentiment seems to serve as the premise for his research. "Soon after my return I entered a laboratory for a year or two," the narrator writes. "I worked steadily, intent on providing a solid basis for my conservative views."[12]

Oya steers away from the conclusion that Mori's science is, at bottom, a simple vehicle for national sentiment. That would indeed be too simple. To avoid conflating nation and science, Oya makes a distinction between literature and science; it is a distinction that leaves the problem of their interactions or interrelations unexamined, even unthinkable. He does this by exploring the rhetorical strategies in Mori's account of Japanese food, finding two such strategies.[13]

Oya shows how, on the one hand, Mori argues deductively from specific treatises on nutrition, then constructs an argument for Japanese food on the basis of certain socioeconomic constraints (the number of cattle in Japan, etc.). That is, Mori argues from premises or propositions that have already been proved; he proceeds from the general or universal to a particular conclusion. On the other hand, Mori also argues inductively on the basis of Japanese customs. That is, he reasons from particular facts to a general or universal conclusion. In the instance of Japanese food, he argues that if people in Japan have survived, or even prospered, on traditional foods such as rice, then a dietary regime based on rice must be adequate, legitimate, and reasonable. Once again, the narrator of "Daydreams" furnishes a summary: "Proper research would be bound to show that the Japanese, who had developed quite satisfactorily over thousands of years, did not lead so irrational a life. It was self-evident."[14]

Thus, Oya parses two rhetorical cum logical strategies in Mori's science: deduction and induction. His argument reaches a stalemate, however, because of the way in which he associates deduction with science and induction with literature. It is induction that imparts an emotive quality and beauty to Mori's scientific essays, prefiguring the sadness of his later literary works (such as "Daydreams"). Moreover, induction rescues Mori from simple nationalism. Mori's observations of "national ecology" (*nashonaru na seitai*)—part of the inductive strategy—open a path to internationalism.[15] Finally, Oya argues that Mori always favors induction over deduction, and so it is that literature triumphs over science, internationalism over simple nationalism, and "nationness" over conservatism.

Now Oya's account of Mori brings forth both the strengths and weaknesses of a rhetorical reading of science. I use *rhetorical* somewhat loosely as a label for Oya's method of analysis, in which the scholar reads science in terms of its truths and sentiments. His method could also be dubbed *referential*, for it presumes that words correspond neatly to objects or ideas. In a sense, my reading of Mori is equally rhetorical, but I read words as things and as effects in themselves. When Oya reads science for its sentiment, he quickly encounters the problem of national subjectivity. This is the strength of his rhetorical reading. He brings the problem of national subjectivity to the fore, hinting that science, too, has a "structure of feeling" (to borrow Raymond Williams's term).[16] Subsequently, however, he strives to break all links between this national feeling and political or scientific institutions. To reestablish the propriety of literature, he separates Mori's impossible mixes of deduction and induction. He glosses over the way in which Mori links nation, science, and literature precisely because his project is to preserve the sanctity of Japanese literature and Mori Ōgai.

What demands attention are the ways in which Mori mixes nationness with nutrition, and structures of feeling with rice and cattle. There is a middle region where science and literature, deduction and induction, instrument and sensation, and things and feelings cannot be neatly separated. It is this middle region that occupies Foucault's early notions of discourse. Foucault writes of two regions: First, there are the fundamental codes of a culture — those governing its language, its schemas of perception, its exchanges, its techniques, its values, the hierarchy of its practices — that establish an empirical order. Second, at the other extremity of thought, there are the scientific theories or philosophical interpretations that explain why order exists. "But between these two regions," he writes, "so distant from one another, lies a domain which, even though its role is mainly an intermediary one, is nonetheless fundamental: it is more confused, more obscure, and probably less easy to analyze." Thus he finds that "between the already 'encoded' eye and reflexive knowledge" there is "a middle region which liberates order itself."[17]

Foucault turns to the dubious sciences to explore this middle region; he eventually arrives at the operations that come into play in the emergence of modern clinical observation and interrogation. "The observing gaze refrains from intervening: it is silent and gestureless," he writes. "Observation leaves things as they are; there is nothing hidden to it in what is given. The correlative of observation is never the invisible, but always the immediately visible, once one has removed the obstacles erected to reason by theories and to the senses by imagination."[18] It would not be much of a stretch to relate Mori's mixture of science and literature to the emergence of analogous operations associated with the formation of the dubious sciences in Japan. After all, what is Mori's method of inducing general conclusions from local customs but the beginning of modern ethnology? Similarly, as a doctor, he was part of the formation of a clinical tradition in Japan. Finally, there are techniques of observation that seem to extend into his fiction and his science. At the close of "Daydreams," when the narrative shifts from first-person narration to third-person observations (on the previous narrator), the scientific gaze and poetic contemplation start to merge: "Apart from books, the old man plays with his small magnifying glass studying the little flowers he brings back from the dunes. He also has a Zeiss microscope with which he examines minute creatures to be found in drops of seawater. There is also a Merz telescope through which he can study the stars on cloudless nights. Odd pasttimes which serve as reminders of earlier scientific study."[19] Even though this literary text differs from clinical reports or observations, it gives a sense of the middle region of which Foucault speaks. Modern apparatuses of vision expand contemplation across vast scales, from microbes to distant stars, and the tone of solitude echoes through the cosmos, out to the limits of the prosthetic eye. Mori Ōgai couples modern instruments with a lyric subjectivity via a silent and gestureless gaze. There arises in this passage, however, a hint of something that might disturb the boundaries of Foucault's discourse — those minute creatures, the microbes, that abound in a drop of water. Foucault explores the discipline of human subjects. Is it possible to account for these microbes? Can one speak of their disciplinization? Do they have a history, an agency, or forms of resistance? With Mori, it becomes difficult to set aside the normal sciences (bacteriology) so as to explore the human sciences (ethnology). One confronts not just the clinic but also the laboratory—and entities that behave at once as objects and subjects in the social field.

It is in response to such admixtures that Bruno Latour attempts to cast the net of analysis much wider. Instead of exploring the middle region between cultural codes and reflexive knowledge, Latour opens a "Middle Kingdom" that spans the space between humans and quasi-objects such as microbes, vitamins, ozone, scripts, or viruses. This completely transforms the way in which one discusses Mori's treatises on Japanese food. Agency, for instance, has to be attributed to rice, and nutrition and hygiene appear not as neutral developments but as key players in the construction of boundaries and networks that continually run through and beyond nations and institutions. How is it possible to analyze the effects of the transformations in dietary regime that unfurl with national empires? How do the Japanese programs for rural revitalization in Japan and Korea transform not only social relations but the realm of quasi-objects themselves?

We are on more familiar ground when it is a question of rice and the Japanese annexation of Korea. After the Russo-Japanese War, policy makers debated the optimal form of national expansion with respect to Korea: Should Japan continue to occupy the country militarily (and risk condemnation or sanctions from foreign powers), or should it promote development in Korea to assure a powerful yet subsumed ally? Initially there was great eagerness to see Korea as a wasteland awaiting cultivation, and with the subsequent discovery that this was not true, Japanese cultivators turned their efforts to acquiring already cultivated lands in Korea. From the end of the war until annexation (1905–1911), various measures were proposed to facilitate the legal acquisition of Korean rice land, but then annexation made these measures moot.[20] If this is familar ground, it is because these are issues that foreground human agency—in the realms of territory, ownership, laws, and treaties. The kind of questions posed by Latour, however, shift our attention to the ways in which quasi-objects act rather like agents in imperial expansion.

Latour frames his argument in terms of quasi-objects to avoid some of the simplistic subject-object oppositions that continually crop up around questions of nature versus culture. A recent example would be the press given to debates about Jared Diamond's book *Guns, Germs, and Steel: The Fate of Human Societies*, in which Diamond proposes to cut short racial speculation about the modern technological ascendency of Europe by showing how environmental factors (not cultural or intellectual superiority) determined the outcome.[21] His critics call attention to his inability to deal

with culture, that is, the ways in which human societies transform and transcend natural limitations and boundaries.[22] Diamond replies that his scale is
so large that "cultural differences become sifted to approach limits imposed
by environmental constraints."[23] In contrast, Latour's notion of a quasi-
object is calculated to situate analysis on the border between "natural" constraints and "cultural" differences in such a way that neither nature nor culture subsumes the other.

Nevertheless, because Latour casts his net so wide, there seems to be a
crisis in specificity. Suddenly, the human sciences have to confront the social
sciences *and* the normal sciences but on a new basis, for Latour cuts short
the epistemological labor that interrogates the status of truth in scientific
documents. (Thus, like Diamond, he has difficulties with cultural differences, or to be more precise, with subjectivity.) Still, his is an important
attempt to resituate analyses of science, discourse, and society. To deal with
this challenge, it is necessary to understand what causes the rise of the new
sociology or anthropology. It is, first and foremost, a response to a certain
type of history of science — such as that which places the debate on Japanese
food within (or as a footnote to) the triumphant advance of science.

Postwar Japan saw the publication of several general histories of science
(previous histories tended to center on mathematics, medicine, or natural history). In the mid-1960s, three scholars — Sugimoto Isao, Satō Shōsuke, and
Nakayama Shigeru — coauthored one of the most important of these general histories of science, *Kagakushi*, for inclusion in a larger series on Japanese history.[24] This work is important not only because it marks the inclusion of the history of science within Japanese historical studies but also
because its authors, particularly Nakayama Shigeru, would profoundly
influence English-language histories of Chinese and Japanese science through
translations of their works and collaboration with Western scholars.[25]
Nakayama included the following passage, in which he mentions Mori Rintarō, in an article on Japanese nutrition:

With respect to our people's disease, beriberi (which produced so many
victims among the troops during the war with Russia and in Manchuria),
regardless of the opposition of army officer Mori Rintarō, the adoption of
boiled barley and rice, based on naval officer Takagi Kanehiro's explana-

tion of our people's nutritive deficiencies, proved effective; but then Suzuki Umetarō, who studied nutrition in Germany, researched the components of rice and, through an examination of rice bran, discovered a new nutritive compound, oryzanin, which research he presented in Meiji 43 [1910]. His discovery, however, was coldly received in Japan; abroad, oryzanin was dubbed a vitamin one year after it was discovered, and later, with the ascendency of vitamin research, it was reevaluated.[26]

Nakayama writes of the victories of science. With respect to the prevention of diseases related to vitamin deficiency (beriberi), science initially acted on what was effective. The causes, however, were not yet clear. If boiled barley and rice proved effective, it was because barley added the required vitamin. Yet until Suzuki Umetarō arrived on the scene and discovered oryzanin (the vitamin component of rice that is polished and bleached away in the production of white rice), it was impossible to deal with the etiology of the disease.

In Nakayama's history, there are traces of a battle between science and superstition. Why was Suzuki's research received coldly? It was because people could not quite believe in minute entities such as vitamins. It was because people could not quite believe that Japanese food contained the essential nutrients, but these were scrubbed away. Only with the ascendency of vitamin research could Suzuki's efforts be properly evaluated and appreciated. In a sense, Mori's conservatism was vindicated, albeit in a strangely invisible register: Japanese food was indeed adequate. Mori felt that science would prove the soundness of custom, and in time it did. Customs, however, never stay the same, for they are subject to incessant observation, rationalization, and standardization.

Transformations were underway that Nakayama's account did not even attempt to explain. In fact, Nakayama simply conjoined the victory of Japanese science and the victory of the Japanese people. From the outset, beriberi was posed as "our people's disease" (*kokuminbyō*), but the site of observation and experimentation was war: our people were in fact soldiers of an imperial army. Maybe Nakayama cannot be faulted for eliding military victory and scientific victory, and for omitting an account of national expansion, on the grounds that this was how it happened. Nevertheless, this should give us pause: scientific victory meant military victory; the success of the Japanese army was directly tied to advances in nutrition and hygiene. When Nakayama evoked this historical moment, he erased any consideration of these momentous transformations, which launched modern armies into Korea and Manchuria. He did this by writing a history of science based on the logic of victory, and because scientific victories are somehow irrefutable, the military victories of the nation were rendered less questionable. In short, science and society are inextricably entwined in a way that makes it difficult to locate a middle region. The so-called normal sciences compound the difficulties, for epistemological inquiry comes to an impasse. It is difficult to call into the question the existence or effectiveness of vitamins, or to treat them entirely as social constructs.

To rethink the relations of science and society, Isabelle Stengers suggests that we adopt a principle of symmetry in our discussions. "What is it about the new 'anthropology' or 'social history' of sciences," she asks, "that so scandalizes scientists?" And she answers,

> It is written explicitly in the track opened by Kuhn, but does not manifest the same respect as he did for scientific productivity. A new discourse has been constructed that explicitly distinguishes between that which is of interest to scientists and that which should be of interest to those who study scientists. The latter, if they wish to be recognized as legitimate participants in the new field, must comply with a discipline that takes the name "principle of symmetry." It is a matter of drawing conclusions based on the fact that no general methodological norm can justify the difference between victors and vanquished.[27]

Stengers thus returns to the battlefield—before "sanctioned" science has won out over "outdated" science. It is not enough to tell of the victories of science, to speak of where it triumphs and where its reason becomes compromised—as in Nakayama's account of the discovery of oryzanin and vitamins, in which the triumph of reason becomes the triumph of the nation. The difference between Mori Rintarō and Suzuki Umetarō cannot be explained in terms of errors and certainties. Conversely, it is not justified to take the position of the vanquished as normative—as in Oya's account of Mori's sadness as a Japanese, in which nationness can be sanctified because it falls short of science.

The principle of symmetry extends beyond the introduction of relativism into the space between victorious science and vanquished science. Symmetry also is introduced into oppositions such as nature and culture, and modern and premodern. It is, in a sense, an anthropology of natures rather than cultures. As Latour puts it, "It is as impossible to universalize nature as it is to reduce it to the narrow framework of cultural relativism alone. . . . From cultural relativism, we move on to 'natural' relativism."[28] There emerges, then, a new region of analysis between science and society—a middle kingdom of natures/cultures. The goal of the principle of symmetry (with its concerted attempt to reduce the modern world to a scale of mobilization) is not simply to make all things relative but rather to pinpoint and critique the emergence of modern sciences in terms of natural effects as well as cultural effects.

Mori Rintarō's arguments against acupuncture provide an excellent point of departure, for in his efforts to prove that acupuncture is not a science, there emerges a strange mixture of "subjective" and "objective" effects. That is to say, he treats linguistic effects as something other than projections of a subject, and his treatment of scientific effect is not quite consonant with natural causality.

Linguistic and Scientific Effects

In an essay titled "Acupuncture Science" ["Shinka"], Mori Rintarō responds to a letter written by Yoshida Kōdō and addressed to the Office of Internal Affairs requesting government sanction and support for the science of acupuncture. Mori addresses the question of whether acupuncture should be considered a science at all: "Yoshida Kōdō and company refer to acupuncture medicine as acupuncture science. In this letter they say: 'In view of the fact that the techniques of acupuncture heal a great variety of illnesses that medicaments do not really reach, the benefits extended to people with respect to hygiene are not insignificant, and therefore these techniques surely may be said to possess powers offering much to our society.'"[29]

Mori then comments on the way in which Yoshida's letter uses Chinese characters. Yoshida, he says, uses a compound of two characters, "stone" and "needle," to refer to traditional therapies that employ not only acupuncture needles but minerals and moxa as well. Thus, according to Mori, Yoshida claims that "stones and needles" reach illnesses that medicaments do not reach. Mori points out that the two characters for "medicament" (*yakuseki*) comprise the characters for "medicinal herb" (*kusuri*) and "stone" (*ishi*). In effect, Mori concludes, Yoshida is implying that stones reach beyond stones, and such illiteracy is surely to be laughed at (641).

Mori trusts a great deal to the use of language in his scientific writings. He mixes poems from ancient collections such as the *Man' yōshū* (c. 759) and the *Kokinshū* (c. 920) in his discussions of hygiene. Frequently, he allies the finer points of language with the ability to order the world rationally. In fact, it would seem that Mori is not exactly sure how to separate the effects of kanji from those of acupuncture needles or of modern hygiene.

Now it is possible to dismiss this as failed or outdated science. The principle of symmetry, however, encourages a closer look, particularly since Mori himself is confident that he can distinguish modern science from outdated science. At this moment in the emergence of modern science in Japan, how does a scientist attempt to distinguish the effects of hygiene from those of acupuncture?

"Nevertheless," Mori writes with respect to Yoshida and company, "to show consideration for their intent, can one say that the use of acupuncture heals a variety of illnesses that are incurable by methods and remedies other than needles and moxa cones?" (641). Mori addresses two aspects of their claims about acupuncture, namely, its medical effects and its social effects: "From the standpoint of this century's international medicine, one cannot say that acupuncture heals illnesses that cannot be cured by other methods of healing. In other words, acupuncture has no special effectiveness" (641).

Note that Mori has great difficulties with the medical effects of acupuncture. He cannot entirely discount the notion that it does have effects. "There are those instances in which acupuncture may replace other methods of healing," he concedes (641). And so he attempts to qualify and quantify those effects. In the first instance, he claims that modern medicine subsumes the effects of acupuncture (its effects are nothing special or additional), and then in the second instance, he proposes that modern medicine works better than acupuncture: "However, in such cases, acupuncture is not superior to other methods. Did not Bardeleben, Gluck, and others all recognize this?" (641).

When Mori argues about the medical effects of acupuncture, he continually resorts to a hierarchy of effects. He turns time and again to the notion that modern international medicine subsumes and outdistances traditional practices. Nevertheless, he continually acknowledges the effects of acupuncture: "Yoshida has said that 'the benefits extended to people with respect to hygiene are not insignificant.' Doesn't 'hygiene' indicate medical practices broadly? If acupuncture has no special effectiveness and is not superior to other methods of healing, its benefits with respect to medical practice are extremely insignificant" (642). Basically, Mori argues that the effects of acupuncture are not sufficiently broad. Even though he avows that it has effects, he can only dismiss them on the basis of larger effects. This is one way in which modern science attempts to prove its ascendency: it lays claims to better and broader effects. But if modern science claims its authority on the basis of effectiveness alone, the difference is one of quantity not quality. In other words, modern science cannot remain on the turf of its opponents (who also argue from the standpoint of effects). How does Mori strive to transform the ground of debate?

"Yoshida wrote that 'these techniques may be said to possess powers offering much to our society,'" Mori continues, "His diction is obscure, but can one say that there are powers in using needles with respect to the development and survival of our society?" (643–644). This is how Mori will finally deal with Yoshida and company. He introduces another manner of discussion, one that moves science into the realm of national progress and survival: "If acupuncture has no special effectiveness, is not superior to other methods, and has few medical benefits, it is an error to say that it possesses powers with respect to the progress and survival of society" (644). In this way, Mori shifts the debate on medical effects to the problem of social effects, in an attempt to transform the field of battle. It is no longer a question of what medicine contributes to society but of how it ensures the development and survival of society. This is an important shift, for it finally allows Mori to introduce a qualitative asymmetry into the question of traditional medicine versus modern science. But what is the exact nature of this asymmetry between traditional practices and modern science? This is the same question posed by Stengers in her discussion of the invention of modern science:

> At what moment does the reference to science transform the conflict between "doctors" and "charlatans"? I will here put forth the hypothesis that it is not some manner of medical innovation that gave medicine the means to lay claim to the status of science, but the manner in which it gave a diagnosis of the power of the charlatan and an account of the reasons for disqualifying this power. According to this hypothesis, "scientific medicine" would begin when doctors "discover" that not all cures have the same value. The cure of itself proves nothing; a common magic powder or a few passes with a magnetic wand may have an effect, even though they do not have the status of cause. The charlatan is, from this point on, defined as that which takes effect as proof.[30]

Stengers's hypothesis aptly describes the moment of Mori's response to Yoshida's group. This is why, for Mori, "acupuncture medicine" can never be "acupuncture science." Although acupuncture may produce its effects and provide cures, it takes its results and effects for proof—with no account of causes. Likewise for the Japanese diet: Mori may be sure that this diet is effective in view of the survival of those who eat rice, but without the discovery of oryzanin or vitamins, these *effects* cannot lay claim to the status of science. This is why Mori stresses the need for laboratory research to prove his conservative views about Japanese customs. He needs modern science to prove that indigenous customs are the *causes* of Japanese longevity and vitality.

Nevertheless, Mori does not express this causal logic directly. In fact, it is significant that he devotes so much attention to the effects of acupuncture. He cites German studies that show needles to have therapeutic, prophylactic, and diagnostic applications. He then stresses that the dangers of needles outweigh these benefits. In short, he seems always to argue from the perspective of effects. It is only when he introduces the notion of social progress and development that the logic of causality truly enters his account. If Yoshida and company are charlatans, it is not because their medicine has no effects but because their effects do not take the causes into account. On this topic, it is important to recall that the hygienic science of Mori's day involved a debate over the relation of bacteria to disease. When Mori publishes his essay "Discussions on Hygiene" ["Eiseitan"], he never doubts the reality of bacteria but outlines the debate between Pettenkoffer and Koch over whether bacteria causes disease or not.[31] What is interesting about his discussion of acupuncture is that it relies first and foremost on the notion of cause-and-effect history to determine what is outdated. Mori attains his final condemnation of acupuncture on the basis of historical progress: "Yoshida and company pursue the Tokugawa government's establishment of a training school for acupuncture healing; they seem to wish to see again in these days a comparable flourishing. As related above, they do not understand the historical progress of society."[32]

This is a complex moment in which teleological history stands in for etiological science to differentiate doctors from charlatans. Often the problem is posed the other way around. It is supposed that the human and social sciences have gone astray by attempting to adopt the parameters of the natural sciences. "The sciences of nature become the paradigm of all rational knowledge," writes Partha Chatterjee of modernity. "And the principle characteristic of these sciences as they are now conceived is their relation to an entirely new idea of man's control over nature. . . . Consequently, the subject-object relation between man and nature is now subtly transferred, through the 'rational' conception of society, to relations between man and man."[33] Mori's discussion, however, disturbs this sense of the priority of the natural sciences in introducing the subject-object divisions that serve to rationalize social relations, for the human sciences guarantee the rationality of natural sciences.

Latour suggests that we misunderstand the operations of the natural sciences. They do not entail a hierarchical division of the world into subjects and objects. On the contrary, the natural sciences enable the proliferation of quasi-objects, quasi-subjects, and hybrid effects. What masks this "middle kingdom" is a particularly modern division of intellectual practice. If we see the natural sciences in terms of subjects and objects, it is because we continue a specific division of intellectual labor.

It is precisely this problem that Latour addresses when he divides our current theoretical approaches into three camps—somewhat arbitrarily, by his own admission—to highlight the reigning divisions of labor in intellec-

tual work. He takes E. O. Wilson, Pierre Bourdieu, and Jacques Derrida—
"a bit unfairly"—as emblematic figures. "When the first speaks of naturalized phenomena," he writes, "then societies, subjects, and all forms of discourse vanish. When the second speaks of fields of power, then science,
technology, texts, and the contents of activities disappear. When the third
speaks of truth effects, then to believe in the real existence of brain neurons
or power plays would betray enormous naiveté." Latour goes on to say that
it has become impossible to think of these three modes at once and that it
would seem grotesque to patch these approaches together: "Our intellectual
life remains recognizable as long as epistemologists, sociologists and decon-
structionists remain at arm's length, the critique of each feeding on the
weakness of the other two."[34] And yet, Latour argues, for all our attempts to
divide our approaches, we face global events—such as ozone depletion or
the AIDS pandemic—that combine facts, power, and discourse in impossible and unthinkable formulations.

Now Latour's characterization is unfair insofar as these same thinkers
can be said to break down many of the traditional intellectual divides.
Moreover, his terminology seems infelicitous in that he characterizes the
three realms as real, social, and discursive—as if discursive or social effects
were somehow not real. After all, a number of levels of interaction and interpenetration of discursive, social, and scientific effects have been explored:
(1) the transformation of language can be said to enable subject-object divisions that ground scientific discourse, and conversely, scientific observation
transforms the linguistic subject; (2) sociologists suggest that scientists tend
to come from particular sorts of families, and so societies that produce scientists must produce certain types of familial relations; (3) the demand for
scientific training transforms education, introducing new ways of perceiv-
ing, knowing, and organizing the world; and (4) competition for governmental or industrial support introduces new power formations.[35]

Nevertheless, Latour issues an important challenge with respect to the
ways in which we read science. Analyses tend to ignore the effects of the
natural sciences because they are just out there, naturally. Or we tend to
treat the effects of the natural sciences with an emphasis on subjective projection and social construction. Karatani Kōjin, for instance, gives an
account of the discourse on pathogens in modern Japanese literature; this

discourse is related to social and political effects that structure new power formations. Thus, Karatani signals that there is something profoundly constructed about microbes. Latour would agree that we cannot deny this constructedness, and yet we remain unable to account for the proliferation of hybrid forms of agency around quasi-objects. For Latour, the emblem of this hybrid agency is the bacterium—neither pure object nor pure subject, neither pure cause nor pure effect.

In sum, if Mori's account of acupuncture confuses linguistic and scientific effects, it is not because he is not able to attain the certainties of modern science but because the field of modern science is replete with hybrid effects— effects that the disciplinary divisions continue to mask. Mori's science is instructive precisely because it often seems to fail to sunder scientific and linguistic effects. It occupies an unthinkable site within contemporary theory. This becomes even clearer when one looks at Mori's science from the standpoint of quasi-objects such as microbes —where war becomes the site of experiment, and conquered territories the site of production and reproduction of "natural" effects.[36]

Linguistic and Bacterial Colonies

A surgeon general in the United States Army, Louis Seaman, received permission to accompany the Japanese army to the front in the Russo-Japanese War to study the effectiveness of their medicine. In one of his books, *The Real Triumph of Japan*, he concludes that the war the Japanese won was fought not primarily against a human enemy but more importantly against a silent and hidden foe, disease. According to Seaman, the real triumph of Japan, "unparalleled and unapproached in the annals of war," was for the Japanese to say, "We are willing to sacrifice the million men, but the element of disease with its terrible cost and impedimenta must be eliminated."[37] Seaman explains that "out of every one hundred men who fall in war twenty die from bullets or wounds, while eighty perish from disease, most of which is preventable. This dreadful and unnecessary sacrifice of life, especially in conflicts between Anglo-Saxon races, is the most ghastly proposition of modern war, and the Japanese have gone a long way to conquering or eliminating it" (2).

The lesson that Seaman wanted his country to learn was that there was another war to be waged in and around the actual war, a war against disease. Surely this was a strange moment in the history of warfare when it was decided that victory lay in removing all impediments to battle before the battle. War was at once deferred and omnipresent. War now entailed a concerted effort in hygiene and nutrition, work that began at home and expanded into the preparations for war and mobilization on the enemy front. Seaman's account brings home another lesson: from the Civil War until the 1920s, the United States did not have every advantage over Japan. In fact, in hygiene and military science (as well as industry), Japan had brought itself into the forefront of modern nations. In the early twentieth century, the United States recognized its deficiencies in military hygiene and assigned personnel to follow the Japanese army into Asia, in order to learn the secrets of its success. What is more, in the postwar period, the eagerness of the American army to exploit the data from Japan's Unit 731 in Manchuria suggests that the enchantment of the American military with Japanese expertise in biological warfare continued beyond Seaman's day.

Seaman attributes the military triumph of Japan in part to its assimilationist capacity:

> Throughout the history of the development of medicine in Japan there has been patent a constant desire to absorb everything of intrinsic value from the outside world. The Japanese trait of discarding that which is valueless and of assimilating that which is of sterling worth has been evident at every age. The encouragement to the study of sanitation has also been striking, and the relation of that to the military success of the nation, where preventable diseases in both army and navy have been reduced almost to a minimum, are worthy subjects for deeper study. (215)

This description of the Japanese character borders on cliché. Yet there are a couple of points of interest. First, because it deals with the Japanese battlefront, Seaman's account reminds us that Japanese expansion involved the assimilation not just of ideas and objects but also of lands and peoples. This is important because the legacy of the American Occupation of Japan has done so much to transform our sense of what Japanese assimilation entailed. The contemporary myth of Japanese racial purity and homogeneity has it that Japanese assimilation is limited to concepts, technologies, and commodities. In the days of Mori Rintarō and Louis Seaman, however, the idea of Japanese purity allowed for certain forms of linguistic and ethnic hybridity. Second, because Seaman's account deals explicitly with the issues of infection and sanitation, it juxtaposes and even blends the logic of bacterial purification and sanitation with imperial assimilation.

In the second half of the nineteenth century, two directions emerged in the study of bacteria and the etiology of disease. In France, Louis Pasteur turned to experimental analysis to determine how infective disease is produced in the body and how recovery and immunity are brought about. In Germany, Robert Koch sought technical methods for the examination and cultivation of bacteria and developed rational principles of hygiene and prophylaxis.[38] In effect, these two directions suggested two interlocking strategies for the elimination of infectious disease: inoculation and sanitation. At the turn of the century, the study of hygiene in Japan gathered its momentum from studies done in Germany by scientists sent there by the Japanese government. Kitasato Shisasaburō, one of the most famous of these scientists, studied under Robert Koch at the Hygienisches Institut in Berlin, as did Mori Rintarō.[39] Thus, the Japanese trajectory followed the hygienic, prophylactic, and sanitary practices associated with Koch.

Koch organized his research around the production of pure cultures of bacteria in the laboratory. He attempted to obtain a good medium for the growth of bacterial cultures, a medium that was at once sterile, transparent, and solid.[40] Pure cultures of bacteria require a certain manual dexterity and ingenuity. The technique Koch developed—the poured-plate method—begins with the isolation of a sample from a natural source (water, air, soil, or food, with their saprophytic bacteria). The sample is introduced into a sterile and transparent liquid medium (sometimes diluted to amplify the separation of colonies), which then solidifies in a petri dish. Bacterial colonies subsequently develop from discrete (aerobic) bacteria that are near the surface of the medium. The medium can be altered to select for certain species, and various levels of disinfectant can be introduced to determine what concentrations kill the organisms. With these simple methods, Koch and his followers isolated bacteria in pure cultures and showed them to be the etiological agents of certain diseases.

It is possible to take this process as an analogy for the production of Japanese cultures in colonies such as Korea and Taiwan. There, analogous attempts were made to construct a transparent medium for cultivation with the establishment of Japanese education and standardized language. It was a process of selection and purification, as it were. This kind of analogy makes everything seem simple because it produces objects and subjects: it adopts the perspective of the administrator who naively thinks that people react passively to institutions. A similar naivete emerges in science if the scientist thinks that the passivity of bacteria allows one to treat them as objects. But there is a hitch in the laboratory construction of pure cultures, one that is often dramatized in science fiction. Bacteria refuse to remain objects. They threaten to exceed their medium and swarm out of their tubes and plates into the world. In fact, the complexity of bacteria lies in their agency, just as the complexity of Japanese colonies lay in the agency of allegedly passive subjects. This is what makes the simultaneity of national colonies and bacterial colonies so instructive. This simultaneity suggests that nation and science together produced a proliferation of quasi-objects and quasi-subjects. The hybridity of bacterial and national colonies begins with the agency of bacteria and peoples in the colonial network.

Now when we look at strategies such as inoculation and sanitation alongside the formation of the nation, we always see the purification of the nation. The nation tries to protect its corporeal sanctity by absorbing just enough of the contagion to make itself immune to invasion. Alternatively, the nation attempts to protect itself from invasion by pasteurizing its environs. In these instances, we see the nation already formed, protecting its integrity. But if we shift the emphasis slightly to the site where bacteria encounter the body, we see a boundary in the process of formation unfurling a zone of proliferation. There arises a diffracted boundary that unleashes the proliferation of hybrid effects. The very productivity of nation and science depends on the construction of these zones. It is there that we see the incredible prolixity, hybridity, and asymmetry of modernity. Latour asks why we overlook these zones from the perspective of the natural sciences. He suggests that if we overlook the real effects of science (such as military expansion through hygiene), we miss the reasons for Seaman's celebration of Japanese military hygiene: science not only transforms our attitudes toward nature, it alters nature; it is not that nature (as an object) has come under the control of humans (as subjects) but that modernity has coupled itself with nature in a particular way, unleashing the proliferation of hybrid positions.[41]

Why do we typically not pay attention to this proliferation and interpenetration of quasi-objects and quasi-subjects? Why do we not think of modern science as a transformation or manufacture of things that operates largely through an isolation and amplification of traits and aspects, as in bacteriology? Why do we not see it as analogous to the production of the Japanese empire, to the isolation and amplification of specific customs and acts? What does all this tell us about Mori Rintarō, military doctor and administrator, on the Japanese battlefront with Louis Seaman trailing after?

Latour calls our attention to the intellectual division of labor that arises historically between social-political representation, natural-scientific representation, and textual-conceptual representation. Such divisions make visible Mori Ōgai, the literary figure, but render invisible the military doctor and administrator Mori Rintarō, who is part of the "real triumph of Japan" in Korea and Manchuria that Seaman so eagerly documents. These divisions begin with Mori Rintarō/Ōgai himself. Mori struggled to establish the independence of literature from science and worked to cover any traces of overlap in their enterprises. One of the most celebrated instances is his response to one of his literary peers, Tsubouchi Shōyō, who ardently proclaimed the principles of naturalism proposed by Émile Zola. Zola based his literary manifesto largely on the ideas of the doctor Claude Bernard, who spoke of the importance of observation and experimentation. Mori, who opposed Shōyō's naturalism, insisted that literature maintains ideals that are independent of science. In particular, literature involves intuition rather than observation and experimentation. Thus, he challenged Zola for "never questioning the sharpness of his knife"—that is, for never doubting that dissection and analysis would reach the truth. For Ōgai, when literature turned to clinical observation, analysis, dissection, and experimentation, it lost its hold on the ideal, on intuition.[42] Since Mori devoted a great deal of effort to conceptualizing the separation of literature and science, it is fair to say that the work of the modern—as a separation of forms of representation that thwarts any attempt to make visible the middle region between political, scientific, and literary representation—begins with him.

Of course, it is easy to locate the ironies and uncertainties of Mori's position. After all, in his attack on the scientific method in literature, he signs
himself Mori Rintarō and does not fail to underline that he writes "as a doctor."[43] In fact, despite his insistence on modern divisions, it is possible to see
the real work of Mori Rintarō/Ōgai in terms of a mixture of scientific,
social, and literary effects on an unimaginable scale. This is particularly evident when we read his science in tandem with his fiction. *The Collected
Works of Mori Ōgai* replicates the compartmentalization of Mori's intellectual labor by cordoning off the essays on hygiene in separate volumes, and
yet within and across these texts emerge so many hybrid positions: crosses
of poem and bacterium, of war and lyric, of hygiene and translation. If we
temporarily forestall the urge to assign a hierarchy to these mixes in terms
of foreground and background, or dominant and subordinate modes, it is
evident that, despite their claims to the contrary, his works are far from separating science, society, and literature. The result is an intensely hybridized
mix of facts, power plays, and fictions. This is Latour's point: only when the
work of separation and purification is complete does modernity unfurl its
impossible hybrids — yet hybridity no longer shows itself as such, for it continues the work of isolation and purification, concealing the production of
hybrids.

There are countless moments when Mori himself demonstrates an awareness that modern productivity lies primarily not in purity but in hybridity —
but these texts are less often read. In a series of aphorisms titled "Shintōgo,"
written around 1900, he constructs a model that crosses the boundaries of
language, diet, and currency to speak of the productivity of hybridization:
"Rice is a staple. Meat and vegetables are supplements."[44] Mori evokes the
logic of supplementarity, which he rapidly extends to other systems, such as
the Japanese phonetic syllabary: "To rescue today's kana from the rank of
supplement, value it as you would rice. There is only one way to be equal to
discharging one's duty for the reform of the national script" (139–140).

Here, Mori is alluding to the debates over the unification of speech and
script (*genbun'itchi*) that were so important in Meiji Japan. The primary
goal of the Movement for the Unification of Speech and Script was to establish a standard Japanese language and script. In his interpretation of *genbun'-
itchi*, Karatani Kōjin points out, quite correctly, that the movement initially

called for phonocentrism. That is, it called for purifying the Japanese syllabary through an elimination of Chinese characters. Karatani goes into the details of this phonocentric purification.[45] And yet, in Mori's account of dietary and scriptural supplements, it is not purification that is the productive moment. Purification of the kana syllabary is merely the first step on the way to hybridization.

"Once we discharge our duty in this matter, will there be anyone not equal to heaping their plate with supplements from the myriad scripts of the world outside our national script?" Mori continues. "We should put in Chinese characters, we should take in Roman letters, even Sanskrit, Hebrew, Greek, Cyrillic—not one may not be inserted"[46] Note how Mori wheels between language, diet, and political duty. First, he insists on the isolation of the Japanese national script from other scripts. But the moment of isolation and purification prepares for that of hybridization, and Mori clearly announces hybridity as the productive moment of language reform. The question arises about the authority for such productive hybridity. Obviously, it is not sufficient for someone indiscriminately to mix metaphors and make analogies to usher in hybridity. Mori cautions that the insertion of multiple scripts should not be indiscriminate. To employ various regional and urban dialects without selection and purification, he suggests, would result in a debased language, one unfit for universal thoughts and global dissemination. Subsequently, he turns to the circulation of capital to describe the moment of dissemination and hybridization. Like precious metals, scripts are to be excavated for circulation; scientists and writers are to dig through the rubbish and extract valuable and valid fragments, and these are to be forged anew and spread through the society or world.

How does Mori Rintarō/Ōgai, who writes so often of the separation of literature from science and politics, arrive at such hybridity? Karatani Kôjin locates the sources of such hybridity in premodern Japan, as opposed to the efforts at purity of modern Japan. He depicts the main trajectory of modern Japanese literature in terms of the production of interiority and transparency, and in those terms, Karatani reserves a special place for the two most revered writers of Meiji Japan, Mori Ōgai and Natsume Sōseki. On the basis of Mori's resistance to the elimination of Chinese characters, Karatani situates Mori on the outside of Japanese modernity. In particular,

Mori's turn to historical fiction signals the resistance of the premodern to the modern:

> Ōgai's deepest desires were therefore realized in the historical fiction where he wrote of samurai characters. In these works Ōgai tried to thoroughly eliminate any trace of the "psychological." In doing this Ōgai had something in common with the later Sōseki who wrote fiction in the morning and lost himself in a world of Chinese poetry and ink-brush painting in the afternoon. For both men "literature" must have retained a certain unfamiliarity; both must have developed a perspective which rejected the concept of "expression." The mainstream of modern Japanese literature continued along lines set forth by Doppo rather than Ōgai or Sōseki.[47]

This is quite appealing: Karatani locates the two most lauded writers of modern Japanese literature outside modern modes of representation. Basically, Karatani can do this because he avoids any association of modernity and hybridity.

For Karatani, modernity entails the production and imposition of subject-object dichotomies; he treats these dichotomies for the most part in symmetrical terms (interiority and exteriority). He never speaks of the asymmetry of subject and object (a subjection of the object), which makes possible not only the purification but also the hybridization of subject and object. As a result, he sees modernity exclusively in terms of the purification and consolidation of the interior, with the elimination of the exterior. Above all, for Karatani, Chinese characters are signs of exteriority that Japanese modernity should attempt to eliminate. And so, when he encounters a writer, such as Mori, who makes no attempt to eliminate Chinese characters, Karatani concludes that that writer is not entirely modern.

It is true that Mori is not primarily interested in the elimination of Chinese characters and the purification of the Japanese language. He is interested in a constant assimilation and hybridization of the exterior, which he relates to scientific research on the importance of dietary supplements and to economic ideas about the circulation of wealth. But contrary to Karatani's interpretation, Mori's stance on Chinese characters shows that modernity involves not just purification but hybridization.

It should be recalled that *genbun'itchi* comprised two phases: In the first phase, Chinese characters were seen as anathema to the establishment of a rationally phonetic script for the Japanese language. In the second phase, the standardization of Japanese for use in the colonies was at stake, and Chinese characters proved extremely useful in creating points of contact between Japanese, Chinese, and Koreans.[48] Mori's discussion of language reminds us that the work of modern Japan involved not only national purification and unification but also national expansion and hybridization. The two operations proceeded apace. And so, if we wish to speak of exteriority in Mori's fiction, we have only to look at his scientific research to see that that exteriority lies not outside Japanese modernity but outside Japanese national boundaries—in the colonies and on the battlefront, in Taiwan, Korea, and Manchuria, as well as in Russia and the laboratories of Europe. Associated with the production of bacterial cultures and the transformation of their agency with respect to humans are global transformations in nature, society, and language. At the level of the bacterium, we see that the unevenness that is part of the modern becomes so pervasive because it begins with the microscopic and extends across unimaginable scales.

Latour stresses that the real work of modernity is to produce and conceal hybrids across vast scales: "Century after century, colonial empire after colonial empire, the poor premodern collectives were accused of making a horrible mishmash of things and humans, of objects and signs, while their accusers finally separated them totally—to remix them at once on a scale unknown till now."[49] Latour suggests that the modern mixing and hybridizing of things and humans, as well as objects and signs, remains invisible because the West is obsessed with the myth of its difference from all the rest. Westerners claim that they differ radically and absolutely, to the extent that Westerners can be lined up on one side and all the other cultures opposite (97). At the heart of modernity, however, lie unthinkable and unrepresentable hybrids; these hybrids, not pure cultures, constitute modern productivity. "Moderns," Latour writes, "do differ from premoderns by this single trait: they refuse to conceptualize quasi-objects as such" (112). As a result, the sciences and technologies emerge in such a mysterious way that Westerners are forced to see themselves as completely different from others.

This generates a cascade of small differences that are collected, summarized, and amplified by the Great Divide, the great narrative of the West, which sets it radically apart from all other cultures.

To countermand this exceptionalism, Latour submits, rather sensationally, that "we have never been modern." The single trait that distinguishes the moderns from the premoderns is a refusal to conceptualize hybridity, a refusal that simply increases the scale of mobilization: "The fact that one collective needs ancestors and fixed stars while another one, more eccentric, needs genes and quasars, is explained by the dimensions of the collective to be held together" (108). Ultimately, Latour presents scientific modernity as a myth that can be easily deconstructed and displaced. In this respect, then, he does not give much credence to subjectivities, much less to qualities and intensities. As a result, for all the insights to be gleaned from his radical dethroning of scientific modernity and Western exceptionalism, a note of caution should be sounded. Is it so easy to annul the desire and subjectivity associated with the West, or modernity, or nationality? Latour's argument would call attention to the middle region, where hybridity arises. Yet the term hybridity itself, with all its echoes of racial thought, draws attention to the persistence of colonial desire.[50] On this topic, the realm of microbes can furnish some additional clues.

The work of bacterial isolation and purification takes the form of speciation (separation by species), and the work of national isolation and purification takes the form of linguistic standardization and education. The dubious term that stands between species and language is race; the term, undefinable biologically or linguistically, encompasses a little of both. This is why both Seaman and Mori speak so authoritatively of medical hygiene and national expansion in the same breath: the battlefield of the modern nation combines bacterial species and linguistic cultures in the unrepresentable site of race, and that is the site of productive hybridity. And just as the evocation and elimination of disease becomes the real military triumph of Japan, so does the evocation and elimination of race become the ideological vocation of pan-Asian colonization. This is why we, like Seaman and Mori, are still modern: as long as we evoke the logic of species alongside language, all our hybridities are mediated through purities.[51]

Linguistic and Hygienic Experiments

It should now come as less of a surprise that Mori Rintarō/Ōgai, after devoting years to various modes for separating conceptual, political, and experimental systems, turned to a mode of writing (historical fiction) in which all of his previous divisions seem to be ignored. Many readers find that the historical fiction does not make for successful literature, for plot and narrative subjectivity fairly vanish into documentation. Then again, as Karatani points out, this apsychological mode can also be a source of literary interest. I would like to suggest a different intrepretation: in the historical fiction, because the work of purification is so firmly rooted, the production of hybrids across the resultant asymmetries can proceed unhindered and unremarked. The result is not literature but a hybrid of science and literature — like ethnology (for lack of a better term).

To achieve this hybridity, Chinese characters must not be transparently representational. They must appear as objects. In one essay explaining his historical fiction, Mori laments that editors have diminished the reality effect of his stories by introducing phonetic glosses on the characters. He wants characters to stand without phonetic readings because he has come to revere the "nature" or "reality" or "spontaneity" (*shizen*) of the Chinese characters that appear in the old chronicles, records, and annals. Mori feels that when one fixes the reading of a Chinese character, one alters its history and reality.[52]

Why is this "nature" or "reality" or "spontaneity" attached to Chinese characters, especially to characters copied from old documents? On the one hand, characters should function like objects in the laboratory, according to Mori. They should speak for themselves, and their representation by the writer or scientist should be invisible. Just as the scientist presents, without mediation, a record of the actions of things, the historian of glyphs merely copies the reality of characters. This realist stance recalls, of course, the comments of Roland Barthes on the rhetorical devices that produce a sense of objective and realist history.[53] On the other hand, Mori attributes an almost subjective or animate reality to characters. Characters are quite real, as are their effects, but their status with respect to object and subject remains uncertain. Recall Mori's comments on Yoshida's use of characters:

Yoshida, he complained, couldn't even arrange and classify their effects. Recall, too, his comments on the productivity of language: characters are supplements, and as such, they assure vitality and productivity. In sum, Mori proposes to use characters objectively, and yet he sees in them a vital force. Like bacteria, they are treated *as if* they were objects, but they remain quasi-objects: their effectiveness depends on their agency and on their ability to be cultivated.

Now one can argue that this view of characters as possessed of vital and generative forces is a throwback to Confucian notions of language. One can as easily argue that it is linked to the currency of vitalist thought in Mori's day. Whatever the source, it is evident that Mori combines notions of generative language with notions of objective, scientific transcription. The result is a place for experiments, full of the quasi-objects of language. I would like to say that this use of characters, in which they become bacteria-like quasi-objects, does not constitute a form of nonmodernity or premodernity in Mori's works. It constitutes the unrepresentable site of proliferation at the heart of modernity. Around this usage of characters, Mori fashions experiments that cross the boundaries between language and science (between textual and real effects, in Latour's terms). "How would it be," he asks with respect to Japanese language reform, "if we were to limit the use of characters in public documents to those found in the Thousand-Character Classic?" His conclusion invokes workplace efficiency: "Such an index (*kensaku*) would surely transform an hour's work into a day's work."[54] The term *kensaku* provides a good gauge of Mori's experiments: they are at once reference works, character indices, and laboratory tests.

Mori experimented with language. He treated it objectively and apsychologically and yet generatively. As a result, words and characters enter into an operation of proliferation and hybridization, which is made invisible by calls to objectivity and unthinkable by calls to purity. The conditions for reproduction of a network of real, social, and textual effects is in place. Just as hygiene and nutrition win the real war against the silent foe by producing and hiding a proliferation of quasi-objects, so language reform produces the solid, stable, and transparent medium upon which cultures are purified, differentiated, and selected so as to mix them on an unimaginable scale.

In conclusion, I would like to look at one of Mori's experiments with language. Although I've mentioned his historical fiction as the locus for his final experiments, I think that his essay "Female Hygiene" ["Joshi no eisei"] provides a better example of how his experiments with language work, especially because Mori directs his attention to the colonial network.[55] In this piece, Mori argues about the differences between men and women and proposes that "we hygienists expound special methods of hygiene for women on account of the special disposition of women" (48). He derives the authority for this distinction from German and Chinese poets, concluding that "men regulate the exterior, women manage the interior; men are active, women are passive; men abound in creative forces, women abound in supportive forces" (48). Two points merit attention in his discussion of men and women: First, although the temptation is to relate such remarks to premodern Japan (insofar as they resonate with neo-Confucian ideals), Mori finds equivalent expressions in German poetry. This is a modern moment—of the translation and transmutation of cultures and natures. Second, Mori treats male and female in terms not only of anatomy but of disposition and generation as well. This confusion of biology and psychology comes not only from Confucian ideas about gender but also from modern science—with hints of vitalism. In other words, Mori's remarks come from a hybrid moment in which various notions of gender converge, but these mixes and hybrids remain unrepresentable even as they proliferate. This is the hybridity of which Mori's modernity is fashioned—and the terms for hybridity will entail the maintenance of unevenness across these apparently symmetrical categories.

Mori approaches an issue that he claims is of the hour—that of the "beauty" of female adornment. He isolates the word for "beauty" (*mi*) and proposes to replace it with "customs" (*zoku*) so as to introduce a global perspective. This replacement moves him from the transcendent to the immanent: "We hygienists have no intention of debating the true meaning of beauty from a philosophical perspective" (50). He gives an overview of female adornment in Delhi, Japan, Damascus, and France and concludes: "Since what is called 'beauty' in female adornment largely returns to a single word, 'custom,' it may be clearly understood that it is a matter of the 'vogues' of a particular era or region" (50). At the same time, Mori delimits this experiment with words or characters: "We have no intention of rubbing out the character 'beauty' only to take up the character 'health' and substitute it for this, in the manner of some recent Japanese hygienists. . . . With respect to female adornment, we have decided that what passes for 'beauty' in the world is mostly a matter of 'custom'" (50). So it is that Mori begins his experiment in the logic of other collectives:

> The women of India color their teeth black as in the past in Japan. The dancing girls of Delhi adorn their foreheads, noses, ears, and fingers with gold and paint their toenails crimson. The women of Damascus draw their eyebrows in black bows, apply rouge to their cheeks, and paint black beneath their eyes all the way to their temples. The ladies of the islands of the South Seas tattoo their legs, shoulders, and the tip of their tongue. Those daughters of black men, who wear nothing but a loincloth and glass beads around their neck, fill coconut husks with water for a mirror and paint their face in shades of blue, red, and white; they pierce the septum of their nose and their lips and place ornaments there. It is all but a single-hearted devotion to displaying "beauty." (29:49)

In the final instance, Mori's conclusions are unimpressive. He proposes not to prohibit corsets (or obi), which adversely affect women with their tightness; he claims that he would like only to prohibit an undue tightening of corsets. In the end, everything is in its place, but now things are sanitized and hygienic. There is strict policing of the distinction between immanent and transcendent—between custom and beauty, science and aesthetics, men and women. Mori sets in place interlocking asymmetries that separate science, literature, and politics in a way that promises to prevent adverse interactions between people and things. And yet this speciation of effects simultaneously enables an uncontrolled hybridization: we are in a realm occupied by lungs, tooth blacking, gender, native dress, social customs, and breathing restrictions. And this hybridization is not discursive alone; it couples nature and society to generate quasi-objects and quasi-subjects at every turn. But it is the premodern collectives that stand accused of confusing matters.

Thus, Mori's experiments with facts and fictions, whether we dub it science, literature, history, or ethnography, lead to a proliferation of effects, none of which can be represented in the terms set up by drawing clear distinctions between real, textual, and social effects. How could pierced noses, pinching corsets, blackened teeth, and tightened obi be related to something like the colonial venture or reducing casualties in war? And yet such unthinkable relationships, which link things and people on a scale that is at once infinitely small and infinitely large, constitute the modernity of Mori's experiments.

Notes

A preliminary version of this paper was presented at the Meiji Studies Conference, Edwin O. Reischauer Institute of Japanese Studies, Harvard University, 6–8 May 1994. I would like to thank Judith Farquhar and Marta Hanson, as well as Brett de Bary, for detailed comments that profoundly challenged and changed many of the initial arguments in this paper. I would also like to thank the Fonds pour la formation de chercheurs et l'aide à la recherche (FCAR) and the Social Science and Humanities Research Council.

1   *The Collected Works of Mori Ōgai* [*Ōgai zenshū*], 3d ed., 38 vols., ed. Kinoshita Mokutarō et al. (Tokyo: Iwanami Shoten, 1971–1975).

2   I summarize Mori's history largely from J. Thomas Rimer, *Mori Ōgai* (New York: Twayne Publishers, 1975). Richard Bowring, *Mori Ōgai and the Modernization of Japan* (Cambridge: Cambridge University Press, 1979), also is an important general source for the background of various literary and intellectual debates.

3   James A. Fujii, "Writing Out Asia: Modernity, Canon, and Natsume Sōseki's *Kokoro*," *positions* 1, no. 1 (spring 1993): 194–223.

4   See Mori Ōgai, *Uta nikki* (Tokyo: Syunyodo, 1907). The poems in this book, which were composed between 1902 and 1905, include a number that refer to Mori's military service. Both J. Thomas Rimer (*Mori Ōgai*) and Richard Bowring (*Mori Ōgai*) translate and discuss some of these poems.

5   Michel Foucault, "Truth and Power," in *Power/Knowledge: Selected Interviews and Other Writings, 1972–1977* (Hassocks, England: Harvester Press, 1980), 109.

6   Karatani Kōjin, *The Origins of Modern Japanese Literature*, trans. and ed. Brett de Bary (Durham, N.C.: Duke University Press, 1993).

7   Latour takes his notion of quasi-objects from Michel Serres, coming around to this definition: "Quasi-objects are between the two poles [of nature and society], at the very place around which dualism and dialectics had turned endlessly without being able to come to terms with them. Quasi-objects are much more social, much more fabricated, much more collective than the 'hard' parts of nature, but they are in no way the arbitrary receptacles of a full-fledged society. On the other hand, they are much more real, nonhuman and objective than those shapeless screens on which society—for unknown reasons—needed to be 'pro-

jected.'" See Bruno Latour, *We Have Never Been Modern*, trans. Catherine Porter (Cambridge, Mass.: Harvard University Press, 1993), 55.

8 Oya Yukiyo, "Mori Ōgai no Nihon shoku ron: 'Hi Nihon shoku ron wa masa ni sono konkyo wo ushinawan to su,' wo yomu," in *Mori Ōgai: Shoki sakuhin no sekai*, ed. Tanaka Minoru (Tokyo: Yūseidō, 1987), 100.

9 Mori Ōgai, "Daydreams," trans. Richard Bowring, in *Youth and Other Stories*, ed. J. Thomas Rimer (Honolulu: University of Hawai'i Press, 1994), 175–176.

10 Oya, "Mori Ōgai," 99–101.

11 Ibid.

12 Mori, "Daydreams," 176.

13 Oya quotes a passage in "The Argument against Japanese Food May Soon Lose Its Foundation" in which Mori writes, "Why abandon induction and take up deduction?" Mori uses the terms *sakugempō* (going upstream to the source) and *junryūhō* (following the current), which Oya associates with the modern Japanese terms *kinaihō* and *en'ekihō*, or induction and deduction. See Oya, "Mori Ōgai," 104.

14 Mori, "Daydreams," 176.

15 Oya, "Mori Ōgai," 104.

16 The term "structure of feeling" occurs in much of Williams's writing. It was first articulated in *Preface to Film* (with Michael Orrom; London: Film Drama, 1954) and was linked explicitly to Gramsci's notion of hegemony in *The Long Revolution* (London: Chatto and Windus, 1961). Basically, as I cite it here, it is a critical term intended to emphasize the political implications of culture without endorsing Adorno's vision of communications and media as fundamentally manipulative. Williams discusses it as an emergent pattern of general experience, primarily in the realm of literature and literary authors, but I would like to extend Oya's discussions of Mori Ōgai/Rintarō's emotion in his scientific writings to the possibility of structures of feeling in scientific communication. As Oya suggests, such structures of feeling would be linked to "nationness," and as Latour and Stengers suggest, to military victory.

17 Michel Foucault, *The Order of Things: An Archaeology of the Human Sciences* (New York: Vintage Books, 1973), xx–xxi.

18 Michel Foucault, *The Birth of the Clinic: An Archeology of Medical Perception*, trans. A. M. Sheridan (New York: Random House, 1973), 107.

19 Mori, "Daydreams," 180.

20 Peter Duus, *The Abacus and the Sword: The Japanese Penetration of Korea, 1895–1910* (Berkeley and Los Angeles: University of California Press, 1995), 201–204, 364–376.

21 Jared Diamond, *Guns, Germs, and Steel: The Fate of Human Societies* (New York: W. W. Norton, 1997).

22 See William H. McNeill, "History Upside Down," review of *Guns, Germs, and Steel: The Fate of Human Societies*, by Jared Diamond, *New York Review of Books*, 15 May 1997, 48–50.

23 Jared Diamond, letter to the editor, *New York Review of Books*, 26 June 1997, 69. See also McNeill's letter to the editor in the same issue of this magazine.

24 Sugimoto Isao, Satō Shōsuke, and Nakayama Shigeru, *Kagaku-shi*, Taikei Nihon shi sōsho, vol. 19 (Tokyo: Yamakawa Shuppansha, 1967).

25 See Oya Shin'ichi, "Reflections on the History of Science in Japan," in *Science and Society in Modern Japan: Selected Historical Sources*, ed. Nakayama Shigeru, David L. Swain, and Yagi Eri (Cambridge, Mass.: MIT Press, 1974), 68. These four works by Nakayama indicate something of the extent of his scholarship in English: *Academic and Scientific Traditions in China and Japan*, trans. Jerry Dusenbury (Tokyo: University of Tokyo Press, 1984); edited with Nathan Sivin, *Chinese Science: Explorations of an Ancient Tradition* (Cambridge, Mass.: MIT Press, 1973); *Characteristics of Scientific Development in Japan* (New Delhi: Centre for the Study of Science, Technology, and Development, 1977); and *Science, Technology, and Society in Postwar Japan* (London and New York: Kegan Paul, 1991).

26 Nakayama Shigeru, "Kagaku gijutsu no bunka to hatten," in Sugimoto, Satō, and Nakayama, *Kagaku-shi*, 415–416.

27 Isabelle Stengers, *L'Invention des sciences modernes* (Paris: Éditions La Découverte, 1993), 16–17.

28 Latour, *We Have Never*, 106.

29 Mori Ōgai, "Shinka," in Kinoshita et al., *Collected Works of Mori Ōgai*, 34:641–644. The dates of composition and original publication of this essay are unknown.

30 Stengers, *L'Invention*, 32.

31 Mori Ōgai, "Eiseitan," in Kinoshita et al., *Collected Works of Mori Ōgai*, 34:242–252. "Eiseitan" was originally published 8 February 1901.

32 Ōgai, "Shinka," 34:644.

33 Partha Chatterjee, *Nationalist Thought and the Colonial World: A Derivative Discourse* (Minneapolis: University of Minnesota Press, 1986), 14.

34 Latour, *We Have Never*, 5–6.

35 James Bartholomew (*The Formation of Science in Japan: Building a Research Tradition* [New Haven, Conn.: Yale University Press, 1989]) raises a number of these issues.

36 Bruno Latour gives an account of the overlap of science, novel, and war in his interpretation of Napoleon's campaign in Russia and the rise of Pasteur. See Latour, *The Pasteurization of France*, trans. Alan Sheridan and John Law (Cambridge, Mass.: Harvard University Press, 1988), esp. his introduction to "War and Peace of Microbes," 3–12.

37 Louis L. Seaman, *The Real Triumph of Japan* (New York: D. Appleton and Co., 1906), 5–6.

38 See William Bulloch, *The History of Bacteriology* (London: Oxford University Press, 1979), 213.

39 See Bartholomew, *Formation of Science*, 166–167; and Bowring, *Mori Ōgai*, 20.

40 Bulloch, *History of Bacteriology*, 227.

41 Latour, *We Have Never*, 94–96, 103–106.

42   Mori Ōgai, "Shōsetsuron," in Kinoshita et al., *Collected Works of Mori Ōgai*, 38:451, cited in Bowring, *Mori Ōgai*, 66. Mori addresses the crisis spawned by Enlightenment science and medicine (which Barbara Stafford describes in the chapter on "sensing" in *Body Criticism: Imaging the Unseen in Enlightenment Art and Medicine* [Cambridge, Mass.: MIT Press, 1991]). When the body is dissected, its life has fled; the blade cannot obtain the very thing that it proposes to examine—life. The blade must thus go deeper. Mori, as some of his stories and essays make clear, wished to reserve the blade as a device for protection rather than examination (see Mori Ōgai, *Vita sexualis*, trans. Kazuji Ninomiya and Sanford Goldstein [Rutland, Vt.: C. E. Tuttle, 1972]). This preference may owe something to samurai ideology, but in any case it promised a strategic and singular asymmetry in the context of Meiji science versus literature.

43   See Hasegawa Sen, "Bungaku to igaku no aida," in *Issatsu no kōza: Mori Ōgai*, ed. Yamazaki Sei, *Nihon no kindai bungaku*, vol. 6 (Tokyo: Yūseidō, 1974), 1–12. Hasegawa gives some background and a detailed account of the rhetoric used by Mori to identify himself in this debate.

44   Mori Ōgai, "Shintōgo," in Kinoshita et al., *Collected Works of Mori Ōgai*, 25:140.

45   Karatani, *Origins*, 51–57.

46   Mori, "Shintōgo," 25:140.

47   Karatani, *Origins*, 71.

48   See Nanette Twine, "The Genbunitchi Movement: Its Origins, Development, and Conclusion," *Monumenta Nipponica* 33, no. 3 (autumn 1979): 333–356. Twine divides the movement into two phases, a utilitarian phase and a literary phase, the latter beginning around 1887 (339). When she discusses remarks against the old style made by Onishi Hajime in 1895, she makes an interesting observation: "This verbal assault was issued soon after the victory in the war against China, when attention was focused on the Japanese language which was then for the first time to be used in territories outside Japan" (352). The coincidence of the "literary" movement of language reform and Japan's linguistic concerns in the colonies is often overlooked or denied.

49   Latour, *We Have Never*, 39.

50   See Robert Young, *Colonial Desire: Hybridity in Theory, Culture, and Race* (London: Routledge, 1995). Young's account of Gobineau (99–117) in particular is important in the context of Mori Rintarō, for Mori responded critically and at length to the racial notions of Gobineau and others as rehashed in Germany.

51   Robert Young makes a similar point about the ways in which the contemporary discourse on hybridity relies on the evocation of prior purity, but he feels that it can be dialectically doubled and redoubled to the point that it undoes its origins. See ibid., 25.

52   Mori Ōgai, "Rekishi sono mama sono banare," in Kinoshita et al., *Collected Works of Mori Ōgai*, 7:105. Bowring translates *shizen* as "nature" (Bowring, *Mori Ōgai*, 217). Darcy Murray renders it "reality" in his translation of this piece in *The Incident at Sakai and Other Stories*,

vol. 1 of *The Historical Literature of Mori Ōgai*, ed. David Dilworth and J. Thomas Rimer (Honolulu: University of Hawai'i Press, 1977), 151. A literal translation of *shizen* along the lines of classical Chinese might be "that which is so of itself," a translation that corresponds well to Mori's interest in "history as it is" and the "past just as it is."

53 See Roland Barthes, "Historical Discourse," *Social Science Information* 6, no. 4 (August 1967): 145–155.

54 Mori, "Shintōgo," 25:140.

55 Mori Ōgai, "Joshi no eisei," in Kinoshita et al., *Collected Works of Mori Ōgai*, 29:48–51. "Joshi no eisei" was originally published under the name "Kenbisaishujin" in *Eisei shinshi*, no. 2 (25 August 1889), in the "Ronsetsu" column.

The Disease of Nationalism, the Empire of Hygiene

Michael Bourdaghs

Reading Broken Commandment

> *Broken Commandment* (novel) (Shimazaki Tōson). The celebrated work of recent days. Taking as its protagonist a *shinheimin* primary school teacher, this novel describes the extent of the hatred and abuse that the world heaps on the class of people called *shinheimin*. Racial prejudice is the true enemy of human sentiment, and we must struggle against it with all our might. That Japanese are looked down upon by Westerners is also due to racial prejudice. If Japanese are angered by this, they must first abandon their own identical prejudice. That is, they must drop their own hateful attitudes toward Chinese and Koreans. And of course the likes of the hateful attitude shown toward *shinheimin* are truly the height of irrationality. Accordingly, we hope that you will read this novel, *Broken Commandment*, and find in it a means of overcoming racial prejudice.—Unsigned review, *Katei zasshi* (1906)

positions 6:3 © 1998 by Duke University Press.

In 1907, one year after the appearance of his first full-length novel, *Hakai* [Broken Commandment], Shimazaki Tōson (1872–1943), one of modern Japan's most respected poets and novelists, published an account of the experiences that lay behind the writing of the work.[1] In the passage, Tōson describes how he began work on *Broken Commandment* when he was a schoolteacher in the rural village of Komoro, just as the Russo-Japanese War broke out. He recounts numerous visits to the Komoro depot to send off pupils and fellow teachers who were bound for the battlefield. He goes on:

> In my far-off mountain home, I heard about the plans of my friends in the city to observe the war, and I too decided to pick up my pen and follow along with the troops—although in the end that wish went unfulfilled. It was then that I began work on the *Broken Commandment* manuscript. Life is a battleground, and an author is nothing but its war correspondent: thinking this way, I comforted myself with the thought that I, writing my novel, and my friends, on the far-off plains of Manchuria, were engaged in the same effort.[2]

Tōson's account of the novel's writing has since been joined by a number of other narratives that likewise attempt to explain the appearance of *Broken Commandment* in 1906. In terms of Tōson's biography, the novel represents the completion of his turn toward fiction and away from the Romantic poetry that had first established his reputation in the late 1890s. In narratives of the rise of modern Japanese literature, *Broken Commandment* has alternately been celebrated as Japan's first truly modern novel; as the first masterpiece of Japanese Naturalism; and as the last glimmering hope for a modern Japanese novel that would include a consideration of public concerns (a hope soon extinguished by the rise of the I-novel with its obsessive fixation on private life).

What I find particularly intriguing about Tōson's own explanation of the novel's appearance is the way in which he figures his writing as participating in the national project of empire. He renarrates the literary triumph he had achieved with *Broken Commandment* as one incident from the greater tale of national triumph achieved by the Japanese military on the Asian continent. This history of imperial expansion and the shifting conceptions of national identity that accompanied it form the background of my own reading of the novel. Accordingly, like Tōson himself, I begin with the national triumph achieved in the Russo-Japanese War.

But of what, precisely, did that triumph consist? Dr. Louis L. Seaman, a former U.S. military surgeon who, unlike Tōson, was able to travel with the Japanese army during the war, had no doubts. In his book *The Real Triumph of Japan* (which appeared in the same month as *Broken Commandment*), Seaman argues that while Japan had of course defeated the Russian army, more important was the victory it had achieved against the insidious "silent foe" of all militaries, disease.[3] The traditional ratio of battlefield deaths resulting from disease to those resulting from combat was four to one, and recent colonial warfare had produced even worse ratios. In stunning contrast, for Japan in its war with Russia, the ratio was one to four, an unprecedented achievement. This accomplishment allowed Japan to mobilize its military resources with the highest degree of efficiency. According to Seaman, the Japanese soldier is drilled in the techniques of modern hygiene; he

> is instructed that his body is a fighting machine which is the property of his Emperor; that he is but one element in a great organization, the army, composed of the Emperor's children, and that it is the function of this organization to uphold and protect the Emperor and his people. He is imbued with the idea that it is just as necessary to maintain his body in the best physical condition as to keep his rifle in a state of efficiency; that to permit either to become impaired through his own carelessness or misconduct is to injure the organization of which he is a part, and constitutes an act of disloyalty to his Emperor.[4]

Modern warfare, Seaman argues, demands modern medicine, and in this field, Japan led the way. Japan's national victory was a triumph for the universal empire of hygiene.

As Seaman notes, the success of Japanese military medicine was the result of a long, deliberate promotion of hygienic thought and practices within Japan. My purpose here is to examine *Broken Commandment* as a participant in this process, a process that is inextricably bound up with questions of nation and empire. I will argue that the novel reproduces the symptoms of Japan's triumph, the textual *markings* of the diseases of nationalism and imperialism. By diagnosing Tōson's (probably unconscious) reinflection of the idioms of hygiene, I hope to trace out some of the contradictory ways in which those hygienic speech genres function ideologically to nationalize and colonize human bodies.[5] In particular, I will examine the ways in which Tōson depicts tuberculosis, a disease so ubiquitous in late Meiji Japan that it was widely known as *kokuminbyō* (our national disease). Tuberculosis admittedly plays a marginal role in the novel; the disease is attached to one character from a marginalized social group. And yet I will argue that this marginal disease should be understood as being central to the work's depiction of human bodies—just as the marginalized social group, the *hisabetsu burakumin* (hereafter abbreviated *burakumin*),[6] became central to the ideologies through which Japanese imagined their corporate national body, both on the pages of *Broken Commandment* and elsewhere.[7] In turn, by focusing my reading on these particular details, I hope to open up connections between Tōson's novel and much broader historical questions. The empire of hygiene, after all, spread far beyond Japan and its colonies.

Broken Commandment is one of a number of late Meiji fictional works that describe burakumin characters. The setting is Iiyama, a rustic mountain village. The protagonist, Ushimatsu, is a well-educated burakumin who has moved to Iiyama and become a schoolteacher, all the while hiding his origins (at his father's command) to avoid discrimination. Gradually, however, Ushimatsu's secret leaks out, aided by a rumor-mongering campaign conducted by the novel's villains, who include a corrupt politician and the principal of the school where Ushimatsu works. While rumors fly, Ushimatsu himself is haunted by a powerful desire to openly acknowledge his status. This desire arises out of Ushimatsu's interaction with his hero, Rentaro, a famous writer and political activist who publicly avows his status as a burakumin. Ushimatsu's struggles with his dilemma are heightened when he finds himself falling in love with O-Shio, the nonburakumin daughter of one of his teaching colleagues. The death of Ushimatsu's father (he is gored by a bull from the herd he tends) provides the first major crisis in the novel. As Ushimatsu stands next to Rentaro watching the bull being slaughtered, he resolves that he cannot disobey his late father's commandment and must keep his secret, even from Rentaro. But the pressure on Ushimatsu to confess continues to mount, and as he reaches the brink of suicide, a second major crisis arises: Rentaro is murdered by cronies of the crooked politician. Facing Rentaro's corpse, Ushimatsu experiences a kind of rebirth and resolves that he must carry on his mentor's legacy. Shortly thereafter, Ushimatsu confesses to the students in his class that he is a burakumin. To his surprise, his students and friends rally to his support. O-Shio even declares her willingness to marry him. But rather than remain in Iiyama, Ushimatsu chooses to emigrate to Texas. The novel closes with Ushimatsu being cheered by his students as he leaves Iiyama in the company of O-Shio and Rentaro's widow.

Broken Commandment has been the object of a flood of critical interpretations that began as soon as it was published.[8] Obviously, my readings of the novel benefit enormously from these studies, but I do want to distinguish myself from much of this earlier criticism on one important point: I do not aim to produce the sort of "total reading" that has been the goal of many past critics. Hirano Ken and Miyoshi Yukio, among others, have bemoaned the split in the critical reception of the novel between critics who see it as primarily a political novel attacking social prejuduce and those who see it as primarily a confessional novel of the inner life. Miyoshi, for example, argues that the novel cannot possibly be split thematically in this way, and he proposes to heal the division through a new attempt at interpreting the novel's meaning "in a unified manner [*tōitsuteki ni*] that is in accord with the novel's internal structure"—that is, through "an evaluation of *Broken Commandment* as a totality, just as it was actually written."[9] While I readily acknowledge the insight in both Hirano and Miyoshi, it seems to me that a total reading must reproduce the structures of knowledge that are characteristic of the ideologies of hygiene, the very structures that I will critique here. A total reading attempts to discipline the polysemic possibilities of an utterance into a single, authorized meaning.[10] The dialogic nature of the reading process is disguised by means of an inversion, whereby the dominant status of the reading subject is projected onto the text as its natural, essential meaning. As I will argue below, the ideologies of hygiene function similarly to transform political and historical contingencies into something natural, something biological.

My readings here, then, are inevitably partial. Moreover, they are an attempt to practice a form of dialogical reading, one that acknowledges that words can never be assigned to a single speaker and that declines to effect a clean separation between text and reader, subject and object, cause and effect. I have no way to get outside of ideology to access the "real" body of the text, "just as it was actually written." To produce a reading that does not authorize itself as a seamless substitute for the text itself, I have to acknowledge that I am implicated in whatever diseases I diagnose: I have no sanitary white position of health from which to read. In my unhygienic laboratory, the "experimenter constitutes part of the experimental system," and "the person who participates in understanding constitutes part of the understood utterance."[11]

In *Broken Commandment*, as Ushimatsu's secret gradually leaks out and he comes to see only suspicion in the eyes that gaze at him, the narrator describes his mental condition: "At times, Ushimatsu came to feel estranged even from his own body as he forgot everything else and single-mindedly recalled his father's commandment."[12] Obviously, it is beyond my power to restore to Ushimatsu sole ownership over his fleshly body. I am limited to beginning a process of dialogic critique, one that probes the text to call into visible existence the idioms it reproduces to imagine the human body as the possession of a national community. My goal is not to produce a systematic theory of the nationalized body or a total reading of the novel but rather to present a case study of differences produced through the often conflicting ideologies of hygiene, nationalism, and imperialism. I also hope that my readings here will be supplemented by further readings that will locate other idioms — those, for example, of gender, sexuality, and class — that also intersect in the bodies described in *Broken Commandment* as they are mobilized to extract the image of a healthy national community from human flesh. While no one has access to the "real" body prior to ideological distortion, we should begin the process of sorting through the various ideologies that attempt to construct the body in specific modes. While all discussions of the body (including my own) are inevitably ideological, not all ideologies function to the same effect.

Embodying the Nation

Infectious diseases are caused by poisons getting into the body from the outside, which can be prevented by proper care. These diseases are caused by microscopical objects called germs. In former times the number of deaths from these diseases exceeded the number of those killed in battle. Therefore never neglect to exercise the utmost caution against these germs. . . . An endeavour shall be made to prevent Japanese people from living in the same houses with dirty natives.— Instructions to Japanese troops in China, quoted by Dr. Seaman (1906)

My diagnosis of *Broken Commandment* must be set against a broader understanding of a shift that occurred during the period roughly coeval with Tōson's life, that is, from the 1870s to the 1940s, a period in which human bodies in Japan (and elsewhere) underwent a remarkable transformation. The rise of new industrial, military, educational, and medical regimens required literal incorporation into human bodies of previously nonexistent physical lifestyles. Simultaneously, a broad range of often conflicting ideologies came into play, each with its own particular set of speech genres that attempted to fix particular meanings to bodies. Issues that became focal points of debate include the proper presentation of the body, including attitudes toward clothing and nudity; new definitions of health and illness, including considerations of diet, cleanliness, and exercise; questions of gender and sexuality that arose out of new views of sexuality and the structure of the family; and new ideologies of heredity, racial identity, and racial hierarchy. Within all of these ideological debates and regimens, the status of individual human bodies was repeatedly linked to the well-being of the nation as a whole.[13]

The increasing medicalization of the body in post-1868 Japan accelerated this process of reconstruction. Medical science served as a primary pivot point linking the health of individual bodies to that of the nation as a whole. In particular, the new disciplines of hygiene and physical education constructed the national population into an object of medical treatment and developed norms for every aspect of daily life. These norms led to the incorporation of national policy directly into individual human bodies. Furthermore, as hygiene shifted the focus of medicine from *curing* disease in *individual* patients to *preventing* disease in *society* as a whole, it expanded the role of medicine beyond the treatment of disease to include the monitoring and regulation of healthy persons as well.[14]

The rise of hygiene as a medical discipline was accompanied by that of germ theory. The discoveries and techniques attributed to figures such as Robert Koch or Louis Pasteur provided a powerful new language through which hygienists could write socially essential roles for themselves, thereby achieving dominance over competing schools. Bacteriology and hygiene were so closely interrelated that in 1906, when *Broken Commandment* first appeared, they were still considered to form a single discipline. Japan played a special role in the worldwide dissemination of the new medicine: the presence of figures such as Kitasato Shibasaburō and Mori Ōgai helped germ theory achieve a hegemonic position within Japanese medical practice in a relatively short time, though even in Japan, germ theory was not without its opponents.[15]

One ideological construct that germ theory transmitted was a view of the human body that rigidly distinguished between "health" and "illness." A number of idioms were invented or translated from other domains, all for use in describing the diseased body as one that had been invaded by foreign elements—germs—which were defined as the causes of illness. Karatani Kōjin is a recent critic of germ theory, calling its view of illness a "theology" aimed at exorcising "evil."[16] But, as Karatani argues, this chain of binary oppositions—health/unhealth, purity/impurity, presence/absence (of microbes)—won wide acceptance and became a fundamental precept in the thought of those who concerned themselves with the health of society as a whole.[17] Human bodies and the national community were now placed in a new relationship, whereby the purity/health of each was dependent upon that of the other.

It is important to stress, as Latour does, that there was nothing inevitable or natural about the rise of germ theory. When Koch isolated the tubercle bacillus in 1882, he did not locate the real cause of a disease that had previously eluded scientists. Rather, he invented a new disease.[18] Where previously there had existed a variety of symptoms and conditions linked to numerous causal factors (heredity, miasma, urban environment, personal morality, etc.), now there existed tuberculosis, a unified effect produced by a single cause. After 1882—at least in the minds of germ-theory advocates—tuberculosis was defined tautologically as the disease caused by the tubercle bacillus.[19]

Moreover, the rapid acceptance and diffusion of germ theory was not due to an inherent explanatory superiority. Germ theory attracted supporters only to the degree that they were able to translate its doctrines to serve their own social and political interests. Germ theory empowered certain branches of medicine at the expense of others. Except for the worldwide flurry of activity that followed Koch's 1890 announcement (soon repudiated) that tuberculin could cure tuberculosis, clinical doctors, whose practice was built on curing patients, saw little relevance in the discovery of the tubercle bacillus. It is hardly surprising that clinical physicians were less eager to subscribe to germ theory than military doctors and hygienists, who were immediately able to write new and powerful positions for themselves through it.[20]

Another factor in the rise of germ theory was its tendency to turn the focus of public-health activities away from the social causes of illness (poverty, urban overcrowding, industrial pollution, etc.) and toward purely biological agents. Accordingly, hygiene was widely promoted as an alternative to socialism: it aimed at curing both disease and social unrest. Socialists, in turn, ridiculed hygiene. This was particularly true in the case of tuberculosis, a disease whose appearance was just as much a symptom of capitalism as was the rise of the proletariat. The sudden epidemic of tuberculosis that struck Meiji Japan cannot be attributed to the tubercle bacillus, which had been present since the dawn of history. Rather, in Japan and elsewhere, the disease became widespread only after the change in living patterns that accompanied the rise of industrial capitalism. This fact was well known to socialists of the day: in 1904, the Christian Socialist activist Kinoshita Naoe attacked hygiene's politics of tuberculosis:

> "The spread of the disease germ of tuberculosis occurs mainly through the sputum of those who have the disease": this is what it says at the beginning of an official notice recently issued by the superintendent general of the Metropolitan Police. But in terms of solving the problem of a social disease such as tuberculosis, this approach can hardly have any effect. . . . When we inquire into where consumption is produced, isn't it the factories of large companies, the dormitories of male and female workers, the back-alley tenements?[21]

Kinoshita argues that tuberculosis was merely a secondary symptom of the diseases of poverty and industrial capitalism and that any effort to improve public health must attack the root diseases. Hygienists, on the other hand, saw socialism itself as a potentially devastating social disease, one that could only be prevented through gradualist improvements in living standards and public health. As I will discuss below, this conflict between hygiene and socialism is played out on the pages of *Broken Commandment*.

Germ theory bore especially important implications for the national community. Hygiene advocates insisted that society had to be mobilized into a coherent whole to wage total war against its newly identified enemy, the germ. In theory, the social totality imagined by hygiene did not necessarily have to take national form. In practice, however, it generally did. Japanese hygienists in the 1900s bemoaned the lack of governmental measures to prevent tuberculosis, noting that the worsening of tuberculosis among the lower classes revealed an alarming lack of national cohesiveness. These tendencies reached a sort of logical conclusion in a 1935 article in a Japanese public-health magazine that argued that only Fascism, with its ultimate unification of the people, could implement hygiene effectively.[22]

This nationalistic conception of hygiene was reinforced by the militaristic imagery rampant in hygiene writings from this period. Moreover, especially in Japan, hygiene developed primarily as a form of military medicine designed to increase Japan's battle readiness in its wars of imperialist expansion. Mori Ōgai's army diet reform proposals, based on his laboratory work in Germany, were part of a highly successful effort to combat diseases that had hampered Japanese military movements in Asia.[23] As we have already seen, the work of Ōgai and other Japanese military doctors in improving hygiene contributed enormously to the success of Japan in the Sino-Japanese and Russo-Japanese Wars. The links between Japanese hygiene and imperialism are further condensed by the career of Gotō Shimpei (1857–1929). Gotō earned his Ph.D. in hygiene in the early 1890s, studying under Max von Pettenkofer. In 1898, after a spectacular career in public health in Japan, Gotō was appointed civilian governor of colonial Taiwan, where he introduced numerous hygienic reforms. In 1906, he became president of the South Manchurian Railway Company, the primary institutional apparatus of Japanese colonial administration on the continent.[24] Gotō's career links the experimental procedures of the bacteriology laboratory to the governing practices of colonial administration. His work in hygiene served to effect both a disciplining of bodies internal to the national community and an expansion of the national body.

Accordingly, as I explore the human bodies constructed in *Broken Commandment*, I will focus primarily on two groups of speech genres. The two derive from somewhat contradictory hygienic techniques: quarantine, which labors to construct an impermeable boundary separating the healthy and the diseased; and vaccination, which attempts to neutralize the effects of pathological agents on the body so as to render their intermingling harmless. Since ideological struggles to define the body are always related, directly or indirectly, to struggles over defining the nature of the community, we would expect these two versions of the body to correspond to two distinct images of the national community. Translated into the idioms of national political strategy, we might call the two hygienic techniques protectionism and expansionism.

Discrimination against/between Diseases

[Antiburakumin prejudice] is truly a severe, living problem. It is a social failing born into existence over many long years, exactly like an affliction in our individual bodies, a pain that cannot be forgotten.

How can we treat this ailment and restore good health? It is not a simple problem.
— Shimazaki Tōson (1928)

The intense concern for public health in Meiji Japan helps form the landscape of *Broken Commandment*. The school where Ushimatsu works, for example, introduces hygienic methods to control an outbreak of trachoma, and it is equipped with such prerequisites of physical education as tennis courts, a gymnasium, and gymnastics equipment. When the school celebrates the emperor's birthday, the ceremonies also honor visiting representatives of the Red Cross.

When we examine the human bodies described on its pages, another hygienic fact leaps out at us: illness is everywhere. Questions are continually raised about the health of Ushimatsu. Other major characters, such as Rentaro (the burakumin activist who becomes Ushimatsu's mentor) and Keinoshin (O-Shio's father), suffer from various diseases. The head priest at

Rengeji Temple, where Ushimatsu lives, commits repeated sexual indiscretions, a pattern that his wife repeatedly identifies as his "illness." The principal at the school where Ushimatsu works repeatedly identifies certain forms of thought, along with the publications that transmit them, in terms of disease.

Perhaps the most noteworthy feature of this textual epidemic is that, throughout the novel, disease is concentrated in the bodies of burakumin characters. This association is introduced in the opening pages. Ohinata, the wealthy burakumin whose expulsion from his lodgings launches the plot into motion, has traveled to Iiyama to receive treatment at a hospital there. Rentaro suffers from tuberculosis. And Ushimatsu, though apparently not physically ill, is constantly discussed in terms of illness—his friends are forever recommending that he visit a doctor because he looks poorly.

This attribution of illness to burakumin characters formed an important component of the "écriture of discrimination." Watanabe Naomi, in surveying a large number of texts that discussed burakumin, describes a tendency they shared to construct burakumin bodies through a set of telltale visible "markings" (*shirushi*).[25] Watanabe compares this écriture to Western orientalism: its reduction of the viewed object (in this case, burakumin bodies) to a fixed set of interchangeable markings creates a relationship of absolute, incommensurable difference between the seen object and the seeing subject. Furthermore, the mastering of the object via this attribution of markings serves to construct the viewer as an unmarked, self-identical subject. Accordingly, Watanabe ties this écriture to the construction of a homogeneous Japanese national identity.

The texts that reproduced this écriture in particular helped disseminate dominant ideologies of heredity, which assigned inferior bloodlines to burakumin as a means of naturalizing their social status. In this way, meanings inscribed onto burakumin bodies intersected with the broader ideologies of blood lineage that underlay the Meiji *ie* (family) system and the emperor system, as well as Western attitudes toward Japan and Japanese attitudes toward other Asians.

But with regard to burakumin, this ideology had a tremendous weak point: the distinctions that blood lineage was supposed to produce were invisible. This lack of corporeal markings became all the more troubling as other markers of burakumin status (dress, residence, occupation) disappeared when legal restrictions were eased following the 1871 Liberation Ordinance. The result was an inability to visually distinguish burakumin from "normal" Japanese. This apparent blurring of boundaries, the deterritorialization of the feudal social order, produced an anxiety that the écriture of discrimination labored to overcome with its visible markings. This constructed visibility, a power/knowledge disciplinary complex, functioned to co-opt burakumin characters into the politics of specularity, thereby containing the social difference they seemed to threaten.

Disease formed one of the most important visual markings. Burakumin-related stories were frequently set in hospitals and clinics. More blatantly, these works tended to portray burakumin characters as diseased, an inversion typical of this écriture in that it shifted the cause of prejudice away from social structure and onto the bodies of those who suffered from prejudice.

In discussing what sets *Broken Commandment* apart from earlier works, Watanabe notes that Ushimatsu himself is free of the corporeal markings that this écriture assigned to burakumin characters. This does not mean, however, that the novel is altogether free of these markings: the features that marked earlier burakumin-related works are reproduced in *Broken Commandment*, but here they tend to be projected onto the exterior surrounding Ushimatsu, rather than onto the protagonist himself. Ushimatsu's interiority is then constructed in reaction to this marked exterior.

In this sense, the presence of disease in other burakumin characters such as Ohinata and Rentaro locates *Broken Commandment* within the écriture of discrimination. There is one subtle but significant difference, however: whereas the diseases most commonly attached to burakumin bodies were hereditary ones, those in *Broken Commandment* (despite the obsessive concern over hereditary disease that Tōson would display in later works) tend to be contagious.[26] They are diseases whose origins are attributed to agents invisible to the naked eye and only recently rendered visible to the medical gaze via the microscopes, cultures, and dyes of Pasteur, Koch, and Kitasato.

In a sense, as Watanabe argues, this difference in type of disease is irrelevant. The écriture of discrimination functions regardless of the particular marking employed. The stock of potential markers are all exchangeable, so long as the fundamental gap between the gazing subject and its object is maintained. But one way to define ideological critique is as a disruption of the principles of exchange that naturalize social hierarchies. While the écriture of discrimination may posit an equivalence between hereditary and contagious diseases, a reader is not obliged to accept the validity of that transaction. A reader can seize upon one of its terms and insist on its irreducibility to the other term. Diseases become interchangeable only when viewed from a subject position that narrates itself as being healthy and uninfected — the subject position characteristic of both the discipline of hygiene and of literary studies when it produces monologic "total readings."

Accordingly, it makes a difference that Rentaro's marking is tuberculosis. For example, this particular marking brings into play yet another ideology of disease that was current in the period. Karatani notes that a metaphoric use of tuberculosis was established with the Romantic movement in Europe, whereby the disease "became an index of gentility, delicacy, and sensitivity among snobs and social climbers."[27] Karatani traces the spread of this vision of tuberculosis in Meiji literature, citing as a prominent example Namiko, the heroine in Tokutomi Roka's *Hototogisu* (1898–1900). Clearly, something similar happens in *Broken Commandment* with the character of Rentaro.

The question arises again and again in *Broken Commandment*: how could an intellectual such as Rentaro have risen from the ranks of the most despised social class? Each time the question arises, the answer is the same: Rentaro's success is due, either directly or indirectly, to his tuberculosis. For characters who sympathize with Rentaro — for example, the newspaper journalist (himself a consumptive) who mistakenly exaggerates the gravity of Rentaro's condition — the disease and the suffering it causes are the source of a particular quality that distinguishes Rentaro's writings. In these cases, we find Romantic tuberculosis: Rentaro's consumption becomes a sign of his individual genius.

Less sympathetic characters also associate Rentaro's status with his disease. But in this context, the attribution takes on a sinister twist: the disease becomes a means for denying Rentaro himself any credit for his accomplishments. Rentaro's agency is shifted onto the tubercle bacilli that he harbors in his body; his writings become nothing more than a pathological symptom. Bumpei and Ginnosuke, two of Ushimatsu's teaching colleagues, speculate on how the eta could have produced a figure such as Rentaro and conclude that it is not so much Rentaro as the disease that has authored his many books: "When you look at it that way, it's not that an eta wrote those sort of things, but rather that the illness made him write them—that's how it is, right?"[28] Furthermore, Rentaro's thought is itself treated as though it were infectious. Ginnosuke and others repeatedly discuss the effect of Rentaro's writings and speeches on Ushimatsu in terms of contagion: "I don't know whether, as a rule, consumptives are like that. They say that when you listen to that teacher's [Rentaro's] speeches, they really strike home. . . . Well, people like Segawa here ought best not to listen—if you listen, it's a sure thing you'll get sick again."[29] For these characters, bent on deriding Rentaro, his tuberculosis provides the answer to the question of how a burakumin could rise in the world.

In this light, Ushimatsu's ability to overcome his initial horror at Rentaro's infectious disease to the point that he willingly shares a bath with his friend assumes a new importance (although in another sense, Ushimatsu already has the disease: his burakumin origins). The erotic charge of this scene, as the reserve between the two men breaks down to the point where they scrub each other's back, is at least partially due to the risk Ushimatsu takes in exposing his own body to disease.[30]

We can take this probing a step further. Tuberculosis, prior to and even after Koch's isolation of the tubercle bacillus, was widely believed to be hereditary. Well into the twentieth century, many persons (including doctors) continued to argue for heredity as its primary cause, either in the form of direct transmission of the disease or of a hereditary disposition toward it. Others tried to synthesize the two explanations, arguing that tuberculosis was in some cases hereditary and in others infectious. Johnston notes that the continued insistence on heredity hindered the efforts of Japanese germ theory advocates to mobilize public-health campaigns to halt the spread of the disease.[31]

There are important parallels between this dual accounting for tuberculosis and the status of burakumin in Meiji Japan. While the official abolition of hereditary eta and hinin classifications in 1871 did not abolish ideologies of heredity that assigned inferior bloodlines to burakumin, it did create an opening for new, more liberal explanations for the existence of the burakumin. That is to say, in addition to the ideology of heredity, a new explanation of burakumin status in terms of social transmission became possible.[32]

In *Broken Commandment*, Tōson proposes a solution to this problem of the doubled burakumin. There are, he argues, two kinds of burakumin. This becomes quite explicit in "Yamakuni no shinheimin," a 1906 newspaper article Tōson wrote to defend *Broken Commandment* from charges that it exaggerated the extent of antiburakumin prejudice. After describing the care he had taken in studying buraku life and declaring that prejudice was in fact severe, he concludes by saying that there seem to be two kinds of shinheimin: "high class" and "low class" (he uses the English). The former group are in "all things—facial appearance, habits, speech, and the like—hardly different from us"; but the latter group show their uncivilized status "the way that lower classes of savages show wildness in their faces." The bone structure of their faces is different, and particularly "remarkable is the difference in skin color. Because they don't marry with other groups and sometimes marry even very close relatives, there seems to be a kind of skin disease rampant among them."[33]

These two groups are reproduced in *Broken Commandment*, where they are distinguished as the subjects and objects of the narrative gaze, respectively. The shinheimin at whom Ushimatsu stares in the slaughterhouse scene are stamped ("branded") at birth with a hereditary marking: the "distinct color of their skin."[34] These unfortunates are doomed by blood to remain objects of the narrative (and national) gaze. But other shinheimin, such as Ushimatsu and Rentaro (those who in "all things" are "hardly different from us"), attain the status of gazing subjects—just like the unmarked heimin. What distinguished *Broken Commandment* from earlier works of Japanese fiction, according to both 1906 readers and later critics, was the remarkable intensity with which it narrated Ushimatsu's inner life: the reader is powerfully solicited to identify with Ushimatsu and to see the world through his eyes. In Ushimatsu, Tōson constructs a burakumin as an interiorized subject, one who is capable of returning the national gaze, of fulfilling the desire of the national gaze for intersubjective recognition.

In other words, Ushimatsu cannot simply be dismissed as a non-Japanese, an alien, despite the school principal's repeated attempts to identify him as a "foreign element" (*ibunshi*) who must be "expelled" (*hōchiku* or *haiseki*) to bring unity (*tōitsu*) to the school. That is to say, whatever there is that is "foreign" about Ushimatsu cannot be attributed to his bloodline. Ushimatsu's father, in delivering his commandment, specifically tells Ushimatsu that their family derives from a samurai bloodline, so that they are not aliens (*ihōjin*), unlike other eta whose ancestors, he says, came from Russia, China, Korea, and other foreign places.[35] Moreover, Ushimatsu's "disease" cannot be understood in terms of a hereditary susceptibility to infection. When Ushimatsu receives the terse telegram notifying him of his father's death, he is surprised—his father was "of the extremely healthy type, who even in that fierce climate never once caught a cold. . . ."[36] At any rate, some other cause besides heredity must be located to explain the difference that the "high-class" shinheimin is thought to introduce into the social body. It is in this context that the tubercle bacillus takes on new importance.[37]

As I have already suggested, the slaughterhouse scene presents a topos saturated with idioms that posit an equivalence between disease and burakumin. The scene contains brutally prejudiced language, in particular manifesting a tendency that scholars have identified in numerous burakumin-related literary works: the tendency to ascribe a bestial nature to burakumin characters, especially in the form of an untamed, animal-like sexuality. A metonymic connection between certain burakumin and animals through traditional occupations spilled over into a metaphor for the group as a whole; burakumin were seen as harboring an animal-like nature in their own bodies.[38]

In a brilliant analysis, Kamei Hideo discusses the slaughterhouse scene in terms of the half-animal, half-human positions it opens up, a characteristic that Kamei argues arises from the coexistence of two kinds of subject-object relationships in the work: one in which the viewing subject labors to share the "landscape" it sees with some other subject, and one in which the viewing subject tries to close itself off from all others to achieve a position of seeing without being seen. This latter way of seeing fears the external "landscape," which it sees as filled with ill omens, and tries to dominate it. The "landscape" of the slaughterhouse situates it in this latter, more ominous mode: Ushimatsu fears that nature is looking back at him. His anxiety produces the half-animal, half-human position into which both the bull and its burakumin slaughterers fit.[39]

When we employ the speech genres of germ theory and tuberculosis to read the slaughterhouse scene, we produce a clearer image of the ideologies that intersect here. The bull that is slaughtered is, of course, being brought to justice for having gored Ushimatsu's father to death. As Kamei points out, the bull is a figure for Ushimatsu's father: in witnessing the death of the bull, Ushimatsu is watching a displaced reenactment of his father's death. The bull stands in for Ushimatsu, too: its killing of the father enacts the patricidal aspects of Ushimatsu's own desire to break his father's commandment. It is significant that each of the human characters projected onto the animal's body is a burakumin. But the interpenetration of burakumin and animal bodies is not limited to this sort of figural projection. Ushimatsu's father dies when the boundary of his human, burakumin flesh is violated by an animal—that is, when his body is penetrated by a foreign agent. The guilty animal is then brought to justice under quasi-human standards, and its punishment reverses the crime: its flesh is violated by human, burakumin hands. The slaughterers bash in the bull's head and then cut through its flesh, hacking the corpse into four large hunks of meat that hang down from the ceiling, dripping blood across the floor. The witness to all of this is, of course, Ushimatsu, whose very name indicates the depth of the problem here.[40]

But there is another displaced burakumin character figured through the bull: the bull's carcass, as it lies bleeding in front of Ushimatsu, prefigures the appearance of Rentaro's corpse, lying in its own blood, in chapter 20. Like Rentaro's corpse, the bull's carcass is viewed by a policeman. But prior to the slaughtering, the bull is also inspected by a veterinarian: "The veterinarian, walking this way and that, circled the cow—he pinched its hide, pressed against its neck, tapped at its horns; finally he lifted up its tail, and with that the examination was over."[41] Readers in 1906 Japan would have understood the significance of this passage: *the veterinarian is inspecting the bull for signs of bovine tuberculosis*. The opening years of the twentieth century saw the rise of an intense, worldwide concern over the possibility that meat and milk from cattle infected with bovine tuberculosis might be an important cause of human tuberculosis. In Japan, the 1901 Domestic Cattle Tuberculosis Prevention Law implemented the first mandatory inspections of cattle, beginning with imported animals in 1901 and extending to domestic animals in 1903. It provoked a social controversy as farmers protested the loss of income it entailed.[42]

The bull in the slaughterhouse scene, then, not only reproduces the figure of Rentaro's corpse through its violent death, it is also monitored for markings of the same disease that has invaded the burakumin activist's body. To summarize the ideologies that intersect on the slaughtering floor, we find there a scandalous violation of animal/human distinctions. Bestial burakumin slaughterers penetrate the flesh of an oddly human cow who had previously penetrated (that is, fatally infected) the flesh of Ushimatsu's father. This cow is suspected of harboring within it the same germs that infect Rentaro, a burakumin present at the slaughtering. If tuberculosis is capable of being transmitted from cows to people, it only makes sense that the germs should be concentrated in burakumin, who are located ideologically somewhere between the categories of animal and human. This is consistent with modern hygiene's reorganization of Japanese society, under which burakumin were frequently situated as the agents of disease. Moreover, we have the presence in the scene of two sorts of burakumin, those in whom the pathogenic status is apparently hereditary (the slaughterers) and those in whom the status must be explained in terms of social transmission (Ushimatsu and Rentaro). It is the mobilization of tuberculosis as a marker of burakumin status that renders possible this whole network of ideological distinctions and blurrings.

Quarantine: Ideological Fantasies of Health

Internationally, [Bolshevik] Russia is the special buraku of thought. They are carriers of a hazardous germ that takes as its ideal the smashing from the foundation up of social organizations, the instigation of revolution in all the nations of the world, and the conquering of the world with the communism in which they believe.—Fukui Kōji (1925)

The redefinition (at least in some cases) of tuberculosis into a contagious disease justifies the exclusion from the social body of even those burakumin who are "purely" Japanese. Quarantine as a hygienic technique requires such a separation of the morbid from the healthy: infected bodies have to be iso-

lated from healthy ones. The social space of Meiji Japan accordingly underwent a massive reorganization as part of an effort to separate out elements
that were posited as introducing difference into the national population—
persons with diseases, criminal offenders, poor people. A controversial network of prisons, isolation hospitals, and poorhouse labor camps was set up
throughout the land to effect a separation of the morbid from the healthy,
to construct a homogeneous national community, and to maintain a constant surveillance on elements that threatened to introduce heterogeneity.
Germ theory, which demanded the unification of national society into a single unit dedicated to total war on the microbe, provided a major ideological
rationale for this social reorganization: "*Disease was no longer a private mis-
fortune but an offense to public order.*"[43]

The conclusion of *Broken Commandment*, in which Ushimatsu decides to
emigrate to Texas after confessing his buraku origins, has been an object of
derision since 1906, even among critics who praise the novel.[44] As many
critics have noted, the ignoble body language of the confession scene and
Ushimatsu's subsequent decision to emigrate undermine whatever value
readers may have attributed to his and Rentaro's earlier struggles; moreover,
the decision to emigrate comes so suddenly as to seem a case of deux ex
machina. The conclusion had become such an embarassment that in 1962,
when Ichikawa Kon directed a film version, he simply rewrote it. Yet the
novel's conclusion, when read against the ideologies of hygiene, does reveal
a certain logic (albeit a double logic, as I will explore below): it can be read
as reproducing the ideologies of quarantine in the broader spatial register
discussed above. Just as disease is seen as the penetration of foreign elements
into the body, so the carriers of those foreign elements—the novel's
burakumin characters—are finally portrayed as the agents who introduce
an unhealthy difference into the community. The diseased must be isolated,
quarantined, even when they boast hereditary pedigrees "hardly different
from us."

Perhaps Ushimatsu did catch something from Rentaro in that bathtub
after all. The promiscuous, irresponsible (that is to say, socialist) Rentaro
actively tries to infect those around him with his unhealthy thought/disease
and therefore must ultimately be repressed—or, in the language of the
Cold War, "contained." On the other hand, Ushimatsu exercises a sense of

social responsibility and implements the self-segregation so essential to hygienic strategies for containing social diseases such as tuberculosis. Once again, we are presented with the conflict between hygiene and socialism. Rather than agitate for social change, Ushimatsu emigrates. In this sense, the climax of *Broken Commandment* reproduces the ideological fantasy[45] of hygiene: a healthy, homogeneous community in which heterogeneous agents voluntarily quarantine themselves.

Accordingly, Ushimatsu is not simply a foreigner, either to Japan or to the village of Iiyama. Rather, he is a faithful subject who carries out the hegemonic duties of hygiene. In fact, the conclusion can be read, paradoxically, as the successful consummation of Ushimatsu's bid for membership in the local Iiyama community. This is one of the revolutionary features of *Broken Commandment*: whereas earlier works describing burakumin characters had tended to ally those characters with sympathetic members of society's elite—the aristocracy, wealthy persons, and so forth—against the irrational prejudice of the uneducated common folk, in *Broken Commandment*, Ushimatsu clearly allies with the local folk against the ruling elements of society.[46]

In *Broken Commandment*, this local Iiyama community and its nature are described in great detail. The community's identity is largely constructed via a center-periphery conflict that pits rural Iiyama and its traditions against the incursions of the centralized state and its bureaucrats.[47] The community is constructed in the face of this other, the exterior that looms just beyond its boundaries, but to establish those boundaries—to simultaneously produce and reproduce the community as a self-identical entity—the need arises for a *pharmakos* figure.[48] Like the pharmakos, the ritual scapegoat of ancient Greek societies, Ushimatsu occupies a position simultaneously inside and outside the Iiyama community; he is the foreign element who nonetheless originates within the community and whose expulsion to the exterior allows the social community to produce/reproduce its internal identity—its health. Moreover, the ideologies of hygiene have so naturalized this exclusion of difference that violent rituals of expulsion are no longer needed: in *Broken Commandment*, the pharmakos excludes himself.

This is because Ushimatsu knows his place in the community. Like the school principal, Ushimatsu comes to Iiyama from outside. But unlike the principal, who represents the interests of the centralized state, Ushimatsu becomes one of the townspeople following his confession. His acceptance is signaled by the reaction to his confession shown by his students and his housemates at Rengeji. A more important sign is O-Shio's willingness to marry him in spite of his being burakumin. Yet this acceptance is paradoxical: under the ideologies of quarantine, the condition of Ushimatsu's becoming a member of the Iiyama community is that he leave Iiyama.

Ushimatsu's confession signals his acceptance and internalization of the pharmakos role. In revealing his secret to his students, Ushimatsu reminds them of two things: his difference from them (as he recounts the traditional social stratification and the rituals used to separate eta from the community) and his similarity to them (as he recounts the activities they have participated in together). He tells them both that he is one of them and that he is not one of them. Ushimatsu, having accepted this position via the confession, is then accepted by the community.

Only Ushimatsu's subsequent departure from the community can fulfill the hygienic logic of his position. The language used to describe Ushimatsu's mental state as he departs from Iiyama suggests the contradictory nature of his situation:

> How Ushimatsu must have breathed in the December morning's cold air and come back to the feeling of being revived after having finally set down a heavy load. *It was like, for example, the nostalgic feeling of a sailor who kisses the soil upon returning to land following a long sea journey.* That was exactly how Ushimatsu felt. No, in fact, he felt even happier. Even sadder. Walking on snow that crunched with each step, he came to feel as if, without a doubt, this world was his own.[49]

Only when he leaves Iiyama can Ushimatsu feel that he has at last come home: his departure is figured as a homecoming. The specific use of contagious disease, as opposed to hereditary disease, as the marking of burakumin status both enables and necessitates this contradictory resolution.

Hence, in its conclusion, *Broken Commandment* reproduces at the level of the Iiyama community the idioms of quarantine, just as it also portrays a victory of Ushimatsu's hygiene over Rentaro's socialism. Furthermore, while the Iiyama community certainly resists the centralized state, the novel's conclusion also hints at the absorption of this peripheral difference into a self-identical national community.

After all, Ushimatsu does not simply leave Iiyama, he emigrates from Japan to join Ohinata's proposed ranching venture in Texas. The assumption behind Ohinata's project (and behind all the other burakumin-related works that proposed emigration as a solution) is that abroad, Ushimatsu will be free from the antiburakumin prejudice that sets him apart from other Japanese. His burakumin status will disappear in Texas, where, in the face of Yellow Peril racism (mentioned in Rentaro's work *Confessions*), he will likely be scorned simply as a Japanese.[50] Accordingly, the same paradox that saw Ushimatsu becoming a member of the Iiyama community when he agreed to leave Iiyama is reproduced at the level of the national community: Ushimatsu finally becomes Japanese at the moment he leaves Japan.[51]

Vaccination: Hygiene Conquers the World

Japan is as healthy as any country similarly situated, and the advanced sanitary measures insisted upon rigidly by the authorities are steadily diminishing the mortality returns. But as it is very difficult to impress upon an ignorant lower class the necessity for observing hygienic rules, it devolves upon the traveler to take certain precautions to guard against the diseases which sometimes prevail. . . . Korean ideas of hygiene are almost as negligible as those of a Hottentot. Travelers should always be on their guard against sampling native dishes and beverages, and on no account should water or milk be drunk unless recently boiled. The average Korean well is little short of a pest-hole, and is often the cause of epidemics. While the progressive Japanese have installed modern waterworks in certain of the large cities, it is difficult to prevent an ignorant populace from defiling the sources.
—*Terry's Japanese Empire: A Guidebook for Travelers* (1919)

As I have argued, the fascination with tuberculosis found in literary works such as *Broken Commandment* arose at least partially from its ambiguity as a disease suspended between conflicting hereditary and contagious explanations. This ambiguity situates it as a particularly potent marking for burakumin status.

A similar ambiguity marks many hygienic texts—Mori Ōgai's hygienic diet reforms, for example, which argue that traditional Japanese foods (miso, rice, tofu) provide the best possible diet for the Japanese Army since they are ideally suited to the Japanese physique. State policies are to be grounded in the natural, ahistorical physique of the Japanese people. Nonetheless, that body is also simultaneously constructed as a project requiring intensive state intervention: hygienic diet reforms are designed to mold the Japanese physique into a more efficient military tool to carry out state policy within Japan and without. That is to say, the Japanese body must become all the more Japanese.

Hygienic nationalism, then, celebrates the national body as it is handed down through heredity and yet at the same time calls for a transformation of that body into something else. Rather than choose between these sets of idioms, it seems more productive to consider the nationalized body as suspended in a disjunctive, liminal space between contradictory constructions —"pedagogical" and "performative" modes of narrating the body that are mutually supplementary and do not "add up."[52] The closure that would assure national, corporeal, and textual self-identity remains inevitably deferred.

A similar ambiguity also marks *Broken Commandment*. The hygienic idioms described above, which can be grouped together under the name quarantine and which effect a separation of the healthy from the morbid, are supplemented by another range of idioms that derive from the techniques of vaccination (or, following Bhabha, vacciNation). In one sense, these two sets of idioms exist in a relationship of temporal succession: in 1906, the focus of hygiene was shifting from quarantine to vaccination, from curing disease to promoting health, from acute infectious diseases such as cholera to chronic diseases such as tuberculosis. And yet, as we see in *Broken Commandment*, the earlier idiom retains currency even as the new idiom is introduced. The nationalized body lies suspended between these two contradictory poles of protectionism and expansionism—each with its own form of colonialism: the leper or penal colony, on the one hand, and the paternalistically administered protectorate or colonial territory, on the other.[53]

In vaccination, one introduces a weakened strain of some agent of disease into the body so as to steel that body and strengthen it so that it will be able to dominate the more virulent microbes it encounters in the future. As a technique, vaccination played a fundamental role in facilitating colonial expansion: to borrow Bruno Latour's language, immunizing European bodies against the microparasites of tropical disease was a necessary step in the transformation of those bodies into macroparasites on non-Western regions.[54] When a body was constructed through the idioms of vaccination, concern shifted away from fortifying the boundaries of the body and from maintaining internal purity. The germ was no longer to be avoided, since, as hygienic texts repeatedly stressed, contact was inevitable. Attention was turned, rather, toward effecting proper hierarchies between body and germ. What was essential was to discipline the body, to reconstruct it to enable it to assimilate the alien germ on the most profitable terms possible.

This is true at the level of the individual human body as well as at the level of the social body: When smallpox vaccinations were introduced into colonial Bombay in 1802, the first phase focused on vaccinating European settlers and their Indian servants.[55] This was accompanied by an effort to restrict contact between these (imperfectly) protected populations and the mass of unvaccinated colonial subjects, thereby effecting a kind of quarantine. Soon, however, and with mixed results, the colonial government launched "benevolent" campaigns to vaccinate the entire Indian population. That is to say, instead of separating the healthy European from the diseased Asian, the new medicine was now deployed as a means of neutralizing the dangers of colonial space so as to allow further penetration by the colonizers.

Accordingly, this vaccination campaign met with strong resistance from colonial subjects — just as vaccination as a form of discipline met with opposition in Britain, Japan, America, and elsewhere. Many of those who were subjected to this colonizing of the body resisted absorption into the neutralized, harmless position that vaccination attempted to assign them. Indian subjects resisted smallpox vaccination because, as a colonial official reported in 1872, they read it as a "mark of subjection to the British Government."[56]

The conclusion of *Broken Commandment*, then, with Ushimatsu's decision to emigrate, can be read not only through the idioms of quarantine but also through those of vaccination. It is important to note that the novel was first published at a time when state policies toward domestic minority groups and toward colonial empire were undergoing important changes.

With regard to domestic others, late Meiji saw a shift in government policy away from isolating those groups toward actively integrating them into the national community; the beginning of official *yūwa* (assimilationist) policies toward burakumin in late Meiji is emblematic of this shift.[57] Simultaneously, Japan's colonial policy shifted from one that defined its colonies as external properties—chips it could manipulate in the game of international power politics it played with other colonial powers—toward one that stressed the integration of the colonies into Japan itself. This new policy was heralded by the 1910 annexation of Korea. While these new policies were never stable and the coming decades saw much back-and-forth movement between the two strategies, nonetheless, by the time *Broken Commandment* appeared, the speech genres of vaccination were available for reinflection.

Accordingly, in *Broken Commandment* and other works describing burakumin, we see not simply quarantine but also vaccination. Certain burakumin figures—"high-class" ones, who carry neither inferior bloodlines nor pathological socialist thought—are constructed for the purpose of assimilating them into the body of the national community. Two important conditions define their construction: they must not actively agitate for change (i.e., evoke domestic difference) within Japan and they must participate in the expansion of the nation beyond its present-day borders. The result of this vaccination is a reenergized national community, one that is strengthened for its encounter with new others (Koreans, Taiwanese, Chinese, Russians). Accordingly, Ushimatsu and Ohinata emigrate to Texas; the heroine of "Immigrant School" emigrates with her husband and other shinheimin to colonial Hokkaido; and—most symptomatically—in Ōgura Chōrō's *Biwa Song* [*Biwa uta*], the hero is a burakumin soldier who serves the emperor bravely on the battlefields of Asia, despite the discrimination he faces from other Japanese.[58] In these works, readers are solicited not to reject the burakumin protagonists but rather to sympathize with their heroic strivings on behalf of the nation.

Accordingly, two sets of speech genres are simultaneously invoked to define individual and social bodies in *Broken Commandment* and its kindred texts. In addition, the publishing history of Tōson's novel in the 1920s and 1930s can also be read through the contradictory idioms of quarantine and vaccination. By the mid-1920s, with the rise of the Suiheisha liberation organization (founded in 1922) and growing public awareness, open expressions of prejudice against burakumin began to go out of fashion in Japanese polite society (although this in no way meant an end to discrimination). With this shift, *Broken Commandment* became controversial. It was attacked not because it urged the inclusion of Ushimatsu in the national community but rather because its most prejudiced language suggested a difference that excluded other burakumin from that same community. In response, for a 1922 edition of his complete works, Tōson made a number of minor changes in the text, revising some of the more blatantly offensive language. A 1929 edition of the work included a few additional similar changes.[59]

Then, in 1929, shortly after the publication of the second revised edition, Tōson withdrew *Broken Commandment* from publication altogether. The text, he implicitly acknowledged, was infected with the disease of prejudice. His conscientious response was to place it in quarantine, lest it spread the disease to the reading public. Despite its status as a classic of modern Japanese literature, it remained out of print for a decade.

But in the late 1930s, as Japan mobilized for Total War, Tōson again changed strategies. In 1939, he reissued the novel, explaining his reasons in a new preface and afterword.[60] The new preface begins, "This is a tale of the past." Tōson goes on to explain that the society and especially the buraku slums that he describes in *Broken Commandment* are those of the past, not of the present. It was precisely for this reason that he had once resolved to "completely bury" the novel from public view. And yet now he has changed his mind because art is supposed to convey a truthful portrait of social life. Moreover, there is a need for Japan to be confronted with this ugly image of its past, a need that can compared to the plot of the novel itself:

> When you think of it, the past can come back to life at any time. In *Broken Commandment*, there are two figures. One [Ushimatsu's father] attempts to conceal the past out of an excessive anxiety over the future; the other [Rentaro] believes that the only way to truly bury the past is to expose it. Yet other persons in this world fluctuate between these two positions. At any rate, I have decided to again place this tale of the

buraku before the readers of the present day with the feeling of one who renews a grave marker for the sake of those persons who would lay to rest the olden days.

It is only by taking the cure offered by a Rentaro and openly confronting even the ugliest aspects of one's past that one can overcome that past: Tōson offers up *Broken Commandment* as a kind of medicine for Japan's disease of prejudice (even as he claims the disease has largely disappeared).

In the 1939 "Afterword," Tōson reiterates these themes. He notes a certain form of historical repetition, which he calls a "coincidence": *Broken Commandment*, which was originally written at the height of the Russo-Japanese War, is being reissued in the midst of yet another war (1939 is the third year of the war in China). He concludes:

> Today, on the occasion of the republication of this text, I have attempted as much as possible to preserve it in its original state and have made no significant revisions. I have done no more than revise or cut out a phrase here and there. It is the case that a number of questions have been raised about this work, but it is my intention to offer up the work itself in place of an answer to all of those.

It is hard to know what Tōson's intention was in writing that last comment because, in fact, the 1939 edition was drastically altered. An incomplete listing in the current edition of Tōson's complete works lists more than 250 distinct changes to the text of the 1939 edition, including major revisions of a number of extended passages.

When we look at precisely what sorts of changes Tōson made to the text, two dominant patterns emerge. First, there are revisions of discriminatory phrases and concepts. Derogatory words such as *eta* and *shinheimin* are replaced with neutral phrases such as *buraku no mono*. Statements made by various characters that suggest that burakumin are racially distinct from other Japanese are cut out. The narrator's descriptions of certain burakumin as being "ignoble" or "branded in the skin" are cut. In sum, the pathological markings of "low class" burakumin characters are erased.

But there are other sorts of revisions as well, revisions that are unrelated to the issue of antiburakumin prejudice. A number of words are avoided or are repeatedly replaced by words that do not carry the echoes of radical thought and social critique; this produces an image of a Japan that is untroubled by class conflict and other forms of social antagonism. For example, *shakai* (society) becomes *yo no naka* (the world), and *kaikyū* (class) becomes *mibun* (social status). Rentaro is no longer a *shisōka* (political ideologue or social critic), but rather he becomes a *kangaeru hito* (thinker). *Rōdōsha* (laborers) become *kinrōsha* (devoted workers—the word loses its socialist connotations). Other words, such as *kenri* (rights, as in "political rights"), disappear altogether.

Another important revision occurs in the list that the novel provides of the titles of Rentaro's published books. The 1906 text lists five books; the 1939 text, however, lists only four: the work titled *Labor* [*Rōdō*] disappears from the list. The title of another book is altered: the book that in 1906 is called *Current Trends in Thought and the Lower Strata of Society* [*Gendai no shichō to kasō shakai*] in 1939 is called *Current Trends in Thought*.

In short, the 1939 edition is heavily doctored. It erases all traces of internal difference, racial or political, and replaces them with language that depicts healthy identity. The agents of disease have been cultivated and domesticated into a beneficial form. That is to say, if the suspension of publication in 1929 was a kind of quarantine, the 1939 revision employs a more aggressive technique, vaccination. This locates the revised edition within the contemporary campaigns being conducted to ensure the total mobilization of all "Japanese," including burakumin and other marginalized nationals —women, Okinawans, Taiwanese, and Koreans. Even the radical Suiheisha movement found itself co-opted into this effort. Suiheisha had taken a strong anti-imperialist stance at its founding, allying itself with Korean and Taiwanese nationalist movements that resisted Japanese colonialism. But by 1939, Suiheisha had come to define its anti-imperialism in terms of supporting the Japanese military in its crusade to liberate Asia. Symptomatic of Suiheisha's decline as an oppositional force is the role of movement leaders in approving the 1939 edition of *Broken Commandment* prior to its publication.[61]

In the ideological fantasy presented by the 1939 revised edition, the 1906 vaccination has been successful. The burakumin have been assimilated into the national body on favorable terms, without pathological infection. Ushimatsu's status as a beneficial microbe is now extended to all burakumin characters, even to the (formerly socialist) Rentaro. Moreover, the text itself has been cultivated and domesticated so as to eliminate its pathogenicity. As a result, in 1939, difference no longer troubles the homogeneous interior of the nation; it is now permitted to exist only in the space between nations. A complicated, contradictory set of bodily images are invoked side by side to define the national community: diseased difference is discovered and quarantined, but then the same potential source of infection is taken internally in a domesticated form, and the body of the national community is thereby strengthened so that it can safely encounter other forms of difference (whereupon the process can be repeated). And the idioms of quarantine (Japanese "uniqueness") that separate internal homogeneity from external difference are supplemented by the idioms of vaccination ("coprosperity"), as the nation steels itself in preparation to absorb even external others into itself.

—

Rather than end my diagnosis of *Broken Commandment* and its case of the disease of nationalism by prescribing a cure, I would simply iterate two theoretical positions I have attempted to sustain in my unhygienic readings here. First, I hope to contribute to the critique of modernity in a way that avoids some of the problematic assumptions that grounded classical modernization theory. Hygiene was clearly an aspect of modernity in Meiji Japan, but I have tried to demonstrate that it was not a matter of simple belated imitation of Western models: the rise of hygiene in Japan was simultaneous with (and often prior to) its rise in the West. Japan was as involved in the production of this new form of knowledge as any nation. Moreover, a critique of hygiene in Japan can (and must) be linked to a critique of Western hygiene, nationalism, and imperialism.

Second, I have tried to foreground the dense complexity of the relationships between ideologies that construct individual human bodies and those that construct communal bodies such as nations. There is no single national body, Japanese or otherwise, that can be easily isolated and analyzed. Contradictory images of the body can be found even within a single utterance, and these contradictions will only multiply when the sphere of analysis is expanded to include plural utterances. Moreover, the dialogic process of reading these bodies adds yet another layer of complexity, for ideological critique is never conducted from a nonideological position. To answer the call that opened this article—that we use *Broken Commandment* to find "a means of overcoming racial prejudice"—and to produce a dialogic critique that does not simply reproduce the power structures of hygiene, we must remain attentive to the chronic instabilities that haunt both the empire of hygiene and our attempts to dismantle it.

Notes

A longer version of this paper has appeared in Japanese as "Nashonarizumu no yamai, eisei to iu teikoku" (trans. Ueda Atsuko and Sakakibara Richi, *Gendai shisō* 25, no. 8 [July 1997]: 24–51). An earlier version was presented at the Meiji Studies Conference at Harvard University in 1994 and is included in the conference volume *New Directions in the Study of Meiji Japan* (ed. Helen Hardacre and Adam L. Kern [Leiden: Brill, 1997]).

The following abbreviation appears in the text:

TZ   Shimazaki Tōson, *Tōson zenshū*, 18 vols. (Tokyo: Chikuma Shobō, 1966–1971).

1 *Broken Commandment* is reprinted in *TZ* 2. All translations from Japanese-language materials are my own, except where noted. There is a translation by Kenneth Strong. See Strong, *The Broken Commandment* (Tokyo: University of Tokyo Press, 1974). I have followed Strong's translations for character names (e.g., dropping macrons, "O-Shio" instead of "Oshiho," etc.).

2 *TZ* 2:303–305.

3 Louis Livingston Seaman, *The Real Triumph of Japan* (New York: D. Appleton and Co., 1906).

4 Seaman, *Real Triumph*, 143.

5 The concept of "speech genres" comes from Mikhail Bakhtin, *Speech Genres and Other Late Essays*, trans. Vern W. McGee (Austin: University of Texas Press, 1986). I am modifying Bakhtin's usage in significant ways, but I retain his basic assumption that the rhetorical level of speech genres is the site of ideological struggle. To determine what speech genres are invoked in a given utterance is to define the boundaries of that utterance, thereby delimiting the sorts of responses that will be permitted to it. Accordingly, the struggles to define the speech genres being invoked in a given utterance are nothing less than struggles to fix in advance the impact that utterance will have in a given social setting. In this sense, to conduct ideological critique means to insist that utterances invoke speech genres other than those that have been commonly attributed to them.

6 That is, descendents (not solely in the biological sense) of those persons classified as *eta* and *hinin* during the Edo period. Despite the official abolition of those pariah status groups in

1871, the derogatory terms *eta* (much filth) and *hinin* (not human) remained in wide use in 1906. *Hisabetsu burakumin* (literally, "people from the discriminated-against districts" [district= *buraku*]) is a polite modern term. In *Broken Commandment*, another discriminatory name is also frequently used: *shinheimin* (new commoners). This term was introduced in early Meiji to distinguish burakumin from "ordinary" commoners (*heimin*) following the official abolition of the eta-hinin categories.

7   Here, my approach is informed by Mary Douglas [1966], *Purity and Danger* (London: Ark, 1984): I will examine how bodies are defined in relation to a community's perception of its boundaries. Unlike Douglas, however, I will avoid assuming that a particular community is given as a consistent whole. I prefer to focus on how conflicting views of bodies reveal the presence of internal difference and undermine the possibility of coherent identity. See, for example, the discussion in Peter Stallybrass and Allon White, *The Politics and Poetics of Transgression* (Ithaca, N.Y.: Cornell University Press, 1986), of how bodily images (in this example, of pigs) are a "site of competing, conflicting and contradictory definitions.... Since they articulate the symbolic and metaphorical resources of different classes and groups whose anchorage points occupy distinct and different sites and locations, they co-exist in an uneven and often incompatible way" (49).

8   A number of studies have appeared in English, as well. The two that I find most useful are James Fujii, *Complicit Fictions* (Berkeley and Los Angeles: University of California Press, 1993); and Thomas LaMarre, "Pain, Filth, and Stupefaction: Forms of Authority and Mediation in the Late Meiji Novel" (Ph.D. diss., University of Chicago, 1992). One important study in Japanese that appeared too late to be considered in this article is Suga Hidemi, "Kokumin to iu sukyandaru: Teikoku no bungaku 1," in *Hihyō kūkan* 2, no.13 (1997): 226–246.

9   Miyoshi Yukio [1962], *Miyoshi Yukio chosaku shū 1: Shimazaki Tōson ron* (Tokyo: Chikuma Shobō, 1993), 115. See also Hirano Ken [1938], "*Hakai*," in *Hirano Ken zenshū* (Tokyo: Shinchōsha, 1975), 2:17–35.

10 Many of the most interesting recent discussions of *Broken Commandment* in Japan have focused on the status of textual materiality; they include Kōno Kensuke, *Shomotsu no kindai* (Tokyo: Chikuma Shobō, 1992); Komori Yōichi, "Shizenshugi no saihyōka," in *Nihon bungaku kōza 6: Kindai shōsetsu,* ed. Nihon bungaku kyōkai (Tokyo: Ōshūkan Shoten, 1988) 95–113; and Fujimori Kiyoshi, "Byōsha ni okeru katari: *Hakai* no byōsha ni tsuite," *Bungaku* 5, no. 1 (winter 1994): 115–127.

11 Bakhtin, *Speech Genres*, 123.

12 *TZ* 2:246.

13 See Hirota Masaki, "Nihon kindai shakai no sabetsu kōzō," in *Nihon kindai shisō taikei 22: Sabetsu no shosō*, ed. Hirota Masaki (Tokyo: Iwanami Shoten, 1990), 436–516; and Narita Ryūichi, ed., *Toshi to minshū*, vol. 9 of *Kindai Nihon no kiseki* (Tokyo: Yoshikawa Kōbun-kan, 1993).

14 See Bruno Latour, *The Pasteurization of France* (Cambridge, Mass.: Harvard University

Press, 1988), 121–122. See also Date Kazuo, *Ishi toshite no Mori Ōgai* (Tokyo: Sekibundō, 1981), on the rise of hygiene as a form of military medicine in mid-Meiji Japan.

15 On Ōgai, see Date, *Ishi toshite no Mori Ōgai;* Richard Bowring, *Mori Ōgai and the Modernization of Japanese Culture* (Cambridge: Cambridge University Press, 1979); and the article by Thomas LaMarre in this issue of *positions*. On Kitasato, see James R. Bartholomew, "Science, Bureaucracy, and Freedom in Meiji and Taisho Japan," in *Conflict in Modern Japanese History*, ed. Tetsuo Najita and J. Victor Koschmann (Princeton, N.J.: Princeton University Press, 1982), 295–341; and Andrew Cunningham, "Transforming Plague: The Laboratory and the Identity of Infectious Disease," in *The Laboratory Revolution in Medicine*, ed. Andrew Cunningham and Perry Williams (Cambridge: Cambridge University Press, 1992), 209–244.

16 "Almost all human beings are infected with either the tuberculosis bacillus or some other pathogen. We coexist with microorganisms, and indeed without them we cannot even digest food to nourish ourselves. Having a pathogen within the body and becoming ill are entirely different matters" (Karatani Kōjin, *Origins of Modern Japanese Literature*, trans. Brett de Bary [Durham, N.C.: Duke University Press, 1993], 106).

17 Foucault argues similarly that the prestige of biological sciences in the nineteenth century derived mainly from their deployment of "a space whose profound structure responded to the healthy/morbid opposition. When one spoke of the life of groups and societies, or the life of the race, or even of the 'psychological life', one did not think first of the internal structure of *the organized being*, but of *the medical bipolarity of the normal and the pathological*" (Michel Foucault, *The Birth of the Clinic* [New York: Vintage Books, 1975], 35; emphasis in the original).

18 The rise of laboratory-based medicine led to a radical reconstruction of diseases, so that, for example, plague became something entirely different once germ theory scientists isolated its "causal agent": "The identities of pre-1894 plague and post-1894 plague have become incommensurable. We are simply unable to say whether they were the same, since the criteria of 'sameness' have been changed. As I have been arguing, this is not a technical medical issue, but a logical, philosophical and historiographic one" (Cunningham, "Transforming Plague," 242).

19 On tuberculosis in Japan, see Fukuda Mahito, *Kekkaku no bunkashi* (Nagoya: Nagoya Daigaku Shuppankai, 1995); William Johnston, *The Modern Epidemic: A History of Tuberculosis in Japan*, Harvard East Asian Monographs, vol. 162 (Boston: Council on East Asian Studies, Harvard University, 1995); and J. Keith Vincent, "Masaoka Shiki to yamai no imi," *Hihyō kūkan* 2, no. 8 (1996): 160–187. On tuberculosis in general, see Rene Dubos and Jean Dubos, *The White Plague: Tuberculosis, Man, and Society* (Boston: Little, Brown and Co., 1952); and Susan Sontag, *Illness as Metaphor and AIDS and Its Metaphors* (New York: Doubleday, 1990).

20 On political and economic factors (in particular, the rise of the bourgeosie) in the debate between contagion and anticontagion theories in the decades leading up to the rise of germ

theory, see Erwin H. Ackerknecht, "Anticontagionism between 1821 and 1867," *Bulletin of the History of Medicine* 22 (1948): 562–592. See also Roger Cooter, "Anticontagionism and History's Medical Record," in *The Problem of Medical Knowledge*, ed. Peter Wright and Andrew Treacher (Edinburgh: Edinburgh University Press, 1982), 87–108.

21 Kinoshita's article originally appeared in *Heimin shinbun*, 8 May 1904. This passage is reprinted in Fukuda, *Kekkaku*, 52–53.

22 See Johnston, *Modern Epidemic*, 272.

23 See Mori Ōgai [1886], "Nihon heishoku ron taii," in *Ōgai zenshū* (Tokyo: Iwanami Shoten, 1974), 18:11–18. Ōgai's dietary research is described in Date, *Ishi toshite no Mori Ōgai*, esp. 101–120 and 177–202. Ōgai himself, incidentally, labored throughout his life to conceal the fact that he had tuberculosis. See Fukuda, *Kekkaku*, 57–97.

24 Gotō's medical career is discussed in Seaman, *Real Triumph*, 220–221; and Johnston, *Modern Epidemic*, 180–181. His colonial career is discussed in Stefan Tanaka, *Japan's Orient* (Berkeley and Los Angeles: University of California Press, 1993); and E. Patricia Tsurumi, *Japanese Colonial Education in Taiwan, 1895–1945* (Cambridge, Mass.: Harvard University Press, 1977).

25 Watanabe Naomi, *Kindai Nihon bungaku to "sabetsu"* (Tokyo: Ōta Shuppan, 1994). See also Umezawa Toshihiko, Hirano Eikyū, and Yamagishi Takashi, *Bungaku no naka no hisabetsu buraku zō: Senzen hen* (Tokyo: Akashi Shoten, 1980); and Kawabata Toshifusa, *Hakai to sono shūhen* (Kyoto: Bunrikaku, 1984).

26 What follows is a belated answer to a question raised by Tomoko Steen to an earlier version of this article. I thank her for her insightful comments.

27 Karatani, *Origins*, 101.

28 *TZ* 2:40–41.

29 *TZ* 2:163.

30 *TZ* 2:113–115. Idehara Takatoshi discusses this in another context in "Rengeji no kane," *Kokugo kokubun* 56, no. 1 (January 1987): 1–23. Ushimatsu's inability to reveal his origins to his mentor also masks the presence of another secret: the scandalous contact with disease overlaps with the scandal of Ushimatsu's desire for Rentaro's body. The text will eventually control this irruption of unspeakable desire by murdering that desired body and displacing Ushimatsu's desire onto O-Shio, the nonburakumin heroine. This displacement is effected through the mediation of a textual corpus: O-Shio, upon agreeing to marry Ushimatsu at the conclusion of *Broken Commandment*, suddenly expresses a desire to read Rentaro's writings. See Kōno, *Shomotsu*, 124; and Shinoda Kōichirō, *Shōsetsu wa ika ni kakareta ka* (Tokyo: Iwanami Shoten, 1982), 20–27.

31 Johnston, *Modern Epidemic*, 70–73.

32 Moreover, the pariah status assigned to potentially infectious tubercular patients under germ theory enhanced the functioning of tuberculosis as a marker of burakumin status. This was not unique to Japan. Germ theory brought an end to Romantic tuberculosis in Europe and

made the disease instead into "a contagion, something unclean. In several modern novels, the infected individual became *almost an untouchable*, a character stimulating repulsion or fear" (Dubos and Dubos, *White Plague*, 66; my emphasis).

33 *TZ* 6:77–84.

34 *TZ* 2:126.

35 *TZ* 2:9. Foreign origins were a popular (and false) explanation for the presence of burakumin in Japan. References to foreign origins were revised out of the 1939 edition of *Broken Commandment*.

36 *TZ* 2:77. We still, however, see here a marking of burakumin status: the father's body, in its unusual resistance to disease, is distinguished from the "normal" Japanese body.

37 Shimizu Shikin's 1899 story "Immigrant School" ["Imin gakuen"] is also of interest. In it, an ambitious burakumin father hides from the world to allow his daughter to succeed in society, and—as in *Broken Commandment*—it is the father's death that causes the strategy to unravel. When the daughter learns of her father's illness, she rushes to him, thereby revealing her origins in the buraku. Here, too, the father's unspecified disease is almost surely contagious: the father was not born of burakumin parents but rather was adopted into the community when he fled his own nonburaku family in his youth. For a translation, see Rebecca Sue Jennison, "Approaching Difference: A Reading of Selected Texts by Shimizu Shikin" (masters' thesis, Cornell University, 1990), 78–118.

38 Hence, the 1922 call to arms of the Suiheisha burakumin liberation organization: "We were the victims of ignoble class policies, and we were the manly martyrs of industry; as recompense for having flayed the skin off beasts, we were flayed of our living human skin; as the price for having cut the hearts out of beasts, we had our own warm human hearts cut out of us . . ." ("Declaration," quoted in Watanabe, *Sabetsu*, 77–78). For background information on Suiheisha, see Ian Neary, *Political Protest and Social Control in Pre-War Japan: The Origins of Buraku Liberation* (Atlantic Highlands, N.J.: Humanities Press International, 1989). Tōson himself was sympathetic to Suiheisha. See the 1923 essay "Mezameta mono no kanashimi," in *TZ* 9:249-252.

39 Kamei Hideo, *Kansei no henkaku* (Tokyo: Kōdansha, 1983), 256–283.

40 *TZ* 2:127–131. As Fujii points out, the first character in Ushimatsu's given name carries the meaning "cow." While this likely indicates the zodiac sign of the year of Ushimatsu's birth, why would Ushimatsu's father, who wants his son to escape his burakumin background, give him this name? For readings of the significance of this and other proper names appearing in the work, see also Shinoda, *Shōsetsu*, 16–20.

41 *TZ* 2:128.

42 See Johnston, *Modern Epidemic*, 216–220; and Fukuda, *Kekkaku*, 69–71. By about 1910, the inspection system had fallen into disuse, owing both to farmer resistance and to growing doubts among hygienists of the relevance of bovine tuberculosis to the disease in humans. The bloodlines of the bull in *Broken Commandment* further complicate matters. Is bovine

tuberculosis hereditary or contagious? The bull's owner says that although he owns many cattle, "none is of bloodlines superior to this one's. Its sire was American-born, its dame was such-and-such, and if only it hadn't any bad habits it would have been the prized bull of the Nishinoiri pastures" (*TZ* 2:127). The bull's American lineage not only foreshadows Ushimatsu's emigration but also renders the animal more suspect. Under the Unequal Treaties, Japan was prevented from enforcing any effective quarantine, and U.S. cattle growers were known to be dumping infected cows onto the Japanese market.

43 Latour, *Pasteurization*, 123; emphasis in the original. On Meiji-period policies toward supposedly heterogeneous elements, see Hirota, "Sabetsu"; and Narita, *Tōshi to minshu*.

44 One characteristic common to most of the early reviews is that critics, including those who praise the novel, see its conclusion as a literary failure. Even reviewers who evidenced little sympathy for Rentaro's politics bemoaned—for aesthetic reasons—Ushimatsu's behavior during his confession and his decision to emigrate rather than to remain in Japan and carry on his mentor's struggle. Hasegawa Tenkei's "Handō no genshō" (1906) is typical: although Hasegawa believes the novel overstates the extent of antiburakumin prejudice, he argues that "because the novel on the one hand provides us with the figure of Rentaro fiercely struggling against society despite his status as an eta, there is a tendency for us to feel less and less sympathy for Ushimatsu's suffering" (*TZ* 18:102–105). Burakumin-liberation activists have also long attacked the novel's conclusion for more overtly political reasons. See, for example, Burakumin Kaihō Zenkoku Iinkai [1954], "*Hakai* shohanbon fukugen ni kansuru seimei," in *TZ* 2:535–540.

45 "Ideology is not a dreamlike illusion that we build to escape insupportable reality; in its basic dimension it is a fantasy-construction which serves as a support for our 'reality' itself: an 'illusion' which structures our effective, real social relations and thereby masks some insupportable, real, impossible kernel (conceptualized by Ernesto Laclau and Chantal Mouffe as 'antagonism': a traumatic social division which cannot be symbolized)" (Slavoj Zizek, *The Sublime Object of Ideology* [New York: Verso, 1989], 45).

46 Kawabata, *Hakai*, 29–75.

47 Fujii, *Complicit*, 76–102. In many places, the 1939 revised edition softened or omitted the language in which this resistance to the centralized state was couched.

48 See Jacques Derrida, *Disseminations* (Chicago: University of Chicago Press, 1981), 128–134.

49 *TZ* 2:293; my emphasis.

50 The comparison to Western Yellow Peril racism was cut from the 1939 revised edition, probably because it implied that burakumin discrimination was a racial problem. An 1890 editorial by the Kyushu Heimin Kai was aimed at shinheimin in Fukuoka: "Those with capital, go to foreign countries and engage in business. Those without capital, go to foreign countries to work and earn your keep. In foreign countries, there is no distinction between heimin and shinheimin. Foreigners will treat you in an equal manner as they do us, as subjects of Imperial Japan." See Kawabata, *Hakai*, 73 n. 12.

51 A similar conclusion is reached in Suga, "Kokumin." See also Katharina May, "Das Motiv des Aussenseiters in der modernen japanischen Literatur," in *Bochumer Jahrbuch zur Ostasienforschung*, vol. 4 (Bochum, Germany: Studienverlag Dr. Norbert Brockmeyer, 1981), 110–129.

52 I am, of course, citing Homi K. Bhabha, "DissemiNation," in *Nation and Narration*, ed. Homi K. Bhabha (London: Routledge, 1990), 291–322.

53 I am indebted to K. Mark Anderson for pointing out these two forms of colonization.

54 Latour, *Pasteurization*, 140–141. See also William H. McNeill, *Plagues and Peoples* (New York: Anchor Books, 1976), 5–13.

55 David Arnold, *Colonizing the Body: State Medicine and Epidemic Disease in Nineteenth-Century India* (Berkeley and Los Angeles: University of California Press, 1993), 116–158.

56 Ibid., 143.

57 On *yūwa* policies, see Neary, *Political Protest*; and Watanabe, *Sabetsu*. For accounts of a similar shift with regard to another domestic minority group, Okinawans, a shift that can only be understood in relation to Japan's expanding overseas empire, see Murai Osamu, *Nantō ideorogii no hassei*, rev. ed. (Tokyo: Ōta Shuppan, 1995); and Tomiyama Ichirō, "Kokumin no tanjō to 'Nihon jinshu,'" *Shisō*, no. 845 (November 1994): 37–56.

58, Ōgura Chōrō, *Biwa uta* [1905–1910], reprinted in *Meiji bungaku zenshū 93: Katei shōsetsu shū*, ed. Senuma Shigeki (Tokyo: Chikuma Shobō, 1969), 365–417. Note that this reprints only the first half of the novel. See Umezawa, Hirano, and Yamagishi, *Bungaku*, 47–53.

59 On the publishing history of *Broken Commandment*, see Umezawa, Hirano, and Yamagishi, *Bungaku*, 1–20; Kawabata, *Hakai*, 210–230; Kitahara Daisaku [1954], "*Hakai* to buraku kaihō undō," in *Nihon bungaku kenkyū shiryō sōsho: Shimazaki Tōson*, ed. Nihon bungaku kenkyū shiryō kankō kai (Tokyo: Yūseidō, 1971), 220–224.

60 The 1939 preface and afterword are reprinted in *TZ* 2:533–535.

61 In the postwar era, as the needs of national health again shifted, the 1939 text was in turn quarantined. In the mid-1950s, Japanese publishers began returning to the 1906 text, often with little explanation of the history of textual variation. Such an exclusion was apparently necessary to disinfect Tōson's problematic activities during the 1930s as part of the process of constructing the tradition of a healthy national literature. The 1939 revised text has been unavailable in any edition since approximately 1970.

Modernity, Medicine, and Colonialism: The Contagious Diseases Ordinances in Hong Kong and the Straits Settlements

Philippa Levine

Nineteenth-century anxiety over sexually transmitted diseases was a powerful mix of moral and sanitary prejudice that routinely viewed promiscuity, and more especially prostitution, as the likeliest route of infection. In a period of widespread Western debate over the limits and rights of public-health enactments, venereal diseases (VD), as they were then known, were a topic of substantial concern and debate. In Britain and its enormous cache of colonial possessions, a series of acts and ordinances known as contagious diseases (CD) legislation specifically named the prostitute as the principal purveyor of VD.

This essay looks at the enactment of CD legislation in two of Britain's Asian colonies, Hong Kong and the Straits Settlements, both acquired by the British in the nineteenth century and displaying many similar characteristics. In the wake of much work on the domestic British legislation, as well as more recent assessments of its imperial implications, it is hardly contentious to argue that CD laws were one of the principal arenas for the codification of female sexuality in the British colonial context.[1] Nor will it sound innovative to insist that such codification was determinedly racial in its distinctions and boundaries. What I want to explore here, however, is how we might connect these questions of race, gender, and sexuality to the broader project of modernity so rhetorically central to late British colonialism. CD legislation reveals an interesting contradiction between the legal fiction of modernity authored by the colonial state and the less "modern" and not infrequently coercive practices colonial peoples experienced as the state effected its route toward the "modern."

CD acts were first introduced to island Britain in 1864, and the legislation was extended and amended in 1866 and again in 1869. The 1869 act, suspended in 1883 after vigorous protests inaugurated mainly by feminists, was finally repealed in 1886. Operable only in those military and naval districts identified by the statute, the acts made women prostitutes but not their customers liable to medical examination and detention. Women suspected of prostitution were subject to arrest for the purposes of examination and, once examined, were certified and committed to regular vaginal inspections. "Lock" hospitals, the traditional centers of treatment for VD, attracted government funding by guaranteeing a percentage of their beds for women detained under the acts. Where no lock hospital existed, general hospitals received grants to establish lock wards for government patients.

Less widely known are the versions of this legislation introduced throughout the British colonial world. These versions seldom distinguished the military from the civil as the domestic legislation had so carefully done. Alongside Malta and the Ionian Islands, Hong Kong anticipated domestic CD legislation by seven years, passing its first ordinance in 1857. Ordinance 12 of 1857 introduced the examination of women and the licensing of brothels by the registrar general, an office established by Governor John Bowring in the 1850s. The ordinance also punished prostitutes and brothel keepers in cases where women allegedly communicated VD to a client. Registration allowed for the designation of brothel localities: the east end of town was reserved for those serving a European clientele and the west end for those with Chinese clients. Ten years later, a new ordinance (No. 10 of 1867) superseded the earlier law. It was less a replacement of the older legislation than it was a refinement, in much the same manner as the domestic acts of 1866 and 1869 built upon that of 1864. Ordinance 10 provided the registrar general and the police superintendent the right of entry without warrant into premises suspected as unlicensed brothels.

The law was introduced in the Straits Settlements in 1870 and implemented in Singapore and Penang in 1872, and in Malacca shortly thereafter. On paper, at least, the Straits ordinance was almost identical to that of Hong Kong.[2] It, too, instituted brothel regulation, routine medical inspections, and a lock hospital in which infected women were mandatorily treated. In application, the two were in fact radically at odds. While in Hong Kong, only women serving a European clientele were brought under the ordinance, in Singapore the ordinance was applied first to Chinese-only brothels and only latterly to others.[3]

At the heart of both ordinances lay two provisions: the compulsory medical examination of women prostitutes, which sparked such a huge controversy in Britain, and the regulation and registration of brothels. This latter requirement had no parallel in the domestic legislation, where such effective legalization of the trade would have produced an even greater uproar than the acts alone ignited. In these two dominantly Chinese colonies, the parallel implementation of a medical regime and an allegedly protective regime, justified as shielding local women from the full force of local brutality, also allowed for far greater intervention and surveillance than was considered necessary in the metropole. For the remainder of the century, the Colonial Office as well as local authorities tended to consider the two colonies in tandem whenever there were amendments to the legislation.

Elsewhere in Britain's colonial holdings, legislation of this stripe was justified as sanitary and medical in intent, a classic modernization argument that consolidated the associations between law, medicine, and modern rational science. But in Hong Kong and the Straits, justifications that stressed these associations as primary were less common.[4] This is worth considering since above all other colonies, these two portended the brightness of the modern colonial future. Hong Kong and the Straits Settlements were seen as beacons of economic success, of the growing benefits of global trade and economic expansion: modernization, in short, was critical in the picture of these port colonies that was painted for public consumption. Medical considerations were far from absent, but they were overlain with a particular and concrete anxiety about modernity and its application in a Chinese context. From the beginning of their controversial history, the ordinances in Hong Kong and the Straits spoke to issues well beyond medical concern, yet they continually annexed the medical position as an unquestionable insignia of the modern.

The Straits Settlements, comprising Singapore, Malacca, and Penang, were established in 1826 as the fourth presidency of India. Uninhabited Penang had been acquired by the East India Company in 1786. Singapore had followed in 1819 when Sir Thomas Stamford Raffles signed a treaty with the local ruler, the Temenggong of Johore, establishing a British trading post.[5] From a modest population of about one thousand, the city's population had quintupled by 1821, and Singapore rapidly developed in significance as a major trading center for the British in Asia and the Pacific; when the Settlements were designated a crown colony in 1867, there were sixty European companies trading in Singapore.[6] International trade through the port was valued at $11.4 million as early as 1824.[7]

Since the population prior to British colonization had been so small, the Straits Settlements developed primarily as immigrant societies.[8] Male immigration was unrestricted and the typical demographics of the "frontier" soon took hold, especially in Singapore, the capital and main port of the colony. Even as late as 1911, men outnumbered women in Singapore by eight to one.[9] By the 1860s, over two-thirds of Singapore's population was Chinese. Menial Chinese labor—the "coolie" system—was crucial in shaping modern colonial Singapore as a major commercial entrepôt.[10] Thirteen or fourteen thousand Chinese immigrants flocked there annually in the mid-nineteenth century, and though the outflow was such that this was also often a transient population, its overall profile is significant to any discussion of modernization. The greater part of this migrant population was from isolated coastal regions in southern China—eastern Kwangtung and southern Fukien in particular.[11] The two dominant dialect groups in Singapore were the Hokkien (the largest Chinese population in the Straits) and Teochew groups. Serious tension between them not uncommonly spilled into the streets of the colony in the nineteenth century.[12]

Migrant workers experiencing the loneliness and harsh conditions of menial work and a bachelor life frequently sought solace in the replication of familiar Chinese traditions, in particular, the formation of clan associations and dialect groups that reminded them of their origins and that provided friendship and support networks.[13] Henry Lethbridge has convincingly argued that, unlike the colonial state, such organizations provided welfare and protection for poorer Chinese.[14] The flourishing of these societies, which were regarded by the British as dangerous and destabilizing, illustrates the potential for tension between the colonial accent on modernizing—to maintain Singapore's sometimes tenuous commercial supremacy in the region—and the significantly un-Western values of its predominant population; this is what Yen Ching-hwang identifies as "the influence of traditional Confucian values on the new social relations."[15] The imposition of British law, as frustrated colonial authorities endlessly discovered, was not a simple matter; both displaced laborers and more prosperous merchants looked to their cultural origins and not to their colonial masters for their primary identification. Writing in the *Straits Chinese Magazine* in the early years of the twentieth century, Soh Poh Thong called for Straits Chinese girls to be encouraged to dress in the Chinese manner and to be schooled in Hokkien or Mandarin rather than in English.[16] This interest in language as a marker of identity was an important one; in Hong Kong, not one of the European police officers (who occupied the entire senior ranks of the force) spoke any Chinese dialects.[17] The so-called secret societies could thus provide important services that were otherwise unavailable to non-English speakers.

On the southern tip of the Chinese mainland is the colony of Hong Kong. The British initially acquired Hong Kong Island for naval and commercial purposes in 1841. They added the mainland peninsula of Kowloon (though not Kowloon City) to their acquisitions in 1860 and leased the New Territory (later the New Territories) in 1898. Though Hong Kong was established from the start as a crown colony, its political structures nonetheless underwent considerable if not always logical adjustments in the first few decades of colonial rule, as governors and council members jostled with the Colonial Office for power and authority. By the last decade of the century, the seagoing tonnage entering Hong Kong harbor made it one of the four largest ports in the world. With no natural or mineral resources and a terrain unfavorable to anything but the smallest scale of agriculture, the fiscal base of business and trade rapidly came to define the stature of colonial Hong Kong; the Hong Kong Chamber of Commerce was established in 1861 and the Hong Kong and Shanghai Banking Corporation in 1865. Part of the colony's extensive trade was also conducted in humans, including women sold into profitable prostitution.[18]

As were the Straits, Hong Kong was home to a large Chinese population, part of the overseas Chinese clinging, in the words of G. B. Endacott, "tenaciously to the Chinese way of life."[19] Demographically, Hong Kong resembled Singapore, too, in the overwhelming presence of unaccompanied male laborers from the Pearl River delta region of neighboring Kwangtung Province. As late as 1865, 63 percent of Hong Kong's population consisted of adult males, most of whose families remained in China.[20] It was this particular connection to which officials often alluded in their defense of local CD legislation, arguing that the presence of so large a population of single men necessitated some control over prostitution and the spread of VD. The preponderance of this population of single Asian blue-collar men was vital to the modern commercial success of both colonies. Their work, their low wages (made lower by the absence of their womenfolk), and their ability to cope with a climate deemed difficult for Europeans made them a cornerstone of economic and thus political stability at the same time as their foreignness and lack of accompanying women made them also a threat. For it was this skewed demographics—in which, according to Hong Kong barrister J. J. Francis, there were "very few families, in the proper sense of the word" in the colony—that allegedly invited a brothel culture.[21]

Colonial knowledge claimed that the presence of "respectable" Chinese women in these two port colonies was negligible and that the vast majority of women émigrés from China came knowingly, if not always willingly, to work in the colonies' brothels.[22] Certainly there were large numbers of brothels in both places, though I remain unconvinced from my own research that there were more of them than in Britain or elsewhere, as contemporary commentaries sometimes suggested. Whatever the statistics, however, the perception that a working-class bachelor population spawned a more urgent and greater demand for brothel services seems to have deeply influenced the particular forms of legislation promulgated here.

The divergence of colonial brothel regulation from the alleged parent law of Britain offers a useful framework for considering the lack of consonance between statute and practice, and between aspects of colonial development and the requirements of colonial rule. Moreover, it points profoundly to the realities of disease legislation that clearly spoke to issues beyond and separate from those articulated and claimed by medical expertise. This flashpoint of tension underscores the fundamental clash between the project of modernization and the colonial attitudes that sustained segregation. It is a gap that, I want to argue, exposes some of the weaknesses in the colonial armor.

The growing power and status of medicine interacted with and fed off colonial modernity. Medical discourse, whatever its inconsistencies, was an increasingly powerful force in shaping what Ann-Louise Shapiro calls "symbolic forms and social practices."[23] Frank Dikötter has shown how science and sexuality became linked critical markers and symbols of modernity in this period.[24] And in a recent essay, Warwick Anderson has explored how what he calls a "new American medical discourse" created and made sense of the bodies of colonial subjects in the Philippines, a project that he argues spoke as much about colonization as about its subjects.[25]

Yet when we try to fit sexually transmitted diseases into the frameworks that medical historians have constructed to see the shaping and making of disease in the colonial environment, some intriguing discrepancies arise. Dominant early in the nineteenth century (though losing ground latterly) was the idea of racial immunity, the notion that local indigenes were less susceptible to disease than were transplanted Europeans.[26] It was this assumption that often informed the widespread use of Chinese menial labor in the Straits and Hong Kong. Venereal diseases, however, could not be — and indeed were not — viewed in the same light since their etiology, while complex, was seen as sexual in origin, or at least largely so. It was a commonplace to view tropical VD as a harsher and more devastating cousin to European varieties, and medical practitioners frequently claimed that such diseases were rampant and even endemic in colonial populations. Soma Hewa's argument that colonial disease was frequently attributed to local religious and cultural characteristics may give us some clue as to the ways in which these most culpable of infections resonated with colonial fears of both contagion and sexuality, and with prejudices about indigenous practice and its hostility to the values of modernization.[27] The stock associations between sensualism and the "Orient" made easy the transition from behavior and custom to disease (and vice-versa) in this instance. The alleged refusal of modernity by local populations and the consequent threat of indigenous disorder coalesced in colonial understandings of how VD might literally poison the body politic. The mobilization of cultural arguments to justify inequalities in the advantages bestowed by modernization—economic and otherwise—is a striking example, moreover, of why a traditionally political reading of colonialism or a wholly institutional reading of medicine cannot suffice.[28]

Stephen Kunitz has cogently argued that different colonial experiences have produced startlingly different disease trajectories, suggesting that, as he puts it, "diseases rarely act as independent forces."[29] His insistence on a relationship between disease ecologies and the social processes within which they emerge has far-reaching implications for the colonial perception of a clash between the old and the new. His critique of a static view of the constituents of "tradition" is useful here since it points to the ways in which colonial medical personnel fixed a portrait of the hopelessly insanitary Chinese, whose stubborn habits made necessary the tragic binary that separated the human face of government from its broader and less kindly imperatives.[30] The older view of local racial immunities faded quite quickly in the nineteenth century, or at least it chaotically coexisted with the increasingly common view of indigenes as carriers of disease.[31] Disease was thus "a potent factor in the European conceptualization of indigenous society."[32] Not surprisingly, given the complex mix of the medical and the moral that shaped debate on CD legislation, the regulation of prostitution enshrined in these laws became an important point of discussion and comparison. The juxtaposition of a modernizing West and a traditional East—in short, an orientalist discourse—was fundamental to the rationale for colonization, as was the seemingly contradictory but important representation of a libertine East and a sexually disciplined West.

The registrar general of Hong Kong argued that the closer surveillance afforded by registration was a vital gesture of humanity: "The Contagious Diseases Acts in England have for their object the protection of Soldiers and

Sailors. The Contagious Diseases Ordinances here have not only that object, *but have also for their object the protection of girls and women against brothel slavery* [emphasis in original] and hence it is that the Colonial Government had to adopt the 'registration' and 'licensing' of brothels, and keep up a complete Police inspection. The liberty of the subject in England is too well-known to all to receive much attention, but in China where girls are bought and reared up as prostitutes," he maintained greater efforts were required to afford the necessary protection.[33]

At the Colonial Office, Lord Kimberley argued similarly in defense of the system adopted in the two colonies: "*On the ground of humanity* [emphasis in original], we cannot shrink from this duty, and the performance of it requires that a much stricter and more direct control shall be kept over these houses than would be required or would be possible in an English community."[34]

In short, while Asian laborers could produce greater Britain's modern economic miracle through their thrifty work habits, it was not possible to afford them the specific benefits of Western liberties. Their habits, customs, beliefs, and practices were allegedly incompatible with the fundamentals of British law and liberty. Thus, to bring about the social and cultural changes without which the civilizing effects of British law would be nullified, laws of a sterner sort were deemed necessary, laws that looked "back" to "local" culture rather than "forward" to modernity, even while they lay claim to the language of humanitarianism.[35] In Foucauldian terms, such justifications point rather to a premodern text of coercion than to a "modern" text of discipline.

Though he sees it as operating in modified form, G. B. Endacott nonetheless acknowledges that the politics of colonial Hong Kong were those of "administrative absolutism."[36] The conundrum of humanitarianism versus good government became an increasingly significant representation of the CD ordinances in Southeast Asia. VD thus became less a specifically epidemiological threat than a representation not merely of bad habits or promiscuity but of backwardness, of unmodernness.

Colonial environments were necessarily and definitionally those that required the firm hand of modernization—medically and sanitarily, as well as economically. And since these environments were produced not only by inclement weather and the local fauna but by the particular habits of the locals, medical men were justified in speaking of behaviors as well as microbes. John and Jean Comaroff have pointed out that throughout "the colonized world, persons were disciplined and communities redistributed in the name of sanitation and the control of disease."[37] Modernity stressed the potential and value of the individual; this homogenization of the mass, despite the clear linguistic, cultural, and social differences that were fundamental to these immigrant societies, again marked them out in colonial eyes as somehow premodern. At one and the same time, colonial officials could point to a refusal of modernity by local populations *and* insist that modern conditions and laws would be useless and disruptive innovations. Commentators often dwelt on the perverse uses to which modern commodities were put by those too ignorant to see their true purpose. Most striking is the horror Westerners seemed to feel at the "misuse" of electricity in the red-light districts of the East. Itinerant social-purity activist and moral missionary John Cowen blasted Singapore's areas of prostitution for "their brilliance of electric light and dazzling display [which] far outshine any other parts of the town or colony."[38] R. H. McKie remembered in his memoirs the "electrically brilliant" brothel quarters of the East.[39] This seeming *misuse* of modern beneficence typified for many the pointlessness of extending to local populations advantages that they would and could not fully appreciate, even while acknowledging their critical presence in the construction of a tangible modernity.

Nicholas Thomas sees a similar policy at work in colonial Fiji, where he notes that the greater part of colonial regulation rested not on assimilation —since indigenes would be likely to distort the model of Western civilization offered to them—but on maintaining local systems.[40] Colonial Hong Kong's doctrine of legal repugnancy mirrors this policy. Promulgated in 1843 and in effect in one variant or another until 1986, this doctrine ruled that Chinese law and custom superseded that of English law except in cases where "the Chinese law was in conflict with the 'immutable principles of morality which Christians must regard as binding on themselves in all places and at all times.'"[41] In practice, then, the colonial state could choose its path, nullifying those local laws and customs it found inappropriate and upholding those of which it approved. The modern British rule of law was, by this doctrine, not terribly well suited to the successful rule, or stability, of nonmodern populations. At one and the same time, then, colonial populations were in need of the control that modernization would impose but were unable to benefit from the good brought about by modernization.

This articulation of the separateness of cultures, and its attendant hierarchical reckoning of British and local practice through a medicalized invocation of modernity, justified a greater invasiveness into colonial lives, and especially those of Chinese women.[42] A senior Straits civil servant reported to the colonial secretary in 1871 that the new ordinance was expected to confer beneficial effects that "would not be required from a similar law in England."[43] He numbered among those benefits not only the protection of brothel inmates but also the check it was hoped the ordinance would have on the activities of the secret societies, who were regarded as deeply involved in the entangled worlds of slave trading, immigration, and commercial sex.[44] To both these ends, the Straits Settlements established the post of protector of Chinese in 1877, an office held by the registrar general in Hong Kong since 1858.[45] Women working in brothels, where licenses had always to be displayed, were brought before the protector to declare in person that they chose brothel work freely and without coercion. The familial structure of pocket-mother and pocket-daughter relations that dominated the world of Chinese prostitution, and which echoed the filial piety of the traditional family, was represented by the British as little more than "brothel slavery," and it was this that required the policing offered by registration.[46]

We can see, then, that in the East, CD ordinances were seldom defended exclusively on medical or medico-military grounds.[47] But if not medical and modern in their thrust, what then were these ordinances? For feminist missionaries Elizabeth Andrew and Katharine Bushnell, they were the enemy of the "true" law, the moral law. Andrew and Bushnell charged colonists with betraying Christian precepts through their "guilty compromise with slavery." For them, the ordinances articulated a sophistry that condemned women to sexual slavery through the "flimsy device of calling the ravishing of native women 'protection' and the most brazen forms of slavery 'servitude.'"[48] For Andrew and Bushnell, the point of the law was to uphold the moral premises of Christianity and not to bend to the perils of indigenous custom. The law was a guide to behavior and a follower of faith: without religion and its attendant moral code, law had neither meaning nor valid authority. At the secular level, their critique was a shrewd dissection of the motley contradictions enshrined in the law.

For others, these laws were sensitive barometers of public opinion, an index both of prevailing social mores and of current attitudes to, and interest in, empire. Colonial Secretary Joseph Chamberlain made this abundantly clear in writing to the governor of the Straits in 1899 when he bluntly stated, "The Contagious Diseases Acts were repealed . . . in deference to a strong expression of public opinion. Whether that opinion was well or ill founded, judicious or the reverse, it is unnecessary now to opine. The fact remains that the Acts were repealed."[49] Ever the politician, the law in Chamberlain's eyes was an electoral vehicle, a marker of the tenor of political opinion and the likelihood of political success. Moreover, his was a position that left no doubt as to the relative importance of metropole and periphery; local opinion, whether indigenous or colonial, was less influential than domestic opinion buttressed, as the latter was, by the growing power of the parliamentary vote.

There were also those for whom these laws represented, if problematically, a notion of Englishness that was exactly converse to the charges made by Andrew and Bushnell and their coworkers. For this group, the law was an icon of fairness and humanity in a faceless sea of Asian indifference and brutality toward the fate of individuals; this was especially ironic in light of the indentured labor entering the Straits from British India. Though the *mui tsai* tradition of domestic servitude exported to these two colonies may have enjoyed cultural sanction in Chinese society and have been helpful to poor families,[50] there was no one representative Chinese position on this custom.[51] In both colonies, we see a range of Chinese opinion on the practice of selling women into families as domestic drudges; it was colonial knowledge that chose to homogenize a single Chinese view rather than to see and to seek a range of different opinions. Hong Kong and the Straits being overwhelmingly Chinese, colonial claims that modern British laws brought enlightenment to an immanently culpable culture found a receptive audience in Britain and among colonists.

These competing contemporary readings of the juridical code demonstrate some of the difficulties that faced the ever controversial CD legislation. Tropical colonies, said Downing Street and the medical men, did not correspond with domestic Britain in any manner. They differed from the mother country "in climate, race, social, moral and religious conditions."[52] Colonizer and colonized led "separate and overwhelmingly segregated lives," based, as Kate Lowe and Eugene McLaughlin have argued, largely on race.[53] This racially determined segregation was replicated in medical and sanitary reports that consistently stressed the foul stench and greasiness of Asian living conditions, the welcoming environment that dirt created for the breeding of disease, and general unwholesomeness. Even before the establishment of the Hong Kong Sanitary Board in 1883, the colonial surgeon (first appointed in 1844) and the medical superintendent (1864) both found indigenous sanitary conditions wanting.[54] High mortality rates appeared to justify their claims: in early-twentieth-century Singapore, the mortality rate fluctuated between an enormous forty-four and fifty-one per thousand, higher than in India, Ceylon, or Hong Kong.[55]

Hygiene as a site of modernity was an increasingly important articulation of the distinctions drawn between colonizer and colonized. Commentaries on the Chinese in the two colonies abound with references to squalor and filth as a way of life. One colonial official described Hong Kong and Singapore as "two vast plague spots . . . two putrid sores . . . infecting an ever widening circle of human creatures."[56] Whenever colonial officials ventured into the Chinese quarters of Hong Kong and Singapore, uppermost in their descriptions of life in these overcrowded areas were the unfamiliar smells and noises they encountered. After visiting some Hong Kong brothels, the colonial surgeon declared emphatically that "without exception, these places were filthy overcrowded dens . . . black with filth and smoke."[57] Though he was optimistic that the pressure he could bring to bear was improving these conditions, others saw the local population as beyond redemption. An 1874 report on Hong Kong sanitation pronounced the brothels "so saturated with filth that they cannot be properly cleansed."[58]

Reporting to the governor of the Straits, a Singapore investigative committee found in 1877 that the living quarters of Chinese prostitutes were "generally ill-ventilated and dirty, [t]he rooms dark and small."[59] Officials, however, did not always connect the squalor they found so offensive with the overwhelming poverty of a working-class Chinese population, for whom crowded conditions and filth were chronic problems.[60] Instead, colonial officials attributed the realities of economic hardship—the result of rapid modernization—to the connectedness of racial traits and moral failings.

This drawing of racial boundaries around an assessment of cleanliness allowed for an easy separation of local and nonlocal areas of town, as we have already seen. Brothels frequented by locals and those catering to Europeans were housed in different parts of Hong Kong and Singapore. This literal edifice of physical segregation made it simpler to justify a de facto system in which different rules applied to different segments of the community; this was precisely what the feminist missionaries found offensive and contrary to the true—moral—law.[61] Moreover, in both colonies, the law actually designated different classes of brothel, divided according to the race of the clientele.[62] First-class brothels, staffed largely by local women (especially in Hong Kong), were reserved for a European clientele, while second-class brothels catered only for the local Chinese clientele. In both colonies, these distinctions endured partly because the examination of a woman was linked to the "class" of brothel in that she worked, but it was not mere convenience that determined this segregation. Similar divisions pertained throughout Britain's nonwhite colonies and were defined everywhere along racial lines.

Despite all these considerations of difference, it was humanitarianism and public order—the fight against slavery—that were the constant vindications of the ordinances. Even after the shift in imperial policy in 1887 abrogated the systematic regulation of prostitution, licensing and registration still found supporters at the Colonial Office: "The system of registration & inspection may not have done all that was hoped for from it, but to sweep it away because it recognises brothels, & therefore shocks the moral sense, & to put nothing in its place, seems to me neither humanity nor good government."[63]

Even within the colonial establishment, however, there were powerfully differing opinions as well as practices. Throughout the empire, colonial governors and their councils made strenuous efforts to hold onto CD regulations while their opponents condemned the system for its double standard and its alleged encouragement of vice. The constant battles over how regulation might be implemented, and even whether it ought to be implemented, produced drastic instabilities not only in the externals of colonial rule but within the innermost circles of power.

Governor John Pope Hennessy's vociferous opposition to the Hong Kong ordinance is well known and was one of the issues that prompted his despatch after five years in office to govern the less important colonial possession of Mauritius. Endacott puts Hennessy at the enlightened end of nineteenth-century British opinion since he upheld "the principle of equal treatment for all peoples."[64] The governor, however, ran aground of his own political philosophy on this question of slavery, including sexual slavery. Endacott rightly notes that "the kidnapping of women and girls raised in an acute form the conflict between British law and Chinese custom that arose over the policy of bringing the Chinese more closely under British administration."[65] Hennessy was hoist on his own petard. His consistently pro-Chinese position was, in this instance, sorely tried by his abhorrence of what he saw as slavery: the unbridgeable gap, as it were, between the modern world of freedom and its incompatible foe, the decidedly nonmodern world of slavery.

But Hennessy was not alone in finding a contradiction in these laws, as the elaborate justifications already noted might suggest. Nigel Cameron has shown how an earlier governor, Sir John Bowring, consistently introduced legislation impinging on the Hong Kong Chinese that "conflicted sharply with the liberal sentiments he expressed at other times."[66] Tracing the many amendments to the CD ordinances and their late-nineteenth-century successors, the Women and Girls' Protection Ordinances (which retained brothel regulation but vetoed compulsory examination), Yen Ching-hwang sees "the frequent shifting of the ground" as indicating "not only a loss of coolness on the part of the Government, but also . . . serious differences between government departments on the implementation of the protection policy."[67]

The constant questioning of the policy and the many and frequent changes in the system confirm Yen's speculation. The Legislative Council of the Straits Settlements took the position in 1875 that their CD ordinance should continue to be modeled on that of Hong Kong, yet practices in the two colonies rarely matched—again suggesting different approaches as to how best or most effectively to govern in this medico-moral arena. As we have seen, in Hong Kong, only women with a European clientele were examined since the registrar general thought it would be impolitic as well as impractical to examine all brothel women.[68] By contrast, all Straits prostitutes were examined, though those with European clients were examined more frequently.[69] And while women entering the Straits were required to attend an interview with the protector of Chinese, Hong Kong kept no check on women immigrants.[70]

While these differences in practice suggest a certain discomfiture with the policy, or merely a confusion as to the most efficient and presumably cheapest means to an end, they also highlight the gap between law and practice, and between rhetoric and intent. Nowhere was the law administered to the letter, and the rationales accompanying this discontinuity underscore the unevenness of the colonial enterprise and of its authority. Colonial officials never tired of complaining that the British public had no appreciation of "the delicacy required in ruling an alien civilisation."[71] Such complaints spoke directly to the clash between Western and non-Western values. Endacott has pointed out that when plague broke out in Hong Kong in the 1890s, the British authorities were brought face to face, through strikes and protests over their interventionist measures, with how little of Western values and medicine were embraced by the local population.[72] It is not surprising, then, that he also argues that "public health measures presented the policy of integrating the Chinese into the colonial administration with its greatest challenge."[73] Writing some forty years ago, Endacott does not point out that in this scenario, integration is to be a one-way process requiring an acceptance of British methods and values, but this is nonetheless a key point. That public health should prove so great a focal point of conflict and difficulty suggests not only the emphasis that colonial authorities laid on "sanitizing" subject lands and populations but also the centrality of sanitary-medical issues to the vision of a modernizing colonialism. At the same time, these instabilities remind us that European attitudes must also not be overly homogenized. While the colonial project clearly rested on an undifferentiated view of Asian squalor, brutality, and unmodernity, differing positions jostled for prominence in colonial opinion. Medical practice itself was at a pivotal moment of consolidating power and authority, and there, too, we can note considerable competition. Not only were medical regimes for the treatment of VD not all that different from those in use by non-Western practitioners but theories of disease, and especially of tropical disease, were in critical flux at precisely this period. Miasma theory had not been entirely discredited, germ theory was slowly gaining a foothold in medical orthodoxy, and notions of racial immunity were being challenged by the vocabulary of contagion; these were not stable technologies but themselves sites of contestation and resistance.

The intent of British law was to consolidate imperial rule, but over and over, it was an approach that proved untenable. Theoretically, since Hong Kong and the Straits Settlements were both crown colonies, their laws were those of English common law. Barrister J. J. Francis was technically correct in pointing out that it was toleration and not legalization that prevailed in the Hong Kong brothel system because the sovereign power held sway, the doctrine of legal repugnancy notwithstanding.[74] This, of course, was exactly what antiregulation reformers such as Andrew and Bushnell had long regarded as an invidious double standard. But the activists had, by no means, a monopoly on critiques of this dilemma. Government officials in the colonies and the metropole consistently negated comparisons between West and East, even while the entire practice of colonialism rested squarely on that comparison. Assessing CD ordinances at Malta and Hong Kong, a London official spurned the notion of comparability: "I do not see how any comparison can be drawn between a place with a wholly European population and one of the Eastern colonies."[75] And the constant and open acknowledgment of the un-Englishness of the laws as promulgated and practiced in Hong Kong and the Straits concurs with that view. The imposition of British law may have been an ideal, but the practice almost always fell short.[76] Britishness, ironically, had ultimately to be inculcated and encouraged by distinctly un-British means. This lay at the heart of colonial rule, and to it, we may surely ascribe some, at least, of the instabilities and ambiguities in that rule that have been noted by so many scholars.

It was not uncommon to find colonial profitability in these two key trading posts asserted as the basis for a less than rigid application of the common law. Even the liberal Hennessy appreciated the force of the market. Elizabeth Sinn argues that in tandem with other British politicians, Hennessy was willing to tolerate some forms of human purchase so as not to alienate the prosperous Chinese merchant class.[77] Sir William Robinson, Hong Kong's governor from 1891 to 1898, urged Colonial Secretary Chamberlain to take steps to deal with the evils of unregistered brothels at a time when the whole registration system was under constant and vociferous attack. Robinson's concern was pragmatic: he feared that such brothels would deter the more "respectable" Chinese from moving to Hong Kong — a decision "which may affect the prosperity of the Colony."[78]

Robinson's distinction between respectable Chinese and traffickers in human commodities was another gray area for officials. While some took the view that the "better class" of Chinese would applaud a crackdown on the sex trade, others saw Asian cultures generally as indifferent to prostitution and lacking in the moral refinements lent Europe by Christianity. It was the missionary feminists Andrew and Bushnell who charged rightly that the colonial government had never sought the Chinese view of the situation. For them, of course, the ordinances represented a treacherous and opportunistic pact with the devil. Historians of both Singapore and Hong Kong have argued that the regulating of brothels and controlling of the spread of sexually transmitted diseases was part and parcel of the British policy to attract cheap Chinese labor to the colonies.[79] Since Hong Kong and Singapore were notorious for being what James Warren calls "clearing houses" for women being shipped to other sex markets (Australia, California, and South America, to name a few), it follows, as he further argues, that the state's concern was less with the trafficking of women (the ostensible object of concern) than with the cleanliness of extant or incoming sex workers, there to service the large laboring population.[80]

In practice, influential men in the Chinese community took matters into their own hands in both colonies. The Po Leung Kuk (PLK), literally the Society for the Protection of the Innocent, monitored the kidnapping of women for prostitution and provided an asylum for "rescued" women. In Hong Kong, the PLK had close associations with the Tung Wah Hospital; indeed, Elizabeth Sinn describes it as "a junior associate of the Hospital."[81] Both she and Henry Lethbridge see the Tung Wah as foundational in the creation of a local Chinese elite that was separate from colonial structures, and it may not be insignificant that it was in the arenas of health care, women's safety, and immigration that this new elite chose to consolidate its standing in the Chinese community.[82] In the Straits, the PLK was founded by the Chinese Protectorate and overseen by a European women's committee. Its day-to-day running, however, was in the hands of local Chinese, who also raised money for its maintenance. The government made a charitable grant toward its upkeep, but continually stressed that it was not a government institution, thus sending a decidedly mixed message as to the government's commitment to women running from coercion.

It was 1888 before Hong Kong law specifically penalized trafficking in women, despite the long-standing rhetoric of concern with this issue.[83] Procuration had become a major issue in Britain in the 1880s, especially after the scandalous revelations of William Stead's attempts at purchasing a little girl in the *Pall Mall Gazette*.[84] The 1885 Criminal Law Amendment Act tightened the domestic law in this respect; it also raised the female age of consent, a policy colonial lawmakers tended to view with grave concern since Asian women were said to mature earlier than their Western sisters.[85]

The state thus frequently found itself in the curious and ambiguous position of upholding the moral and political authority of the modern Western judicial mode but simultaneously seeking to reassure the foreign populations subject to that code that it would not unduly interfere with either their laws or customs. Endacott notes an absence of "Western forms of political liberty" in Hong Kong, but he justifies that lacuna as consonant with the protection of Chinese interests.[86] James Warren, as already noted, sees that same absence in the Straits as a conscious labor policy in the modern development of the colony.

This constant balancing of imperial considerations had a major impact on the medico-moral rhetoric that accompanied CD legislation when, in 1887 and 1888, the Colonial Office directed colonial administrations to repeal extant legislation in accordance with the demands of the House of Commons, and in the wake of domestic repeal in 1886. It is difficult to gauge whether the Colonial Office anticipated the level of dismay that speedily ensued in the face of their directive. Many colonial governments raised protests at the loss of the CD legislation: in India, Fiji, and Ceylon, as well as Hong Kong and the Straits, colonial authorities unsuccessfully demanded the right to maintain the full force of the ordinances. Hong Kong was by no means the only colony in which repeal was "forced through a dissenting Legislative Council by the use of the official majority."[87] The Straits Settlement Association, a London-based mercantile booster group for the colony, claimed that the CD ordinance was repealed "under the peremptory orders of the Colonial Office" and "against the protests of the Local Government, of the non-official members of Council, of the officers of Her Majesty's Forces, of the Medical Staff (Civil and Military), and of the general public of the Straits Settlements."[88] If one accepts the association's implicit definition of the "general public" as a European public, then their claim is an accurate one. Repeal was as widely opposed by whites in the Straits as it was in Hong Kong.

The appeal for retention of the legislation in Hong Kong and the Straits focused not on the anticipated rise in VD rates, as it did in India and elsewhere, but rather on the alleged efficacy of brothel registration in dampening the trade in women. In both colonies, a compromise position successfully championed the abolition of the compulsory examination so anathematic to the British protesters alongside the retention of brothel registration. In the Straits, a Women and Girls' Protection Ordinance replaced the old ordinance in 1888, and legislation of the same name followed in Hong Kong a year later. Hong Kong had previously maintained two separate legal tracks. Before the enactment of the new law, Ordinance 4 of 1865 and Ordinance 2 of 1875 prohibited the procuration and sale of women and girls for prostitution.[89] These two laws were so seldom invoked, however, that one Hong Kong historian has pronounced them "a dead letter."[90] The new laws in both colonies in the 1880s maintained the existing system of brothel registration but specifically outlawed any compulsory examination of women; both spelled out the penalties for trafficking in women and for detaining them against their will.

The legislative separation of these two clearly related issues until late in the 1880s, when the defense of a law under attack became an issue of political urgency, is suggestive. If the local CD ordinances had been framed, as was so often argued, primarily to procure and protect the apparently fragile liberty of Chinese women, it would surely have made sense, and saved money, to have combined the related laws far earlier. That the procuration ordinances were seldom invoked and rarely discussed by politicians, prosecutors, or lawmakers contrasts strikingly with the constant and critical attention devoted to the earlier disease-specific ordinances. While the procuration laws focused on those who profited from the sale of women, the CD laws, conversely, put the spotlight on the women themselves; whether women were being made victims of the associated rhetoric or were blamed by it (as the medical reading of the law implied), attention was effectively diverted from the men and women who actually ran the trade. The gesture of protection was just that, a gesture.

We can push this separation of intent a little further through an investigation of the kinds of prosecution that were pursued under these and similar ordinances. The Hong Kong CD ordinances of 1857 and 1867 both allowed for the prosecution of brothel keepers for ill-treatment of the women whom they employed. There were 411 prosecutions of unregistered women and unregistered brothels between 1858 and 1868, and 590 between 1868 and 1877. Prosecutions of brothel keepers for ill-treatment of the women, on the other hand, numbered only fourteen between 1869 and 1873, the years for which figures are available.[91] Even given the discrepant time span here, it is evident that the latter variety of prosecutions was pursued less frequently.

Under the new legislation implemented after 1888 and in theory aimed more specifically at protecting women from exploitation, there was little change. The PLK reported having brought only sixteen cases under the Hong Kong Women and Girls' Protection Ordinance between January 1892 and May 1892;[92] ten of these explicitly detail instances of forced prostitution.

The situation in the Straits was not dissimilar. Mr. Justice Wood of the Singapore Court found Ching See Soh guilty of kidnapping, abducting, and purchasing a girl child in the early 1880s but imposed only a paltry twenty-dollar fine and no prison term. Justifying his sentencing, Wood claimed he was persuaded by none other than the protector of Chinese that "such sale of children by parents and relatives was legal and customary in China," a clear reference to the *mui tsai* tradition.[93] Though the Colonial Office strenuously objected to Wood's departure from the common law, such instances were not uncommon where the offense was procuring rather than failing to appear for a venereal examination or for transmitting such diseases to a client. Indeed in Hong Kong, 288 complaints were laid against registered women for infecting clients with VD in 1888, a far greater number of complaints than we see in either colony against those who were alleged to traffic in and profit from the sale and employment of these women.[94] And with the number of registered brothels well into the hundreds (539 in the Straits in 1914),[95] the disparity between prosecutions of workers, on the one hand, and of traffickers and even brothel managers, on the other, is certainly worth questioning.

These discrepancies in prosecutorial vigor suggest again a slippage between rhetoric and rule centered around the more coercive strands of modernity. The laws in both colonies inscribed a picture of vulnerable women who required protection from their own kin and kind but who were nonetheless unwilling to follow the protective European model without the extra "push" of coercion. All the evidence points clearly to brothel women declining the examination after it became a voluntary procedure.[96] This was explained by medical officials as indicating ignorant prejudice against European medicine—yet another sign of Chinese stubbornness in the face of the modern.[97] And while the imperial government had been unable to ignore the strenuous efforts of colonial legislators to maintain some form of control over brothel prostitution in the late 1880s, the opposition to such legislation by the local population was more easily dismissed. In Singapore, anti–CD ordinance riots had broken out in late 1872 but were barely reported to London.[98] While nothing on this scale erupted in Hong Kong, antiordinance Governor Hennessy did recognize that there was serious unhappiness among the local population over the rules. To the annoyance of many metropolitan officials, the governor ordered an inquiry into the working of the ordinance, and especially into the deaths of two women who, in 1877, fell from a rooftop in their hurried efforts to escape detection.[99] Hennessy, of course, was less interested in magnifying the potential sanitary benefits of the ordinance than in detailing its coercive qualities and dubious application. Ultimately, however, the separation he sought is conceptually untenable since what made the law coercive was so intimately connected to its medical as well as its allegedly humanitarian intent. The tensions and contradictions in promulgation and in application were smoothed out by the central role accorded modernity in the passing—and the partial dismantling—of these controversial ordinances.

Warwick Anderson's insistence on the fundamental connectedness between the framing of disease, of race, and of environment points up the ways in which we might read disease as a construct that is critically poised to demonstrate and elucidate the practices of modernity, with public health very much the "front line of imperialism."[100] Resistance could be negated and in effect depoliticized by its association with a rejection of the palpable benefits of a modern and medical approach: Chinese discomfort with the interventionist and coercive aspects of CD legislation in this critical period of modernization became one more emblem betokening the value of modernity and the inability of subject populations to appreciate the full worth of its munificence.

Oppositional assumptions about the West's role (or more literally the British role) as modernizers and about the "Orient" as a corrupt and degraded backwater are fundamental in appreciating hiccups in the application of the colonial law, which Angela Zito and Tani Barlow describe as "'the never finished outcome of constant discursive negotiation."[101] That antagonism produced, on the one hand, invocations as to the preciousness of individual liberty, and on the other, some powerfully coercive mechanisms for negating that liberty in practice. If the British purported to find their Asian subjects stubborn in the face of change and modernization, it is perhaps ironic that their own absolute readings of the meaning of liberty and the rule of law forced them into compromises that served to illuminate powerfully the tenuousness even of coercive forms of rule in ostensibly modern circumstances. For the Asian subjects of these British colonies, the experience of modernity was one of coercion and confusion rather than of benefit and advantage. The resistance that their colonial masters took for stubborn traditionalism might better be seen as an eloquent critique of the costs of colonialism and its quest for the modern.

Notes

This research was supported by generous funding from both the National Endowment for the Humanities (Humanities Studies in Science and Technology Award: £RH-21243 95) and the National Institutes of Health (National Library of Medicine Award: £RO1LM05678). An earlier version of this essay was presented at the 1995 North American Conference on British Studies, where the comments of Ian Fletcher were of great help in its later development. I would also like to thank Antoinette Burton, Margo Bistis, and Charlotte Furth for their helpful comments on drafts of this paper, as well as the incisive comments of both an anonymous reviewer for *positions* and the guest editors for this issue, Marta Hanson and Judith Farquhar. Doug Peers provided invaluable advice on the precise chronology of relations between the Straits Settlements and India. Kate Lowe provided immense assistance in orienting me in the history of Hong Kong, as well as in Hong Kong itself.

1 For the British CD Acts, see Judith Walkowitz, *Prostitution and Victorian Society: Women, Class, and the State* (Cambridge: Cambridge University Press, 1980); and Paul McHugh, *Prostitution and Victorian Social Reform* (London: Croom Helm, 1980). For imperial legislation, see Kenneth Ballhatchet, *Race, Sex, and Class under the British Raj: Imperial Attitudes and Policies and their Critics, 1793–1905* (London: Weidenfeld and Nicholson, 1980); Arnold P. Kaminsky, "Morality Legislation and British Troops in Late-Nineteenth-Century India," *Military Affairs* 43: (1979) 78–83; Philippa Levine, "Rereading the 1890s: Venereal Disease as 'Constitutional Crisis' in Britain and British India," *Journal of Asian Studies* 55, no. 3 (1996): 582–612; Levine, "Venereal Disease, Prostitution, and the Politics of Empire: The Case of British India," *Journal of the History of Sexuality* 4, no. 4 (1994): 579–602; Elizabeth B. Van Heyningen, "The Social Evil in the Cape Colony, 1868–1902: Prostitution and the Contagious Diseases Acts," *Journal of Southern African Studies* 10, no. 2 (1984): 179–191; James F. Warren, *Ah Ku and Karayuki-San: Prostitution in Singapore, 1870–1940* (Singapore: Oxford University Press, 1993); Norman Miners, "State Regulation of Prostitution in Hong Kong, 1857 to 1941," *Journal of the Hong Kong Branch of the Royal Asiatic Society* 24 (1984): 143–161; and Susanna Hoe, *The Private Life of Old Hong Kong: Western Women in the British Colony, 1841–1941* (Hong Kong: Oxford University Press, 1991).

   Three pertinent articles have, unfortunately, appeared too recently for proper consideration here. They are Kerrie L. MacPherson, "Conspiracy of Silence: A History of Sexually Transmitted Diseases and HIV/AIDS in Hong Kong," in *Sex, Disease, and Society: A Comparative History of Sexually Transmitted Diseases and HIV/AIDS in Asia and the Pacific*, ed. Milton Lewis, Scott Bamber, and Michael Waugh (Westport, Conn.: Greenwood Press, 1997), 87–112; Brendan O'Keefe, "Sexually Transmitted Diseases in Malaysia: A History," in Lewis, Bamber, and Waugh, *Sex, Disease, and Society*, 155–175; and Brenda S. A. Yeoh, "Sexually Transmitted Diseases in Late Nineteenth- and Twentieth-Century Singapore," in Lewis, Bamber, and Waugh, *Sex, Disease, and Society,* 177–202.

2 Legislative Council of the Straits Settlements, *Proceedings of the Legislative Council of the Straits Settlements, 1875: Annual Medical Returns of the Civil Hospitals for 1873,* (Singapore: Government Printing Office, 1876), lxxiii.

3 On Hong Kong, see Public Record Office, London, Colonial Office [hereinafter CO] 129/239 (22188), 23 November 1888; on the Straits, see CO 273/65 (2546), Sir H. Ord to Lord Kimberley, Colonial Office, 13 February 1873.

4 For an interesting contrast, see Kerrie L. Macpherson's analysis of lock-hospital legislation in

Shanghai, where she sees a medico-military initiative for the municipal legislation intro-
duced there in 1877 (Macpherson, *A Wilderness of Marshes: The Origins of Public Health in
Shanghai, 1843–1893* [Hong Kong: Oxford University Press, 1987], esp. 237). One Hong
Kong historian who does see a largely medical initiative for the CD ordinances is Elizabeth
Sinn ("Chinese Patriarchy and the Protection of Women in Nineteenth-Century Hong
Kong," in *Women and Chinese Patriarchy: Submission, Servitude, and Escape,* ed. Maria Jaschok
and Suzanne Miers [London: Zed Books, 1994], 141–170).

5 For a consideration of the strategic issues making for British interest in the region, see
Wong Lin Ken, "The Strategic Significance of Singapore in Modern History," in *A History
of Singapore*, ed. Ernest C. T. Chew and Edwin Lee (Singapore: Oxford University Press,
1991).

6 C. M. Turnbull, *A History of Singapore, 1819–1988*, 2d ed. (Singapore: Oxford University
Press, 1989), 13, 90.

7 Wong Lin Ken, "Commercial Growth before the Second World War," in Chew and Lee,
History of Singapore, 42.

8 For a discussion of this process, see C. M. Turnbull, *The Straits Settlements, 1826–67: Indian
Presidency to Crown Colony* (London: Athlone Press, 1972), chap. 1.

9 Turnbull, *History of Singapore*, 95. Lee Poh Ping argues that the steady growth in the female
population evidences both settler desires and successes: "Only those whose jobs allowed for
some permanence would be willing and able to send for their wives from China" (Lee Poh
Ping, *Chinese Society in Nineteenth-Century Singapore* [Kuala Lumpur: Oxford University
Press, 1978], 94). For a discussion of women's agency in making the move to the Straits, see
Claire Chiang, "Female Migrants in Singapore: Towards a Strategy of Pragmatism and Cop-
ing," in Jaschok and Miers, *Women and Chinese Patriarchy*, 238–263.

10 Warren, *Ah Ku*, 379; Turnbull, *History of Singapore*, 58. For a discussion of Singapore's commercial history, see Wong, "Commercial Growth." Indian convict labor was also a crucial
factor in the development of the Straits before the 1870s.

11 For an analysis of the exodus of laborers from Kwangtung and Fukien to Hong Kong, see
Jung-Fang Tsai, *Hong Kong in Chinese History: Community and Social Unrest in the British
Colony, 1842–1913* (New York: Columbia University Press, 1993), esp. 20–22.

12 Edwin Lee, *The British as Rulers: Governing Multi-racial Singapore, 1867–1914* (Singapore:
Singapore University Press, 1991), 34–47.

13 Edwin Lee, "Community, Family, and Household," in Chew and Lee, *History of Singapore*,
243; Turnbull, *History of Singapore*, 52; G. B. Endacott, *Government and People in Hong Kong,
1841–1962: A Constitutional History* (Hong Kong: Hong Kong University Press, 1964); Endacott, *A History of Hong Kong* (London: Oxford University Press, 1958), 90.

14 Henry Lethbridge, *Hong Kong: Stability and Change, a Collection of Essays* (Hong Kong:
Oxford University Press, 1978), 55; Tsai, *Hong Kong in Chinese History*, esp. 26.

15 Yen Ching-hwang, *A Social History of the Chinese in Singapore and Malaya, 1800–1911* (Singa-

pore: Oxford University Press, 1986), 255. See, too, Warren, *Ah Ku*, 227; and Gail Hershatter, "The Hierarchy of Shanghai Prostitution, 1870–1949," *Modern China* 15, no. 4 (1989): 480.

16 Soh Poh Thong, "Concerning Our Girls," *Straits Chinese Magazine* 11, no. 4 (December 1907): 141–143.

17 Nigel Cameron, *An Illustrated History of Hong Kong* (Hong Kong: Oxford University Press, 1991), 105.

18 Maria Jaschok, *Concubines and Bondservants. A Social History* (London: Zed Books, 1988), 86; Endacott, *History of Hong Kong*, 173.

19 Endacott, *Government and People*, 90.

20 Tsai, *Hong Kong in Chinese History*, 47.

21 British Parliamentary Papers. House of Commons [hereinafter PP. HC.]. 1882. [c. 3185]. Enclosure No. 5 in No. 18, 1 October 1880.

22 See, for instance, PP. HC. 1881. [c. 3093]. *Observations on the Report of the Commissioners on the Contagious Diseases Ordinances in Hong Kong*, 22; and Turnbull, *History of Singapore*, 57.

23 Ann-Louise Shapiro, "Disordered Bodies/Disorderly Acts: Medical Discourse and the Female Criminal in Nineteenth-Century Paris," in *Gendered Domains: Rethinking Public and Private in Women's History: Essays from the Seventh Berkshire Conference on the History of Women*, ed. Dorothy O. Helly and Susan M. Reverby (Ithaca, N.Y.: Cornell University Press, 1992), 124.

24 Frank Dikötter, *Sex, Culture, and Modernity in China: Medical Science and the Construction of Sexual Identities in the Early Republican Period* (Honolulu: University of Hawai'i Press, 1995), 7.

25 Warwick Anderson, "'Where Every Prospect Pleases and Only Man Is Vile': Laboratory Medicine as Colonial Discourse," *Critical Inquiry* 18 (1992): 507.

26 See Warwick Anderson, "Immunities of Empire: Race, Disease, and the New Tropical Medicine, 1900–1920," *Bulletin of the History of Medicine* 70 (1996): 94–118.

27 Soma Hewa, *Colonialism, Tropical Disease, and Imperial Medicine: Rockefeller Philanthropy in Sri Lanka* (Lanham, Md.: University Press of America, 1995), 6.

28 For a further discussion of this point, see Levine, "Rereading the 1890s."

29 Stephen J. Kunitz, *Disease and Social Diversity: The European Impact on the Health of Non-Europeans* (New York: Oxford University Press, 1994), 5.

30 See Dikötter, *Sex, Culture, and Modernity*, 11–12, on the fundamental ahistoricity of dualized East-West notions of "tradition" and "progress."

31 Lenore Manderson, *Sickness and the State: Health and Illness in Colonial Malaya, 1870–1940* (Cambridge: Cambridge University Press, 1996), 8.

32 David Arnold, "Introduction: Disease, Medicine, and Empire," in *Imperial Medicine and Indigenous Societies* (Manchester: Manchester University Press, 1988), 7.

33 CO 129/203 (21149). Registrar General of Hong Kong to Acting Colonial Secretary, 21 September 1882.

34 James Stansfeld, *Lord Kimberley's Defence of the Government Brothel System in Hong Kong* (London: National Association for the Repeal of the Contagious Diseases Acts, 1882), 35.

35 It is worth noting that Elizabeth Sinn argues that in Hong Kong, this was a compromise to "minimize resistance to colonial occupation" (Sinn, "Chinese Patriarchy," 141).

36 Endacott, *Government and People*, 26.

37 John Comaroff and Jean Comaroff, *Ethnography and the Historical Imagination* (Boulder, Colo.: Westview Press, 1992), 216.

38 John Cowen, "Extracts from a Report upon Public Prostitution in Singapore," *The Shield*, 3d ser., 1, no. 3 (October 1916): 184.

39 R. H. McKie, *This Was Singapore* (Sydney: Angus and Robertson, 1942), 100.

40 Nicholas Thomas, "Sanitation and Seeing: The Creation of State Power in Early Colonial Fiji," *Comparative Studies in Society and History* 32, no. 1 (1990): 156.

41 Elfed Vaughan Roberts, Sum Ngai Ling, and Peter Bradshaw, *Historical Dictionary of Hong Kong and Macau* (Metuchen, N.J.: Scarecrow Press, 1992), 127.

42 Other women, Japanese in particular, were also affected. For Japanese women in Singapore, see Warren, *Ah Ku*. See, too, the following discussions of Japanese women working as prostitutes elsewhere: Yamazaki Tomoko, "Sandakan No. 8 Brothel," *Bulletin of Concerned Asian Scholars* 7 (1975): 49–54; and Motoe Terami-Wada, "Karayuki-san of Manila: 1890–1920," *Philippine Studies* 34 (1986): 287–316.

43 CO 273/51(12747). Administrator, Straits Settlements, to Earl of Kimberley, 21 November 1871.

44 It was 1889 before the Straits government moved openly against the secret societies, preferring to cloak public-order policies in guises such as this.

45 The post of registrar general was renamed secretary for Chinese affairs in 1913. In the Straits, the protector of Chinese also oversaw the CD ordinance in the years it was in effect. Colin Crisswell and Mike Watson claim that the registrar general at the time of the passing of the 1857 Ordinance, D. R. Caldwell, was a brothel owner. See Crisswell and Watson, *The Royal Hong Kong Police (1841–1945)* (Hong Kong: Macmillan, 1982), 77. I have been unable to verify their claim.

46 On relations in Chinese prostitution, see Yen, *Social History*; Jaschok, *Concubines and Bond-servants*; and Gail Hershatter, "Prostitution and the Market in Women in Early-Twentieth-Century Shanghai," in *Marriage and Inequality in Chinese Society*, ed. Rubie S. Watson and Patricia Buckley Ebrey (Berkeley and Los Angeles: University of California Press, 1991), 256–285. Peter Hodge makes the point that European administrators consistently misunderstood the Chinese distinction between kidnapping and the *mui tsai* (mei zi) system. See Hodge, "Prostitution in Hong Kong," in *Community Problems and Social Work in Southeast Asia: The Hong Kong and Singapore Experience*, ed. Peter Hodge (Hong Kong: Hong Kong University Press, 1980), 196–197. See, too, Lethbridge, *Hong Kong*, 78–79.

47 There were, of course, always some officials who continued to maintain that the need for

these ordinances was wholly medical. Dr. Murray, Hong Kong colonial surgeon in 1869, claimed their "sole object" was to restrict contagion and cure VD. See CO129/296 (4718).

48 Elizabeth Andrew and Katharine Bushnell, *Heathen Slaves and Christian Rulers* (Oakland, Calif.: Messiah's Advocate, 1907), ii–iii.

49 CO 129/286 (28461), f. 105. Draft of letter from Colonial Secretary Joseph Chamberlain to Governor Sir C. B. H. Mitchell, 28 April 1899.

50 Cameron, *Illustrated History*, 108.

51 Jaschok, *Concubines and Bondservants*, 83.

52 CO 129/286 (28461), f. 107. Draft of letter from Colonial Secretary Joseph Chamberlain to Governor Sir C. B. H. Mitchell, 28 April 1899.

53 Kate Lowe and Eugene McLaughlin, "Sir John Pope Hennessy and the 'Native Race Craze': Colonial Government in Hong Kong, 1877–1882," *Journal of Imperial and Commonwealth History* 20, no. 2 (1992): 230, 224. See, too, Endacott, *Government and People*; and Endacott, *History of Hong Kong*, 122.

54 For a discussion of alleged Asian dirt in another colonial context, see Donald Denoon's account of the policies surrounding Asian immigration to the Cape after the Boer War in Denoon, "Temperate Medicine and Settler Capitalism: On the Reception of Western Medical Ideas," in *Disease, Medicine, and Empire: Perspectives on Western Medicine and the Experience of European Expansion*, ed. Roy McLeod and Milton Lewis (London: Routledge, 1988), 130–131. See also Brenda S. A. Yeoh, *Municipal Sanitary Surveillance, Asian Resistance, and the Control of the Urban Environment in Colonial Singapore* (Oxford: University of Oxford School of Geography Research Papers, 1991).

55 Saravanan Gopinathan, "Education," in Chew and Lee, *History of Singapore*, 270.

56 CO 129/276. Unsigned, undated internal Colonial Office memorandum, 1897.

57 CO 129/189 (13163). Annual Report of Colonial Surgeon, 1874.

58 CO 129/189 (16884). *Sanitation in Hong Kong*, 1874. Endacott, *History of Hong Kong*, alludes to the constant official concern over Chinese dirt (183).

59 CO 273/91 (6629). *Report of the Committee Appointed to Inquire into the Working of Ordinance 23 of 1870, Commonly Called the Contagious Diseases Ordinance* (1877).

60 Manderson, *Sickness and the State*, 173.

61 According to Hong Kong policeman Kenneth Andrew, even in the mid-twentieth century the practice of housing brothels for different races of clients on separate streets was still common. See Andrews, *Chop Suey* (Ilfracombe, England: Arthur M. Stockwell, 1975) 27; and Andrew, *Hong Kong Detective* (London: John Long, 1962), 90.

62 PP. HC. 1880 (118). *Copy of Report of the Commissioners Appointed by His Excellency John Pope-Hennessy to Inquire into the Working of the Contagious Diseases Ordinance, 1867*; Norman Miners, *Hong Kong under Imperial Rule, 1912–1941* (Hong Kong: Oxford University Press, 1987), 149.

63 CO 129/259. Handwritten internal Colonial Office memorandum initialed M [probably Frederick Meade], 9 January 1894.

64 Endacott, *History of Hong Kong*, 170.

65 Ibid., 173.

66 Cameron, *Illustrated History*, 84.

67 Yen, *Social History*, 257–258.

68 CO 129/286 (28461), ff. 77–78; Hoe, *Private Life*, 145.

69 CO 129/286 (28461), f. 77 (verso).

70 CO 129/259 (12527). Colonial Office Memorandum, G. W. Johnson to Mr. Bramston, 23 November 1893. Such checks as were carried out at Hong Kong were of women leaving the port; they were undertaken not by government officials but by the Po Leung Kuk (PLK), which was founded in 1870 to fight kidnapping, particularly of women and girls. See Sinn, "Chinese Patriarchy," 153–154.

71 CO 129/533/10, f. 46. *Note on the Legal and Practical Position of Brothels in Hong Kong*, 16 May 1931.

72 Endacott, *History of Hong Kong*, 219. Megan Vaughan sees a similar resilience in the maintenance of indigenous African healing traditions. See Vaughan, *Curing Their Ills: Colonial Power and African Illness* (Stanford, Calif.: Stanford University Press, 1991), 24. While Vaughan sees a relatively easy absorption and adaptation of Western medical ideas into these practices, it was only with reluctance that the Tung Wah Hospital, the leading Chinese socio-medical institution in Hong Kong, offered patients a choice between local and Western treatments after the 1890s.

73 Endacott, *History of Hong Kong*, 183.

74 PP. HC. 1882. c. 3185. Enclosure No. 5 in No. 18, 1 October 1880, 100.

75 CO 129/186 (17899). Colonial Office Memorandum, author unknown, 1879.

76 For a cogent analysis of a renowned case in which the clash between imperial and local law had significant repercussions for Britain's imperial prowess, see Sudhir Chandra, "Whose Laws? Notes on a Legitimising Myth of the Colonial Indian State," *Studies in History* 8, no. 2 (1992): 187–211. See, too, Antoinette Burton, "Conjugality on Trial: The Rukhmabai Case and the Debate on Indian Child Marriage in Late Victorian London," in *Disorder in the Court: Nineteenth Century Trials*, ed. Nancy Erber and George Robb (New York: Macmillan, forthcoming).

77 Sinn, "Chinese Patriarchy," 149.

78 CO 129/276, Sir William Robinson to Joseph Chamberlain, 30 June 1897; reprinted in PP. HC. 1899 c. 9523.

79 Warren, *Ah Ku*, 35; Maria Jaschok and Suzanne Miers, "Women in the Chinese Patriarchal System: Submission, Servitude, Escape, and Collusion," in Jaschok and Miers, *Women and Chinese Patriarchy*, 12.

80 Warren, *Ah Ku*, 115, 68; James F. Warren, "Prostitution and the Politics of Venereal Disease: Singapore, 1870–98," *Journal of South East Asian Studies* 21, no. 2 (1990): 369.

81 Elizabeth Sinn, *Power and Charity: The Early History of the Tung Wah Hospital, Hong Kong* (Hong Kong: Oxford University Press, 1989), 116.

82 Ibid; and Lethbridge, *Hong Kong*, 62–63. Lethbridge has also argued that the PLK's strict distinction between a legitimate *mui tsai* tradition and coerced kidnapping served to maintain the flow of *mui tsai* to wealthy Chinese families through a fear that a rising female-infanticide rate would follow any outright ban on the sale of children (Lethbridge, *Hong Kong*, 79–82).

83 The Penal Code did prohibit trafficking, but the political significance of an ordinance that specifically articulated a crime and its punishment was not lost on either offenders or reformers.

84 See Deborah Gorham, "The 'Maiden Tribute to Modern Babylon' Re-examined: Child Prostitution and the Idea of Childhood in Late Victorian England," *Victorian Studies* 21 (1978): 353–379; Michael Pearson, *The Age of Consent: Victorian Prostitution and Its Enemies* (Newton Abbott, England: David and Charles, 1972); Raymond L. Schults, *Crusader in Babylon: W. T. Stead and the Pall Mall Gazette* (Lincoln: University of Nebraska Press, 1972); Charles Terrot, *The Maiden Tribute: A Study of the White Slave Traffic of the Nineteenth Century* (London: Frederick Muller, 1959); and Judith Walkowitz, *City of Dreadful Delight: Narratives of Sexual Danger in Late Victorian London* (Chicago: University of Chicago Press, 1992).

85 Colonial opposition to following British law on this issue was not limited to Hong Kong and the Straits Settlements. The Indian government held that such a law could interfere profoundly with Hindu marriage customs. For discussions of the controversy over age-of-consent legislation, which was introduced into India in the early 1890s, see, for instance, Padma Anagol-McGinn, "The Age of Consent Act Reconsidered," *South Asia Research* 12 (1992): 110–118; and Dagmar Engels, "The Age of Consent Act of 1891: Colonial Ideology in Bengal," *South Asia Research* 3, no. 2 (1983): 107–132.

86 Endacott, *Government and People*, vii.

87 Frank Welsh, *A History of Hong Kong* (London: HarperCollins, 1993), 264.

88 Straits Settlements Association to Colonial Secretary Joseph Chamberlain, 8 November 1897, London, Fawcett Library. Josephine Butler Collection. Box H2. File 663A.

89 PP. HC. 1882. [c. 3185], 100–104.

90 Sinn, "Chinese Patriarchy," 142.

91 PP. HC. 1880 (118) *Report to Inquire into Contagious Diseases Ordinance*, 23, 59.

92 Hong Kong Legislative Council, *Proceedings of the Hong Kong Legislative Council, 1893* (Hong Kong: Government Printer, 1894), 625.

93 CO 273/120. (11257). Mr. Justice Wood to Governor Sir F. A. Weld, 9 May 1883.

94 Hong Kong Legislative Council, *Proceedings of the Hong Kong Legislative Council, 1889* (Hong Kong: Government Printer, 1890), 206.

95 *Annual Report of the Protector of Chinese, Straits Settlements*, 1914, 5, Fawcett Library, Butler Collection. E2/4.

96 See, for example, CO 273/179 (4880), Governor C. C. Smith to Lord Knutsford, Colonial Office, 12 February 1892; and CO 273/237 (18321), Max F. Simon, Principal Civil Medical Officer, Straits, to Colonial Secretary, 14 July 1898.

97 CO 273/162 (464), 8 February 1890.

98 Lee, *British as Rulers*, 40.

99 PP. HC. 1880 (118). *Report to Inquire into Contagious Diseases Ordinance*.

100 Warwick Anderson, "Disease, Race, and Empire," *Bulletin of the History of Medicine* 70 (1996): 63. See also Manderson, *Sickness and the State*, 14.

101 Angela Zito and Tani E. Barlow, "Body, Subject, and Power in China," in *Body, Subject, and Power in China* (Chicago: University of Chicago Press, 1994), 6. See, too, Gyan Prakash, "Subaltern Studies as Postcolonial Criticism," *American Historical Review* 99, no. 5 (1994): 5. Prakash's point that historical questions have continued to structure the West and its interests as "truly'" modern and the "Orient" as failing some critical test of modernity adds a further dimension to this discussion.

Leprosy and Citizenship

Warwick Anderson

Gradually, an administrative and political space was articulated upon a therapeutic space; it tended to individualize bodies, diseases, symptoms, lives and deaths; it constituted a real table of juxtaposed and carefully distinct singularities.— Michel Foucault, *Discipline and Punish*

"These uniforms must be far too heavy for the tropics," the traveler said instead of inquiring about the apparatus, as the officer had expected.

"True enough," said the officer, washing his greasy, oily hands in a pail of water that stood ready, "but they represent our homeland, and we do not want to lose our homeland."— Franz Kafka, "In the Penal Colony"

How was it that lepers, so radically excluded from civil society, were retrained as model citizens in the colonial Philippines?[1]

In the first decade of the twentieth century, the United States' colonial administration conducted a "census" of lepers in the archipelago, then col-

positions 6:3 © 1998 by Duke University Press.

lected the unfortunates and exiled them to Culion, a barren island in the Calamianes group. A conventional historical account might end at this point: it would be the usual sad tale of stigmatization and segregation. We all know this story. For thousands of years, Europeans have represented lepers as unclean, tainted, and dangerous; contact with leprosy often has been equated with moral and physical contamination. Thought to have disappeared from western Europe and most of the United States in the nineteenth century (yet still endemic in Scandinavia), leprosy was rediscovered during this period in the imperial world and associated with the customs and habits of "inferior races." First at Molokai, Hawai'i, in the 1870s, then at Culion, public-health officers from the United States organized the rigorous segregation of any afflicted local inhabitants. While the criteria for exile at Molokai had initially been clinical, by the end of the century the medical definition of leprosy focused on the presence of Hansen's bacillus, *Mycobacterium leprae*, in the nasal scrapings of suspects.[2] Once identified bacteriologically, the leper faced permanent separation from family and village. Most of those sent to Molokai had to fend for themselves: their isolation was sufficient in itself.[3] But life at Culion was ordered differently.

Identified as lepers, banished from their communities, the colonists of Culion became the improbable subjects of intensive medical reformation and retraining in civic responsibility. The modern leper colony was planned as an exemplary site of production of self-possessed, disciplined colonial (and protonational) subjects. Public-health officers urged the inmates to transcend their tainted embodiment, to abstract themselves from class and traditional community, and to abstain from promiscuous contact of any sort. Individuated through treatment protocols, lepers were expected to work diligently, tend their gardens, play in brass bands, take part in baseball games, vote responsibly, and police themselves. Drawn repeatedly into the medical and civic present, they were warned away from idleness and nostalgia. Paradoxically perhaps, the leper colony became a laboratory of modern citizenship in the archipelago.[4] Leprosy itself was translated into a language of modernity, of civic consciousness, of public interest—a vocabulary that both imperial officials and Filipino nationalists could share.[5]

An emphasis on the micropolitics of subject formation allows us to extend into the civic present an earlier assumption that lepers would be especially susceptible to the gospel. According to Megan Vaughan, leprosy had "offered to the missionaries the possibility of engineering new African communities" for the performance of collective, tribal identities. This represented an impasse for modernity rather than its creation. In Africa, during the early twentieth century, the leper "could never be 'just' a leper—she or he was, first and foremost, an 'African,' and, beyond that, a member of a 'tribe.'"[6] But what, one wonders, happened to this collectivization when government medical officers took over the leper settlement? Rita Smith Kipp has described the evangelical uses of leprosy among the Karo of Sumatra during the first decades of the twentieth century, but she assumes that as the boundary between the religious asylum and the outside world became increasingly permeable, the opportunities for social control dissolved. Thus she implies that "new therapeutic approaches to leprosy lessened its evangelical uses";[7] yet here I suggest that the production of the individual civic subject was predicated on this medicalization. Even Harriet Deacon, who discusses an early secularization of a Cape Colony leprosarium, emphasizes segregation and repression more than subject formation, but this may merely indicate the deficiencies of medicalization before 1910.[8]

I want to suggest that colonial medicine—and isn't all modern medicine in a sense colonial?—extended the boundaries of civility and citizenship initially in the Philippines and later, through agencies such as the Rockefeller Foundation, throughout the rest of the world.[9] A new therapeutic optimism became the means of forgetting the unhomely moment of leprosy through the creation of a hygienic, recovering civic subject. In this essay, then, I look at the medical framing of leprosy and the development of governmentality as though these processes were two transparencies laid over each other.[10] An affirmation of the colonists' new, totalized medical identity permitted them to be treated, or to treat themselves, more or less as citizens within Culion. First identified as figures in a pedagogical narrative, lepers soon learned to perform themselves (as cases, convalescents, and citizens) through the conventions of civic address. But these painstaking clinical and civic performances, as we shall see, rarely if ever satisfied the standards of the asylum keepers, the framers of disease, and the custodians of citizenship.

The Census, the Collection, and the Colony

"They say of Doctor Heiser," Eleanor Franklin Egan wrote in the *Saturday Evening Post* in 1918, "that he has handled with bare hands from two to three thousand lepers in all the horrible stages of that most horrible of all diseases; and I myself have seen him pick up a helpless leper in his arms and carry him aboard the leper ship to be taken to Culion with as little apparent concern for his own safety as he would display under the most ordinary circumstances."[11] A shrewd self-publicist, Victor Heiser had taken a special interest in leprosy while director of health in the Philippines. This "loathsome" disease became his principal research interest, and he remained an authority on the subject long after he left the archipelago.

Fashioning himself as a secular Damien, Heiser regarded the scientific treatment of leprosy at Culion as his major legacy to the islands. "As long as [the leper colony] remained in his care," fawned Katherine Mayo, "it challenged the world's admiration."[12] Heiser had spent a large part of each year between 1904 and 1914 sailing from port to port collecting leper suspects, examining them, and exiling the confirmed cases at Culion. While other scientific colleagues collected botanical and geological specimens, Heiser had collected lepers. His writings betray a potent blend of fascination and disgust with the disease, both reinforcing and then undermining his own sense of self-mastery. Heiser, like the other American experts on leprosy, could readily compare his own prim abstracted body with the exudating abject lepers that he assembled; positioning himself against their impurity, he would then also repeatedly seek their approval. He regularly sought out the company of those lepers he meant to reform. On the day he left the archipelago, he confided to his diary his feelings for those he had so assiduously classified and displaced: "There is much sadness," he wrote, "that as yet I do not live in the hearts of the people. . . . I wonder if I will ever be understood and if the lepers will sometime look upon me as their friend."[13] In leper work, it was not just the identity of the leper that was being refashioned. As Heiser collected and segregated and retrained the lepers he was imposing an equally rigid and productive discipline upon himself.[14]

Segregation had only recently become medically popular again. When Dr. N. C. MacNamara described leprosy in the early 1890s, he emphasized that with leprosy, the old notion of diathesis, or hereditary predisposition to an ailment, had been discredited over the past few decades. "Pathology," he declared, "has at last led us to recognize the fact that leprosy is the effect of a micro-organism." Most physicians now believed that the disfiguring and disabling granulomatous disease was communicable, though not readily so. Therefore, MacNamara concluded, "strict isolation of lepers must be the proper and only way of stamping it out." Yet his own experiences in India had suggested that "the religious feeling, customs and habits of the natives, as well as the number of lepers . . . all prevent the government from attempting to introduce a system of compulsory segregation in that country."[15] In 1898, Sir Patrick Manson agreed that leprosy was basically a "germ disease," although he suspected that "bad food and bad hygienic circumstances" were predisposing factors. Transmission of the mycobacterium probably required prolonged and "intimate personal contact." In the first edition of his classic text, Manson paraphrased MacNamara's apparently quixotic call for rigorous segregation of sufferers.[16] In the 1914 edition, not much had changed, except that Manson began to cite medical authorities who had "very sagaciously and truly remark[ed] that leprosy is more especially a disease of semi-civilization." That is, "when the savage begins to wear clothes and live in houses he becomes subject to the disease." Thus the best way to control the condition was either to complete the civilizing process or never to begin it. If the goal was completion of the evolutionary trajectory from tribal to peasant to proletarian, then ideally this should be attempted in an isolated colony.[17]

For most of the Spanish colonial period, medical authorities had assumed that leprosy was hereditary. Accordingly, the rare instances of isolation of sufferers occurred more often for aesthetic and social reasons than for medical purposes. The disease was first identified in the archipelago in the early seventeenth century, and since then it had spread rapidly. The Franciscans took charge of charity work among lepers, building several asylums and hospitals for the severely afflicted. Institutions such as the San Lazaro Hospital, north of the old walled city of Manila, and the Cebu Leprosarium offered a refuge for those who sought it, along with palliative care in the last stages of their illness. In some of the larger towns, groups of lepers often lived together in separate bamboo and nipa shacks. But the Spanish colonial regime did not try to isolate lepers from their communities in order to prevent the spread of the disease.[18]

With the arrival of the United States forces in 1898, lepers soon became a valuable medical commodity. Heiser estimated that there were at least six thousand lepers distributed over the archipelago, and each year some twelve hundred more contracted the disease. A few hundred sufferers resided in the San Lazaro Hospital and in provincial leprosaria, but most roamed freely among the unaffected population. Many had been mistakenly diagnosed as lepers and did not in fact show Hansen's bacillus in their nasal scrapings; still others were infected with the microbe but appeared clinically normal. Heiser, increasingly preoccupied with leprosy, urged all medical officers to take a census of lepers in their region and report their findings to him in Manila. A review of the medical literature had convinced him that only isolation and segregation could accomplish the eradication of the disease. "This policy," he observed, "at first sight seems to impose many hardships upon the lepers themselves and their immediate relatives and friends, but it is believed to be fully justified not only by the fact that hundreds may be annually saved from contracting leprosy, but also that the victims may be given as pleasant a life as possible."[19] He hoped that the apparent cruelty of segregation would eventually be recognized as epidemiological foresight and benevolent tutelage.

Using Molokai as a model, Heiser and his colleagues sought a distant island on which to establish a colony.[20] A committee of inquiry studied a number of locations, concluding that Culion "afforded an ideal site for the proposed colony, and furnished abundant and suitable lands for agriculture and stock raising." Water was available and the harbor was extensive and safe. The population of three hundred or so nonleprous "poor day laborers" could be moved to an adjacent island. The committee believed that "nowhere else in the archipelago can there be found an island so healthful, extensive and fertile, which has so small a population." It urged the government to preserve the island for lepers, with land "to be set apart for every leper willing and able to cultivate the soil," and houses for the accomodation of male and female lepers in "two widely separated areas."[21] But the work of constructing an entire new town suitable for two or three thousand lepers would take time. The houses, the hospital, the school, the theater, the dining halls and kitchens were not ready until 1906. Heiser sent out 365 lepers from San Lazaro in May of that year.

Among them was a "Spanish-mestizo" boy, Eliodore G., who had entered San Lazaro in 1901, at the age of seven. Two brothers and two sisters had died of leprosy. Eliodore had noticed a red spot on his left hip, and later other spots appeared on his cheeks and ears. The laboratory determined that he was "positive microscopically" for leprosy. Like many others in San Lazaro he had no one willing to care for him in his barrio. Treated experimentally with radiation and medications, he remained positive microscopically after his transfer to Culion and died there within ten years, as one of Heiser's "prisoners of hope."[22] It is difficult to say whether his story is typical, as so few case reports remain, but the formulation of this record is certainly conventional: Eliodore G. has been abstracted from his surroundings as a "leper," and his life has been further translated into a medical vocabulary. He was silenced in the medical narrative — his existence reduced to a diagnosis, his future structured as a prognosis. And yet, the same case record has made him visible; it has mobilized him as an individual in need of corporal and social reform.

Once all institutionalized lepers such as Eliodore G. had been transferred to Culion, Heiser began to collect those still living in their local communities. A year or so before the visit of the "leper ship," the government would begin an education campaign in each region to inform lowland Filipinos of the "manner in which leprosy spreads and the improved conditions under which lepers themselves would live at Culion." Doctors from the Bureau of Health gave lectures on leprosy and showed photographs and films of the colony. Teachers discussed the government's leprosy work with their students and encouraged them to identify hidden cases.[23] Heiser was convinced that Filipinos must be taught "that the leper who concealed his disease was a constant and deadly menace to the community in which he lived."[24] In his journal, he noted that "the keynote to success [is] to educate the masses to a fear of the disease."[25] And, in general, the suitably educated population seemed to cooperate with the leper collections. Force was rarely required. "When it is remembered," Heiser wrote, "that this often involved the lifelong separation of wife from husband, sister from brother, child from parents, and friend from friend, it will be appreciated that forbearance was necessary under such circumstances."[26]

Beginning with the outlying islands, Heiser and his colleagues proceeded to examine and classify suspected lepers. At an arranged date, the provincial governors and municipal presidents would gather all known lepers to meet the ship at the harbor. The preliminary diagnosis usually had been made by the district health officer. The leper boat always brought at least three physicians, one of whom was especially qualified in the diagnosis of leprosy, and all of them had to be satisfied that the label was correct before a leper was taken to Culion. In addition, a microscopist from the Bureau of Science examined the nasal scrapings of each leper, seeking to identify *Mycobacterium leprae*. After these precautions against error had been taken, the boat loaded the confirmed cases and sailed towards Culion.[27] By 1913 Heiser could claim that every recognizable leper in the archipelago was confined; over eight thousand had been sent to Culion, and thirty-five hundred were still alive. As the incubation period for the disease might last as long as twenty years, new cases would continue to develop. Nonetheless, the Philippines "enjoy[ed] the distinction of being the only oriental country where complete segregation is being attempted."[28]

In this rigorous medical collecting of lepers, a classificatory order was being substituted for personal history and context of origin. Whatever they had been before, they were now nothing but lepers, defined by the collection.[29] As soon as they were tracked down, lepers such as Eliodore G. underwent a "role dispossession," becoming physically and morally vulnerable to the bureaucratic machinery of the public-health department and to the routines of the leper institution.[30] Thus a scientific diagnosis of leprosy conferred on the exiles both a new identity and a displaced future: in this sense Heiser was right, they had become "prisoners of hope." The conditions of asylum demanded that they conform as "responsible lepers" to relentless medical supervision and discipline: in other words, that they accept not just a mortification but a *self*-mortification. In the hermetic world of Culion they were repeatedly to affirm their diagnosis in the hope of the recognition that might confer both medical relief and moral elevation.

The Field, the Laboratory, and the Miniature

Culion was an idealized medical miniature of the larger colony, and as such, it served as a container of "aphoristic and didactic thought," in Susan Stewart's words. Its spatial closure, its infinite detailing, its theatricality, were all characteristic features of the miniature. "The miniature world," Stewart has observed, "remains perfect and uncontaminated by the grotesque so long as its absolute boundaries are maintained." As a space of representation, the leper colony asserted a control of nature, a possible transcendence of disease and death. Culion was nothing if not orderly: once lepers admitted their condition they could become the responsible subjects of treatment and regimen. Given a prognosis, they were given a future. Their experience of an absolute interiority marked "the pure body, the inorganic body of the machine and its repetition of a death that is thereby not a death."[31] Built on an attempted denial of death (or, rather, the absorption of death into life), the medical miniature — whether hospital, asylum, or colony — is thus a prime instantiation of modernity.[32]

At the center of the new colony, the government built a town hall, a store, a general kitchen, a jail, a school, and the Leper Club, which contained "a piano, a pool table, and many newspapers, some recent, and miscellaneous discarded 'charity' magazines and books unintelligible except for the pictures."[33] Around this cultural center lay dormitories that housed some two thousand lepers by 1923, all segregated according to sex. Many of these buildings were simple "tenement houses," five-room structures with twelve people assigned to each room. Another ten dormitories contained over 650 children. But most of the inmates lived in small bamboo and nipa huts. Many visitors, approaching the town by water, received "a most unfavorable first impression of a dreary, parched, poverty-stricken settlement on stony, unproductive hillsides." But the physicians who worked at Culion, while conceding some "distinctly unfavorable features," felt that the "simple, orderly, not uncheerful lives of the inmates" greatly modified the visitors' initial misgivings.[34]

Treatment of the orderly and not-uncheerful lepers was organized from the General Hospital, which until 1921 consisted of six wards (with three hundred beds crowded into them), a kitchen, a pharmacy, and a small morgue. The principal effort was directed at dispensing chaulmoogra oil and monitoring the response to the medication. Each inmate had a case record documenting his or her origin, clinical signs, laboratory results, and compliance with treatment. Medical activity at Culion thus focused on the specific, routinized, and yet individuated treatment of one disease. Little attention was paid to acute, unrelated illnesses or to the tuberculosis that was rife in the colony. Over forty-five hundred patients were registered for antileprosy treatment in nine clinics, a majority of whom received injections of chaulmoogra oil once a week. Each clinic was managed by a physician, assisted by a nurse and two leper nursing aides. In the 1920s, the rations of patients who evaded treatment were held up until they returned to the clinics. Cases that became bedridden, unable to care for themselves as a result of the ravages of neural lesions, were admitted permanently to the General Hospital.[35]

Culion became famous as a laboratory for the chemotherapy of leprosy. In the 1890s, N. C. Macnamara had achieved only poor results treating the disease in India: he had tried moving lepers to a "healthy and bracing district," improving their sanitary condition, and even rubbing chaulmoogra oil into their skin two or three times a day. But to no avail. Nerve stretching and tubercle excision provided local amelioration at best. "Efforts must be directed," Macnamara concluded, "to discovering some chemical substance which will kill the leprosy bacillus."[36] A few years later, Manson enjoined "scrupulous attention to personal and domestic hygiene," frequent bathing, and "the free use of soap." Although many of his colleagues had favored doses of chaulmoogra oil, and others had recommended ichthyol, perchloride of mercury, and thyroiden, Manson could not help wondering if the success they claimed for these remedies had derived instead from a remission in the disease's naturally fluctuating course. In his opinion, there was nothing yet specific for leprosy "in the sense that mercury and iodide of potassium are specific in syphilis."[37]

But before long, Heiser and his colleagues in the Philippines were trumpeting the effectiveness of a new preparation of chaulmoogra oil that could be given by hypodermic injection. Although it would take "many years and exhaustive experimentation" to establish the fact definitely, it appeared that this gift of "Western science" had cured at least a few dozen lepers in the islands. Uncertain still whether this was the true specific for leprosy, Heiser nevertheless believed that it promised "more consistently favorable results than any other that has come to our attention."[38] John Snodgrass, for instance, could cite the case of a twenty-seven-year-old Filipino admitted to Culion in May 1909. Smears made from lesions on the nose and ears showed leprosy bacilli. Beginning in August 1909, he received "vaccine therapy" for one year, but with no signs of improvement. Between September and November 1910, he took crude chaulmoogra oil by mouth until he could no longer tolerate it, after which he was tried on the new injectable form. His condition improved dramatically, with all the lesions disappearing by May 1911. For the next year "he remained negative microscopically."[39]

By 1914, even Manson was extolling the benefits of chaulmoogra oil when given hypodermically as in the Philippines. He had seen the marked clinical improvement; but other laboratory studies had tempered his confidence in the drug's true specificity. Reports indicated that bacilli were "just as abundant in the nodules during and after as before treatment." A new drug, nastin in benzoyl chloride, had promised more etiological specificity in laboratory investigations, but so far, the clinical effect was "dangerous to life," a problem that unfortunately "imposed limitations upon the general use of the remedy."[40] These limitations were so severe that its use was restricted to a few painful clinical trials. Thus in 1918 Heiser could claim, with a degree of self-satisfaction, that "chaulmoogra oil alone has stood the test of time." With unrivaled clinical experience of the drug, he was convinced that although it might occasionally cause "fever and cardiac distress," its hypodermic administration offered lepers their best hope of continued remission. All the same, he still insisted that his patients take 2-percent hot bicarbonate baths every other day.[41]

If lepers still could conventionally be classed as unclean and dangerous, then the protocols of modern medicine might now remove their taint and purify their bodies.[42] But the positioning of these colonial subjects as lepers had first required an implicit admission from the victims of their own putrescence or stigma, so that they might become medically serviceable objects. On arrival in the colony they would be lepers and nothing but lepers, in need of salvation. Indeed, if they did not accept the subject position given by the totalizing institution, then they could not even be recognized on Culion. As Michel de Certeau has argued in another context, "the victim must be the voice of the filth, everywhere denied, that everywhere supports the representation of the regime's 'omnipotence.'"[43] Thus Heiser and his colleagues saw everywhere around them the needy leper, the accepting leper, the grateful leper, the responsible leper—in short, the leper who engaged in their discourse. It was a performance of abjection, but to what end? Perhaps it was the hope of a sublimation or control of abject embodiment through science and progress; perhaps, ultimately, it was the promise of fashioning a thoroughly modern identity, just as Heiser had. But this labor of repression, of amnesia, of purification, of "civilization," was still more likely to end in death at Culion than in liberation.[44]

Culion thus institutionalized a kind of "grotesque of the service relationship," in that the sovereign diagnostic category serviced the asylum, by reducing its management problems, as much as it helped the inmates. Lepers were expected to develop a stable, contented existence within the institution; the most promising ones would convert to the staff view of themselves and try to act out the role of the civic-minded, compliant leper. (Of course, as in any colony, many others messed up or remained intransigent.) The goal of Culion was a self-regulating "change" in the lepers: in a sense, American officials were staging a binary opposition between themselves and the "typical leper" and then asking the leper to resolve this typological difference through a personal conversion, thus demonstrating that the affliction, the failing, was not unalterable. As in other asylums, the "ideals of proper conduct must be held up as desirable, infractions inveighed against, and the patient treated as a 'responsible person.'"[45]

Rituals of modern citizenship inflected the protocols of the isolated disease community. Heiser praised the attempts of the administration to engage the lepers in the running of the town. "The lepers," he noted, "are given all possible liberty, and are, to a large extent, controlled by regulations which they themselves make."[46] As part of the treatment, the diseased were to discipline and govern themselves. The community elected its own mayor and council. (Women were given the vote as early as 1908—the first female suffrage in Asia.) A police force of lepers saw that the town was "kept in good sanitary condition" and made "arrests of offenders against their own ordinances."[47] Paid leper sanitary inspectors, under the command of a nonleprous chief, also helped to maintain the sanitary condition of the colony. A leper brass band greeted new arrivals and gave occasional concerts.[48] (Heiser once joked that they were so enthusiastic that they "literally played their fingers off.")[49] Several times a year, the lepers put on a play; indeed, they "took eagerly to dramatics," recalled the director of health.[50] And twice a month in the large concrete theater, inmates could dress up to watch "very cheap films."[51] "The disease does not deprive its victims of their desire to look well and to please," wrote Dr. A. J. McLaughlin. "Lepers love neckties and hand-kerchiefs, and things that are pretty and attractive."[52] Athletic gatherings, though held rarely, elicited considerable enthusiasm for baseball. "That they possess the true American baseball spirit," wrote Snodgrass, "was demon-strated at one of the games when both teams attacked the umpire with ball bats."[53]

Medical protocols and social life in the asylum were endlessly theatrical. The diseased body was repeatedly exposed to public view, as if to justify the disciplinary apparatus of the colony. Testing and treatment (especially injec-tions) were generally performed on these bodies as a display of sovereignty for an audience of other lepers. And if medicine had to be seen to be done, so too did citizenship: treatments of the body and of social life all required enactment. The theater—for plays, not operations—was one of the first buildings in the civic center of the colony: while the staff often directed, the players and the audience were lepers. The tiresome emphasis on perfor-mance animated social life throughout the colony: lepers at Culion were on stage in medical and civic dramas during the whole of the day. It was not enough that they were represented as responsible patients or incipient citi-zens, they had to perform themselves as the subjects of civic narratives.[54]

But in spite of these stipulated enactments of civility, it seemed to Heiser that the leper was still "naturally apathetic." In front of each house, for instance, was a small flower garden, "and every effort is being made to instill a sufficient civic pride in the lepers to maintain them; but so far these efforts have not met with much success." The inmates appeared shiftless and dependent on government aid, yet "the streets must be swept, the garbage cans emptied, assistance rendered at the hospital, and supplies car-ried."[55] When Heiser observed the neglect of civic responsibilities he "held a little meeting with the residents affected and asked them to attend to this matter, and they promised to do so."[56] The lepers were expected to work diligently in between their doses of chaulmoogra oil. Heiser lamented that "contractions of the limbs, destruction of tissue, losses of fingers and toes . . . and general debility" meant that only a few lepers could perform sufficient manual labor to supply food for themselves. Some had tried cattle raising or started "tiny sugar plantations." The bulk of the food still was cooked in a large central kitchen by leper cooks: the lepers marched by in single file piling up the food onto their plates. But many of the afflicted remained capable of carrying out simple domestic duties for a small salary: cooking, dressmaking, taking care of streets, making repairs to buildings, and so on. To produce the "conditions prevailing in ordinary communities," a store and, later, two bakeries and an ice-cream restaurant were opened to sell the lepers' manufactures. So that the money handled by lepers never reached the outside world, the authorities coined a special currency to serve as the medium of trade.[57] In effect, this was an insular schooling in abstracted small-town American pieties.

Carceral Citizenship

Like all laboratories, this laboratory of citizenship allowed a variation of scale from the "micro" to the "macro" and, when necessary, back again.[58] Filipinos could be displaced into an exemplary therapeutic community; lepers were translated more or less successfully into citizens; a few might be reformed or cured and then sent out; colonizers and the colonized would learn to speak the language of self-mastery, modernity, and progress; and Heiser and his colleagues might feel good about themselves. To understand the American colonial project it is necessary to study Culion, for the leper colony had become an allegory of the prospects of the macrocolony: the geographical archipelago was eventually to become a carceral archipelago.[59] As the carceral net widened, the nonleprous as much as the leprous would be "taught to speak, and to reason, and to . . . get their rights as citizens among those who have been so long their superiors."[60] Culion was a model for "the making of men out of savages, the regeneration of a conquered people by the conquerors by teaching them the benefits of labor and industry." This was the progressive American's "work of civilization . . .

of regeneration and instruction," organized through a multitude of individual medical careers.[61] In the abstracted space of the microcolony—the space, indeed, of regimen and universalized heirarchy—lepers had been enrolled in modernity in advance of the nonleprous. In this miniature, which was both bounded and yet infinitely expandable, a character-building amalgamation of hygiene and citizenship was structured.

But it was, of course, a deferred and incomplete citizenship, as repressive as it was liberating: civic and medical responsibilities were always more salient at Culion than civil rights. As Bryan Turner has deduced from his typological account of civil society, where "political space is limited, citizenship is passive and private."[62] This was certainly the case in the leper colony. As an exemplary part of the colonial process of modern subject formation, such carceral citizenship permitted no history beyond an individual's standardized medical history and would not sanction any public self-assertion: the leper-citizen became an individualized case record, oriented away from a messy past of illness and superstition toward a contained, therapeutic future. "Citizenship" at Culion thus was predicated on the displacement, erasure, and transcendence in private and domestic life of native embodiment. Configured as moral reformation, medical protocol, and race elevation, this simulated citizenship was to be conferred as a discipline, not demanded as a right. A controlled laboratory of subject repositioning, Culion allowed colonial officials to think of "citizenship" in terms of universalism and progress, just as it enables us now to rethink this category as a problem of social order and civility in modern society.

At the same time, even a carceral citizenship will provide a language of entitlement. As early as 1912, many of the lepers were writing to the Manila newspapers to complain about the neglect of their rights. The editors of *La Vanguardia* questioned Heiser's representation of the leper colony as "a model administration where men and women, more advanced than the rest of the archipelago, enjoy the fullest suffrage, voting as equals for the election of officials; . . . [where] they have the best sanitary service, police, schools, gardens, walks, abundant and healthy food, and everything characteristic of modern life and comfort." Recent protests from the inmates had undermined the view that Culion was "a happy community in the full exercise of self-government."[63] It seems that the food was poor, the housing was overcrowded, the police were oppressive, and the newspaper was often censored. One leper lamented that he was "composed of lentils and salt up to the crown of [his] head." Others complained about forced labor on public works.[64] The lepers addressed the government in a language of civic entitlement, arguing that their corner of the archipelago, "abandoned by the hand of God but not the hand of Mr Heiser," was apparently not the "earthly paradise" for lepers that he had promised.[65]

During the 1930s, lepers held several meetings demanding an end to segregation; they asserted that leprosy was not nearly as contagious as the health department had claimed and that they had a right to freedom of movement. (Medical facts and social potential were thus linked by doctors and patients alike.) The attendant doctors were threatened and a few inmates called for a strike.[66] In 1932, three hundred young men had forced their way into one of the female dormitories in protest against the ban on leper marriages: on this occasion, "the Culion police force was too small to disperse the ardent swains, who refused to pay attention to the law forces."[67] Leper "sweethearts" were later permitted to marry. But the most popular forms of civic activism or performance were the petition and the public hearing. At Culion, in July 1935, Vice Governor-General Joseph Hayden listened to the fractious lepers present their complaints. Ernesto S., invoking "individual rights and liberties of individuals," demanded that everyone receive a gratuity since they had all been brought to Culion against their will; Ciriaco S. P. protested against the reduced appropriation for the colony; Graciano A. directed attention at the delapidated conditions of the school buildings; and Rufino M. noted that lepers "clean and cultivate" land without hope of owning it. In response, Hayden told the lepers that he could now see that although they were still "afflicted," they "nevertheless, live in a well-ordered, well-directed, and well-operated community." He had been impressed by the review of scouts, pioneers, and police, and so he would consider their demands.[68]

In 1935, the passage of the Nolasco Bill effectively ended segregation at Culion, substituting for it group treatment stations throughout the archipelago.[69]

Conclusion

In this essay I have attempted to locate the entry of the colonial leper into disciplined society. Not simply isolated and enclosed in an undifferentiated mass, the leper becomes "caught up," to use Michel Foucault's words, "in a meticulous tactical partitioning in which individual differentiations were the constructing effects of a power that multiplied, articulated and subdivided itself." At Culion we see a belated instance of the great confinement, but we also see the correct training that Foucault predicted even for those most rejected from society.[70] In the colonial Philippines, one might say *especially* for those most rejected from a society that American officials sought to reform. Thus, the iatrocratic disciplines of the leper colony were not supposed to reproduce the denigrated Philippine social body but rather were meant to normalize American ideals of civic responsibility. Accordingly, exile to Culion was represented not as the deprivation of liberty but as its creation. Lepers had been selected for disciplinary normalization not because they were especially delinquent but because they were deemed more medically needy, desocialized, and hence more docile. Moral reform was linked symbiotically to corporal reform, and both were endlessly deferred. At Culion, lepers were never so much delinquent as premature, in remission rather than cured. They were inseparably both recovering lepers and incipient citizens.

It was through the production of such necessarily hybrid subjects, and through these mechanisms of deferral, that colonial power (and perhaps all power) has worked. Development and modernization would remain incomplete processes, always in view but never achieved; similarly, the citizen-subject remains deficient or redundant—an unfinished project—always in the melting pot and never melted. But it is precisely these medical and civic failures, these "contaminations" of an imagined original, these congruent anachronisms of native and modern, that make possible an ambivalent space for colonial discourse.[71] The colonial citizen is produced as a mutation, a procedural hybrid: it is an unstable hybridity that, according to Homi Bhabha, "unsettles the mimetic or narcissistic demands of colonial power but reimplicates its identifications in strategies of subversion that turn the gaze of the discriminated back upon the eye of power." Civil (and medical) disobedience is possible, even permissible, so long as it occurs "within the discipline of civility."[72]

It was not until the 1980s that medical segregation and retraining in citizenship was again proposed in the Philippines—this time, during the early stages of the spread of HIV infection and AIDS. But to explain the contemporary (perhaps just "temporary"?) rejection of the institutional model would require another essay, one not so much on the expressive localization of biopower as on its dispersion through the carceral texture of the modern nation.

Notes

1 I use the term *citizen* not in a narrow legal sense, but with a more sociological inflection, to denote someone who conforms to "a set of social practices which define the nature of social membership" (Bryan S. Turner, "Contemporary Problems in the Theory of Citizenship," in *Citizenship and Social Theory*, ed. Bryan S. Turner [London: Sage, 1993], 4. See also T. H. Marshall, "Citizenship and Social Class," in *Citizenship and Social Development* [New York: Anchor Books, 1967]).

2 Zachary Gussow, *Leprosy, Racism, and Public Health: Social Policy in Chronic Disease Control* (Boulder, Colo.: Westview Press, 1989). Hansen, in Norway, had identified the mycobacterium in the 1870s. Lepers were sent to Molokai from the 1860s, but the first major effort at segregation occurred in 1873. The first lepers arrived at Culion in May 1906. The few lepers in the United States were also segregated during the 1890s, principally at Carville, Louisiana, which became the National Leprosarium in 1921. See Philip A. Kalisch, "Lepers, Anachronisms, and the Progressives: A Study of Stigma, 1889–1920," *Louisiana Studies* 12 (1973): 489–531.

3 See John Farrow, *Damien the Leper* (Garden City, N.Y.: Doubleday and Co., 1966).

4 See Turner, "Contemporary Problems"; Bryan S. Turner, "Postmodern Culture/Modern Citizens," in *The Condition of Citizenship*, ed. Bart van Steenbergen (London: Sage, 1994), 153–168; Chantal Mouffe, "Feminism, Citizenship, and Radical Democratic Politics," in *The Return of the Political* (London: Verso, 1993), 74–89; and Ana Maria Alonso, "The Politics of Space, Time, and Substance: State Formation, Nationalism, and Ethnicity," *Annual Review of Anthropology* 23 (1994): 379–405. I am most concerned here with the links between citizenship, civility, modernity, and the politics of the body. (On the earlier European relations of civility, police, and civilization, see Lucien Febvre, "*Civilisation*: Evolution of a Word and a Group of Ideas," in *A New Kind of History from the Writings of Febvre,* ed. Peter Burke, trans. K. Folca [London: Routledge and Kegan Paul, 1973], 219–257; and Norbert Elias, *The*

Civilizing Process, vol. 1: *The History of Manners*, trans. E. Jephcott [New York: Pantheon, 1978].)

5 See Dipesh Chakrabarty, "Of Garbage, Modernity and the Citizen's Gaze," *Economic and Political Weekly* 7–14 March 1992, 541–547. See also Benedict Anderson, *Imagined Communities: Reflections on the Origins and Spread of Nationalism*, rev. ed. (London: Verso, 1991). Tani Barlow has described nationalism appositely as "the politics of the construction and mobilization of subjectivity inside the spaces offered by the discourses of colonial modernity" (Barlow, "Editor's Introduction," *positions: east asia cultures critique* 1 [winter 1993]: viii). On U.S. imperialism during this period, see Amy Kaplan and Donald Pease, eds., *Cultures of United States Imperialism* (Durham, N.C.: Duke University Press, 1993).

6 Megan Vaughan, "Without the Camp: Institutions and Identities in the Colonial History of Leprosy," in *Curing Their Ills: Colonial Power and African Illness* (Stanford, Calif.: Stanford University Press, 1991), 79, 97. More generally, Vaughan tries hard to show that European medicine in Africa was predominantly aggregative and repressive and was not much concerned with the production of individual subjectivities.

7 Rita Smith Kipp, "The Evangelical Uses of Leprosy," *Social Science and Medicine* 39 (1994): 176. For another account of leper evangelizing, see Sanjiv Kakar, "Leprosy in British India, 1860–1940: Colonial Politics and Missionary Medicine," *Medical History* 40 (1996): 215–230.

8 Harriet Jane Deacon, "A History of the Medical Institutions on Robben Island, Cape Colony, 1846–1910," (Ph.D. diss., University of Cambridge, 1994), esp. chap. 6.

9 On the history of twentieth-century tropical medicine, see John Farley, *Bilharzia: A History of Imperial Tropical Medicine* (Cambridge: Cambridge University Press, 1991). For accounts of early U.S. public-health efforts in the Philippines, see Reynaldo C. Ileto, "Cholera and the Origins of the American Sanitary Order in the Philippines," in *Imperial Medicine and Indigenous Society*, ed. David Arnold (Manchester, England: Manchester University Press, 1989); and Rodney Sullivan, "Cholera and Colonialism in the Philippines, 1899–1903," in *Medicine, Disease and Empire: Perspectives on Western Medicine and the Experience of European Expansion*, ed. Roy MacLeod and Milton Lewis (London: Routledge, 1988). On the development and dispersion of these models, see Paul Weindling, ed., *International Health Organizations and Movements, 1918–1939* (New York: Cambridge University Press, 1995); and Warwick Anderson, "Immunities of Empire: Race, Disease, and the New Tropical Medicine," *Bulletin of the History of Medicine* 70 (1996): 94–118.

10 "This contact between the technologies of domination of others and those of the self I call governmentality" (Michel Foucault, in *Technologies of the Self: A Seminar with Michel Foucault*, ed. Luther H. Martin, Huck Gutman, and Patrick K. Hutton [Amherst: University of Massachusetts Press, 1988] 19). See also Michel Foucault, "The Subject and Power," *Critical Inquiry* 8 (1982): 777–795; and Foucault "On Governmentality," *Ideology and Consciousness* 8 (1981): 3–14. On framing disease, see Charles E. Rosenberg, "Framing Disease: Illness, Society, and History," in *Framing Disease: Studies in Cultural History*, ed. Charles E. Rosenberg

and Janet Golden (New Brunswick, N.J.: Rutgers University Press, 1992), xii–xxvi. While Ann Stoler has examined the production of self-possessed hygienic Dutch colonizers in the East Indies, in her discussion of this "cultivation of whiteness," she assumes a relative fixity of the "racial Other" (Stoler, *Race and the Education of Desire: Foucault's History of Sexuality and the Colonial Order of Things* [Durham, N.C.: Duke University Press, 1995], especially pages 62, 163). See also Ann L. Stoler, "Rethinking Colonial Categories: European Communities and the Boundaries of Rule," *Comparative Studies in Society and History* 31 (1989): 134–161; and Stoler "Sexual Affronts and Racial Frontiers: European Identities and the Cultural Politics of Exclusion in Colonial Southeast Asia," *Comparative Studies in Society and History* 34 (1992): 514–551.

11   Eleanor Franklin Egan, *Saturday Evening Post,* 2 February 1918. See also Warwick Anderson, "Victor G. Heiser," *American National Biography* (New York: Oxford University Press, forthcoming).

12   Katherine Mayo, *The Isles of Fear: The Truth about the Philippines* (New York: Harcourt Brace, 1924), 154.

13   Heiser diary, 13 July 1914, Heiser Collection, American Philosophical Society, Philadelphia.

14   On the culture of the American colonial bureaucracy in this period, see Warwick Anderson, "The Trespass Speaks: White Masculinity and Colonial Breakdown," *American Historical Review* 102 (1997): 1343–1370.

15   N. C. MacNamara, "Leprosy," in *Hygiene and Diseases of Warm Climates*, ed. Andrew Davidson (Edinburgh: Pentland, 1893), 426, 448, 448–449.

16   Patrick Manson, *Tropical Diseases: A Manual of the Diseases of Warm Climates* (London: Cassell and Co., 1898), 412, 417. Difficulties in transmitting the disease through inoculation led to disputes over the degree of contagiousness, but few authorities doubted that infection would eventually take place. Heiser concurred that "prolonged intimate contact" was necessary for infection, but he was understandably far more optimistic about the feasibility of segregation (Victor G. Heiser, "Tropical Diseases," in *Handbook of Medical Treatment*, ed. J. C. DaCosta [Philadelphia: F. A. Davis and Co., 1918], 1:195, 204).

17   Patrick Manson, *Tropical Diseases: A Manual of the Diseases of Warm Climates*, 5th ed. (London: Cassell and Co., 1914), 627. On the supposed susceptibility of "dressed natives" to tuberculosis (caused by another mycobacterium), see Randall Packard, *White Plague, Black Labour: Tuberculosis and the Political Economy of Health and Disease in South Africa* (Berkeley and Los Angeles: University of California Press, 1989).

18   Heiser later claimed that the attitude of Filipinos "fluctuated between a great horror of [leprosy] amounting almost to a panic, and the greatest callousness" (Victor G. Heiser, *An American Doctor's Odyssey: Adventures in Forty-Five Countries* [New York: W. W. Norton and Co., 1936], 220).

19   Victor G. Heiser, "The Culion Leper Colony: One of the Outgrowths of Our Occupation of the Philippine Islands," 14 December 1914, 1–2, Heiser Collection, American Philosophical

Society, Philadelphia. See also Victor G. Heiser to Secretary of the Interior, "Memorandum, 1911," United States National Archives, Washington, D.C., RG 350-1972-31.

20 For a description of Molokai, see Charles Warren Stoddard, *The Lepers of Molokai* (Notre Dame, Ind.: Ave Maria Press, 1885); and Gussow, *Leprosy*, 85–107. Heiser himself visited Molokai in 1908.

21 Dean C. Worcester, "Report of the Committee Appointed to Select a Site for a Leper Colony," 1 January 1902, 447, 449, United States National Archives, Washington, D.C., RG 350-1972-2. Worcester, the secretary of the interior, was chairman of the committee.

22 Case report, United States National Archives, Washington, D.C., RG 350-1972-16. See also Heiser, *American Doctor's Odyssey*, 235.

23 Heiser, "Culion Leper Colony," 5.

24 Heiser, *American Doctor's Odyssey*, 220.

25 Heiser, diary, 1 September 1908.

26 Heiser, "Culion Leper Colony," 6.

27 See Victor G. Heiser, "Memorandum of Leper Collecting Trip, June–July 1913," Heiser Collection, American Philosophical Society, Philadelphia.

28 Heiser, "Culion Leper Colony," 7. Heiser estimated that there were over fifty thousand lepers in Japan, few of whom had been isolated; in China, the problem was still the responsibility of missionaries; in Java, too, the government had done little. In India the number of lepers was so great that the financial burden would far surpass the resources of the Indian treasury. Only in the Federated Malay States had the government tried systematically to isolate lepers: a colony was planned at Pulau Jerajak. See Victor G. Heiser, "Leprosy in the East: Its Treatment and Prevention, November 3, 1915," 10–11, Heiser Collection, American Philosophical Society, Philadelphia.

29 See Susan Stewart, *On Longing: Narratives of the Miniature, the Gigantic, the Souvenir, the Collection* (Durham, N.C.: Duke University Press, 1993), esp. 151–163.

30 See Erving Goffman, *Asylums: Essays on the Social Situation of Mental Patients and Other Inmates* (New York: Anchor Books, 1961), 14.

31 Stewart, *On Longing*, 45, 68, 69.

32 On the link between death and the experience of modern individuality see Michel Foucault, *The Birth of the Clinic* (London: Tavistock Publications, 1976).

33 H. W. Wade and José Avellana Basa, "The Culion Leper Colony," *American Journal of Tropical Medicine* 3 (1923): 402.

34 Ibid., 399. See also Ernest R. Gentry, "Report of a Leper-Collecting Trip in the Philippine Islands, 1912," United States National Archives, Washington, D.C., RG 112-E26/68075-123.

35 Ibid., 410–414.

36 MacNamara, "Leprosy," 451.

37 Manson, *Tropical Diseases* (1898), 419, 420–421. The reference to a specific therapy for syphilis was dropped in later editions. On the search for specific therapeutics, see John

Harley Warner, *The Therapeutic Perspective: Medical Practice, Knowledge*, and *Identity in America, 1820–1885* (Cambridge, Mass.: Harvard University Press, 1986).

38   Victor G. Heiser, "Fighting Leprosy in the Philippines," *World's Work* 31 (1916): 311, 312. John E. Snodgrass describes unsuccessful early attempts made in the Philippines to treat the disease with X rays. See Snodgrass, *Leprosy in the Philippine Islands* (Manila: Bureau of Printing, 1915), 27, United States National Archives, Washington, D.C., RG 350/3465-84. For an overly optimistic discussion of X-ray treatment, see Victor G. Heiser, "The Progress of Medicine in the Philippine Islands," *Journal of the American Medical Association* 47 (1906): 245–47. See also Casimiro B. Lara, *Leprosy Research in the Philippines: A Historical-Critical Review* (Manila: National Research Council, 1936).

39   Snodgrass, *Leprosy*, 27–28.

40   Manson, *Tropical Diseases* (1914), 634, 637. For more on the results of nastin treatment, and of immunological therapies, see Richard P. Strong, "Leprosy," in *Forchheimer's Therapeusis of Internal Diseases*, ed. Frank Billings and Ernest E. Irons (New York: D. Appleton and Co., 1914), 387–400. (Strong was the director of the biological laboratory of the Bureau of Science and, later, the first professor of tropical medicine at Harvard.)

41   Heiser, "Tropical Diseases," 203. In 1921, the new governor general, Leonard Wood, a former military medical officer, inaugurated an intensive treatment program at Culion. Over 4,000 lepers were injected weekly with the ethyl esters of the oil. It was claimed that by 1925, 196 cases were sent away as cured and 499 were bacteriologically negative and undergoing the required two years' observation period for release. See George R. Callender, "The Leprosy Problem in the Philippine Islands," *American Journal Tropical Medicine* 5 (1925): 351–358; and *Annual Report of the Philippine Health Service, Fiscal Year 1922* (Manila: Bureau of Printing, 1923) 15, United States National Archives, Washington, D.C., RG 350/3465-172. By the early 1920s, Bayer had developed antileprol, a derivative of chaulmoogra oil that was better tolerated orally and that soon displaced the parenteral oil. See E. R. Stitt, *Diagnostics and Treatment of Tropical Diseases*, 5th ed. (Philadelphia: Balkiston, 1922), 266.

42   See Tani Barlow, "Theorizing Woman: Funü, Guojia, Jiating (Chinese Woman, Chinese State, Chinese Family)," in *Body, Subject, and Power in China*, ed. Angela Zito and Tani E. Barlow (Chicago: University of Chicago Press, 1994), 253–289, on individuation through the correct enactment of protocols. See also Julius A. Roth, "Ritual and Magic in the Control of Contagion," *American Sociological Review* 22 (1957): 310–314, on institutional magic.

43   Michel de Certeau, "The Institution of Rot," in *Heterologies: Discourse on the Other*, trans. Brian Massumi (Minneapolis: University of Minnesota Press, 1986), 41. He goes on to point out that the institution "lodges rottenness at the same time as it designates it" (46).

44   See Julia Kristeva, *Powers of Horror: An Essay in Abjection*, trans. Leon S. Roudiez (New York: Columbia University Press, 1982). See also Warwick Anderson, "Excremental Colonialism: Public Health and the Poetics of Pollution," *Critical Inquiry* 21 (spring 1995): 640–669.

45   Goffman, *Asylums*, 369, 366.

46 Heiser, "Leprosy in the East," 16.

47 Heiser, "Fighting Leprosy," 316–317.

48 Snodgrass, *Leprosy*, 24.

49 Heiser, *American Doctor's Odyssey*, 236.

50 Ibid.

51 Wade and Basa, "Culion Leper Colony," 406.

52 A. J. McLaughlin to Mrs. G. H. Burwell, 5 April 1909, United States National Archives, Washington, D.C., RG 350-1972-10. McLaughlin was the assistant director of health in the Philippines.

53 Snodgrass, *Leprosy*, 25.

54 Goffman (*Asylums*, 99) describes the institutional theatrical; Stewart (*On Longing*, 54) describes the theatricality of the miniature; and Homi Bhabha ("DissemiNation: Time, Narrative, and the Margins of the Modern Nation," in *The Location of Culture* [London: Routledge, 1994], 139–170, esp. 145–146) refers to the performativity of "people" in the narrative address of the nation. See also Timothy Mitchell, *Colonising Egypt* (Berkeley and Los Angeles: University of California Press, 1991), on the "exhibitionary order."

55 Heiser, "Fighting Leprosy," 318, 316, 320.

56 Heiser, "Memorandum," 1. Yet when the evangelist Rev. James B. Rodgers visited Culion, he admired the same gardens ("Culion, the Leper Colony of the Philippines," *Silliman Truth* (Negros Oriental), 1 May 1911, 2, 4, United States National Archives, Washington, D.C., RG 350-1972-19.

57 Heiser, "Leprosy in the East," 17–18. For a comparison with the increasingly disciplined Molokai colony (population 600), see Frederick Hoffman to Forrest F. Dryden, 10, 11 March 1915, "Special Reports on Leper Colonies," Hoffman Papers, National Library of Medicine, Bethesda, Md. On the asylum at Carville, La., see Hoffman to Dryden, 13 April 1916, ibid. Hoffman, well known as a race theorist in North America, was selecting a site for the federal leprosarium.

58 Bruno Latour, "Give Me a Laboratory and I Will Raise the World," in *Science Observed: Perspectives on the Social Study of Science*, ed. Karin Knorr-Cetina and Michael Mulkay (London: Sage, 1983), 140–170. Susan Stewart observes that the miniature "has the capacity to make its context remarkable" (Stewart, *On Longing*, 46). Lucien Febvre discusses the assumption that civilization is achieved through "experiment" (Febvre, "*Civilisation*," 256).

59 See Michel Foucault, *Discipline and Punish: The Birth of the Prison*, trans. Alan Sheridan (Harmondsworth, England: Penguin, 1991), 298.

60 Albert E. Jenks, "Assimilation in the Philippines as Interpreted in Terms of Assimilation in America," *American Journal of Sociology* 17 (1912): 789. Jenks, formerly the chief of the Bureau of Ethnology, thought that in the archipelago more generally, "to accomplish all this against their natural inertia of race, and the inertia of social and physical environment, is not a task that can be completed by the year 1921" (789). Culion was designed to disturb this "inertia."

61 Atherton Brownell, "What American Ideas of Citizenship May Do for Oriental Peoples," *Outlook*, 23 December 1904, 975. Brownell claimed that the United States' policy was "the subject of scoff by every other colonizing nation" because it "considers each of the subject people to be a human being, entitled to certain unalienable rights, which we not only freely grant, but *teach to him*" (975; my emphasis). See also Atherton Brownell, "Turning Savages into Citizens," *Outlook*, 24 December 1910, 921–931.

62 Turner, "Contemporary Problems," 9.

63 "Culion and Its Inhabitants," *La Vanguardia*, 27 August 1912.

64 "What Is Happening in Culion?" *El Ideal*, 16 September 1912.

65 "The Culion Lepers," *La Vanguardia*, 2 October 1912.

66 "Will Continue Segregation in Leprosy Work," *Manila Bulletin*, 7 October 1936. The activists pointed out that after thirty years of strict segregation, there had been no decrease in the admission of new cases to Culion.

67 "Police Force Helpless As Mob Rushes," *Manila Times*, 1 April 1932.

68 Joseph R. Hayden, "Hearing in the Colony Hall, July 26, 1935," 1–4, Joseph R. Hayden Papers, Michigan Historical Collections, Bentley Historical Library, University of Michigan. For another account linking medicalization with unrest, see Sanjiv Kakar, "Medical Developments and Patient Unrest in the Leprosy Asylum, 1860–1940," *Social Scientist* 24 (1996): 62–81.

69 "Million-Peso Leprosy Plan Being Evolved," *Manila Bulletin*, 12 August 1936.

70 Foucault, *Discipline and Punish*, 198. Foucault wrote: "Treat 'lepers' as 'plague victims', project the subtle segmentations of discipline onto the confined space of internment, combine it with the methods of analytical distribution proper to power, individualize the excluded, but use procedures of individualization to mark exclusion" (199). The leper, though, appears in Foucault's work only as a symbol of the confined.

71 Gyan Prakash, "Science between the Lines," in *Subaltern Studies 9: Writings in South Asian History and Society*, ed. Shahid Amin and Dipesh Chakrabarty (Delhi: Oxford University Press., 1996), 59–82.

72 Homi K. Bhabha, "Signs Taken for Wonders: Questions of Ambivalence and Authority under a Tree outside Delhi, May 1817," *Critical Inquiry* 12 (1985): 154, 162.

Commentary

The History of Chinese Medicine: Now and Anon

Nathan Sivin

Our effort to understand the evolution of Chinese medicine has been greatly limited by the tendency of sinologists to ignore new departures in the history of medicine, and vice versa. It would be otiose to take up larger trends of thought, of which both have remained sublimely innocent. The tendency of some of the very few trailblazers in Chinese studies to write hermetic, jargon-strewn prose has only encouraged this oblivion. I will review what innovation there has been in each field, survey the state of studies in Chinese medicine as it has recently benefited from both, and indicate where the field can go if it overcomes its double parochiality.

Medical History

The history of medicine took new directions late in the nineteenth century as physicians canvassed the past to map the march of medical progress. The issue that engaged them was how their forebears had come to apply biological, chemical, and physical knowledge to clinical research and practice, giving medicine the cachet of modern science despite its undiminished responsibility to care for the sick and suffering.

Medicine's cachet did not begin recently. Researchers have traced the shared intellectual horizon of science and medicine ever farther backward, beyond William Harvey and his experimental, quantitative proof that the blood circulates, beyond the medieval professors of medicine who argued that what they taught was a *scientia*, beyond Galen's trove of detailed observation and philosophic controversy, to the beginnings of systematic thought in the fifth century B.C. in Greece, when the Hippocratic physicians were as prominent as the *physikoi* and hardly less insistent on rational argument.[1]

The history of medicine, when by 1960 it became a recognized discipline, was concerned with the accomplishments of doctors, primarily with their knowledge and secondarily with their practice. It recognized the social dimension of medicine only to the extent of studying physicians' statuses and professional organizations.[2] This tight focus led to considerable strides in ascertaining what physicians knew, establishing its relation to scientific knowledge, and justifying intellectually what was consistently portrayed as the medical profession's well-earned prestige and income. Not surprisingly, in view of these emphases, historical studies found a secure home in medical schools.

One can imagine quite different histories of medicine emerging from the sources and methods available, devoted perhaps to therapeutic practice or to the patient's experience. Eventually some of them came into being.[3] A metamorphosis of the history of science in the 1970s greatly affected the history of medicine. The change was to a large extent due to a change in historians. Authors originally trained as scientists, physicians, and engineers were increasingly replaced by those trained in the humanistic disciplines of history. Although many historians in that generation had substantial technical backgrounds, they were more willing than their forebears to see change forming and evolving spontaneously rather than taking steps somehow destined to generate modern scientific knowledge.

In the United States, for instance, scholars of medical history increasingly were educated and employed outside the medical schools. That directly involved them in the shift of orthodoxies from "internalism" (the study of ideas without reference to their social formation) to "externalism" (the study of the interaction of scientists with each other or with society without regard to the content of science). Externalism reflected, among other things, a growing awareness that science could be used toward heedless and destructive ends. This new orthodoxy was also attractive because scholars without technological training or experience could make important contributions.

Internalism and externalism faded away as innovation focused on interrelations. Through the 1980s, the most influential historians of science, and those historians of medicine close to them, acknowledged that a dichotomy of ideas and social relations made it impossible to see any historical situation whole. In this effort they were greatly aided by tools and insights borrowed from anthropology and sociology. To take the most obvious example, the notion of culture provides a unitary view of concepts, values, and social interactions. Out of this synthesis has emerged a history of medicine that is precise about the large role of bluff in the Greeks' presentation of their theories as rational and demonstrative, and about the competition for livelihood that made bluffing productive; well informed about the astrological and religious as well as the anatomical side of seventeenth-century English medicine; and attentive to the therapies and social statuses of the "quacks" who provided most of the medical care in France ca. 1800.[4]

Sinology

Over the last half century, occidental scholars have transformed their methods of approach to the academic study of China. The sinological branch of orientalism began at the confluence of two traditions. It was formed not only by the enterprising philology of the European Renaissance, but by the Chinese tradition of evidential research (*k'ao-cheng* 考證), which, culminating two thousand years of critical scholarship, had developed equally powerful methods for testing and interpreting textual evidence.[5]

Naturally enough, in view of these patrimonies, sinologists tended to concentrate on explaining with the greatest possible care what ancient books said, recapitulating their gist in topical or chronological order. They paid little attention to the motivations, interests, and social circumstances that made such sources a good deal less than objective testimony. The European specialists' taste for early classics and for conventional topics reflected those of the orthodox Chinese scholars who taught, advised, and assisted them.

Here, as in the history of medicine, the multiplication and expansion of universities and the introduction of new subjects following the end of World War II opened secure careers for large numbers of scholars who could show their proficiency according to established standards. The Cold War of the 1950s multiplied governmental support for studies of China, mostly, but not only, in the United States. The scale of research thus rapidly expanded. At the same time, the added investment encouraged two shifts that turned out to be fundamental.

As sinologists established a noticeable presence in university departments, colleagues in history and other departments, who had come to think of philology as a tool, challenged their reliance on it as an end in itself. Advances in language teaching in this period stressed intensive oral drill with native speakers to provide an active command of the modern language. That enabled the best programs to give students a sound grasp not only of modern but of classical Chinese in three years or less. Language ceased to be a career-long fixation. Young scholars could be expected to learn a discipline before they began dissertation research. No Occidental specialist today, however experienced, finds reading ancient Chinese texts effortless or free of uncertainty, but the same can be said of their East Asian colleagues. With remarkably ample classical dictionaries and concordances, recently published, one text after another has become fully accessible to those systematically trained. This is now merely one among the many perennial difficulties of scholarship.

Another important change, natural enough when so much of the volition (and funding) for Chinese studies came from enmity toward Communist China, is that their center of gravity shifted toward the present. By now, outside China there are many more academic experts on the period after 1800, which hardly existed as an academic subject in 1950, than on the period before. And the literature on early China, once largely concentrated in the late Chou dynasty, is coming to be evenly spread across at least the major dynasties.

Research in Asia

The most valuable contributions to the factual documentation of Chinese science and medicine have originated in China and Japan. The circumstances in which this work has been done differ considerably from those I have outlined above. In 1937, when Ch'en Pang-hsien 陳邦賢 published the first modern-style history of Chinese medicine, the Rockefeller Foundation's Peking Union Medical College, one of the leading medical schools of the world, was being abandoned to the Japanese occupation. The influence of this research-oriented medical school, and the effect of biomedicine generally on China's health-care system, remained negligible until the second half of the century.[6] Nor did modern medicine greatly influence Ch'en's book. His work was characteristic of the best historians of the time in its great erudition, its tendency inherited from the evidential research tradition to juxtapose summaries of primary sources rather than to explain change, and its silence about the social context of medical practice. Also characteristic, the sole exception to this silence was detailed sections on the organization of the palace medical bureaucracy in each major dynasty. There is no evidence that officials were responsible for much of the significant change in health care over the centuries, but in the 1930s a career in the civil service remained, as it had been for two millennia, the one occupation that scholarly families urged on their offspring.

The Sino-Japanese War, the end of the Kuomintang government on the mainland, and the vicissitudes of the People's Republic led to remarkably little net change in the writing of medical history, at least once authors were no longer required to apply (or even quote) the thought of Marx, Engels, Lenin, and Mao. But the scale of publication expanded greatly due to the growth of support in China for specialized research. In addition to the proliferation of full-time researchers in central institutes of the history of medicine and of science, teachers and physicians have responded to the prestige that strong government support gave the field. A survey of 1987 counted a total of roughly five hundred historians of medicine publishing the results of their inquiries into original sources and artifacts.[7]

This swelling band has poured forth monographic studies on individual authors and sources, reprints, critical editions, translations into modern

Chinese, and reference books.[8] Although the chaotic book-distribution system makes this literature difficult to find inside China as well as elsewhere, with access to a good library it is possible for the first time to find accurate information about a great deal of the ancient medical landscape.

There has been no corresponding revolution in methods or conclusions. Almost all the historians of medicine in China were trained in medicine rather than in history. The training of Ph.D.'s in the field began in the late 1980s, but the curriculum does not yet provide a substantial introduction to the modern humanities and social sciences. Students are still being rigorously trained in evidential studies.

Before the late 1980s, history remained in China a risky occupation. In a consciously totalitarian society, reinterpretation of the past is an essential means of control. Any issue may become politically charged; any position, ideologically incorrect. Although such threats have largely abated, intellectuals who grew up earlier have not forgotten that they were periodically terrorized in public, and that periods of calm have regularly been succeeded by new terrors. This is not the sort of atmosphere that encourages methodological innovation.

Authors aware of the risks and sincerely eager to be correct, even when there are no government bans or party persecutions, have to some extent censored themselves, shunning risks in subject matter and interpretation. At the same time, high officials who aim to build national pride have tended to support history only to the extent that specialists can identify discoveries or inventions that appeared first in China. Such exercises fight with its own weapons the Western parochialism that believed Chinese mentally incapable of technical innovation. Thanks to the work of Joseph Needham and others, that parochialism has become less assertive, but few Chinese policy makers are aware of the change. It is unlikely that Chinese "leaders" would stop exerting pressure to claim priority in technological innovation even if they knew that who did what first has ceased to be what the history of technology is about.[9]

A scholarly tradition that explicates texts without much conscious interpretation, historians mostly trained as scientists or physicians and thus inclined toward positivism,[10] recognition and praise awarded mainly for claiming priority in scientific discovery, and self-censorship to avoid being linked to the "bourgeois liberalism" of colleagues abroad: these have conspired to inhibit qualitative change proportionate to the quantitative growth. This picture has begun to change over the past decade or so as economics has taken the helm. Pride has come increasingly to depend on wealth, and campaigns against "spiritual pollution" have begun fading into the featureless past. But it will be some time before iconoclasm becomes nothing more than an intellectual issue. At the same time, many colleagues in China consider the system in crisis, because it has become practically impossible to recruit first-rate graduate students. Exceptional university graduates want a high income quickly.

Work in Japan and Taiwan is also methodologically very conservative, for different reasons. In Japan, where the public esteems the indigenous tradition of Chinese-style medicine, there are well-organized traditions of historic research. Some of the world's most comprehensive and painstaking studies have been carried out by Japanese scholars, to the point that a reading knowledge of modern Japanese is essential for historians of Chinese medicine.[11] The political constraints that operate in China are of course absent in Japan. But Japanese academic careers depend on maintaining the traditions of one's mentor, cultural barriers to iconoclasm and foreign influence remain high, and the evidential research tradition still shapes method.[12]

In Taiwan, lack of government support in a culture that is focused on central approval and initiative has made specialization in technical history rare. A handful of enthusiastic young scholars, educated abroad, reflect new insights and methods in their work, and have begun to train successors. But the impact on the educational system remains negligible. Few institutions are interested in hiring anyone whose qualifications must be evaluated by any other criterion than skill at evidential research.

This survey of local proclivities perhaps makes it easier to understand what has happened, and what has not happened, as the study of Chinese medicine has evolved. It is now appropriate to consider the future.

Current and Future Research Issues

The intersection of a changing sinology and a changing history of medicine is bound to be a quickly moving point. From new successes in the study of early Europe, initiatives in the last generation, and scattered innovations of the last decade or so, we can identify some research questions that can serve as first steps toward a comprehensive history of Chinese medicine:

1. What were the traditions of health care? How were they related? To what extent did medicine compete with religious and other popular forms of therapy? How was each tradition situated in society? What was the economic base of each? How were their intellectual content and social forms related?

2. What were the social settings of medical practice and scholarship? Were these separate activities? If so, how were they related? If not, how were they articulated to form a single complex?

3. What were the sources of new ideas, techniques, and problems? To what extent did these stimuli come from outside medicine? What role did foreign influence, and the influence of non-Han people within the Chinese realm, play in their formation?

4. What were the directions of change in the long term? What caused medicine to move in those directions? What were the constraints on change?

5. To what extent have changes in technology affected medicine? Have innovations in medical technique found nontherapeutic uses?

6. How were medical ideas related to other kinds of thought and activity? The interplay with politics, philosophy, and religion obviously played out differently. How can concrete instances illustrate the diversity of these links?[13]

It is obvious that in order to investigate these issues, they must be resolved into a multitude of concrete questions, of which I will now give some examples. Some of this work has long since been done for occidental medicine, but very little for that of China.

European and American Medicine

More than half a century ago Henry Sigerist, who greatly influenced the formation of medical history, observed that "we know much about the history of great medical discoveries but very little on whether they were applied or to whom they were applied." He tried to redefine his field as "the history of healers and sick people seen within the actual context of their interaction (social and intellectual)." He was not calling for social history, but for something broader.[14]

Historians of Western medicine have begun to study all healers, not only the eminent. They have learned to gather the very scattered records from which they can reconstruct the experience of patients. "Medical pluralism" (see p. 746), they realize, is found to some extent in every society, from ancient Sumeria to modern France. It implies, among other things, that studying physicians alone cannot lead to an adequate picture of health care.

Historians now understand that most patients who choose modern medicine do not passively accept a physician's diagnosis and therapy; medical care still involves negotiation. The doctor may feel that his special knowledge gives him the last word in therapeutic encounters, but the multiplicity of healers greatly limits that power.[15]

Historians no longer choose between social, cultural, and intellectual contexts, but see them as part of one picture. They now examine aspects of this picture that their predecessors overlooked. An important aspect is how differences in gender, ethnic group, and social class affect health, sickness, and therapy. Historians no longer analyze therapy only as a curative technology that is either effective or ineffective. They see it instead as a kind of social interchange in which the drugs and other measures may be less important than ritual or other symbolic acts,[16] and in which the doctor is less important than other people present at the medical interview, in affecting patients' concrete conditions. They are attempting to see the many dimensions of disease in a unitary way. Here is a recent definition of "disease": "at once a biological event, a generation-specific repertoire of verbal constructs reflecting medicine's intellectual and institutional history, an occasion of and potential legitimation for public policy, an aspect of social role and individual—intrapsychic—identity, a sanction for cultural values, and a structuring element in doctor and patient interactions."[17]

Sigerist's prescription is now widely taken. It has given the history of medicine, as practiced at the research frontier, great vitality and scope. It has widened the focus beyond medical ideas to incorporate the whole spectrum of health care—establishment practice and alternative practice, public practice and private practice. Scholars of European history now know something about the costs of therapy in 1650; the enormous differences between practice in cities and in small towns around 1750; the rivalry between the many kinds of healers, respectable and marginal, around 1800; and the unimportance of medical advances in increasing lifespans before about 1900.[18] By throwing light on questions of political policy and social change, historians are helping people to make sensible decisions about today's urgent health-care problems.

Chinese Medicine

If we turn our attention to the study of Chinese medicine, we see, in contrast, an approach to forming problems that has hardly changed in fifty years. When its specialists speak of the history of medicine they seldom mean, as historians of the West do, explaining change. Histories of Chinese medicine continue to be summaries of primary sources in chronological order. This sometimes gives a good idea of what changes took place in the interval between two texts, but it does not explain why. When we find attempts at explanation, they tend to be guesses based on untested generalizations. The history of East Asian medicine has never evolved a methodology to account for change, and has ignored that of other fields. This somnolence has begun to dissipate as a number of newly qualified scholars begin to publish, but it is still the norm.

We know next to nothing about the economics of medical practice in traditional times, about occupational organization, or about the careers and practices of ordinary practitioners. The histories of medicine do not investigate physicians who were not elite authors.[19] They ignore the health care that was performed by priests, healers not educated in the classics, and laymen. Although non-classical healers greatly outnumbered physicians, the historians dismiss their therapy as worthless superstition or quackery instead of studying it. They say nothing concrete about the experience of patients. When they mention such topics, they usually give offhand opinions rather than the conclusions of research.

A well-known example is the question of when medicine came to be widely considered a respectable livelihood for the offspring of elite families.

Nearly everyone who asked it has given a different answer. We are told that this was a very gradual development, or it never happened, or it happened in one dynasty or another from the Sung on. The only systematic study, which was based on the rich documents of only one Chiang-nan prefecture, proves that it happened there in the Yuan period. As Robert Hymes puts it, this was one result of "a permanent shift among elite families from exclusive concentration on the achievement of high office to a broader strategy focusing on local position." This shift took place around the fall of the Northern Sung. The Yuan transition brought other changes, including fewer opportunities to teach, that accelerated the move into medicine.[20]

Conventional work on traditional topics will continue to be necessary and valuable. We have learned a great deal about Chinese scientific and medical concepts in the past couple of decades. We need no longer rely on disembodied, undefined notions such as Confucianism and Taoism to explain intellectual change.

Studies of recently excavated manuscripts earlier than the *Inner Canon* (*Huang ti nei ching* 黃帝內經, first century B.C.?) have fundamentally changed our view of the beginnings of medicine.[21] New studies have led to a redating of most classics that used to be considered pre-Han, and to a new view of how the earliest books came together.[22] This has made us reconsider how science separated from philosophy to form distinct bodies of knowledge, and how the high tradition of medicine emerged from a combination of popular religion, philosophy, techniques of self-cultivation, and lore about effective cures.[23] Historians are clarifying technical issues that used to be dismissed without examination, for instance, the importance of bloodletting in early medicine.[24] We have learned a good deal for the first time about health care among the minority peoples of China.[25]

There remains plenty of work of familiar kinds for specialists in textual study (*k'ao-cheng*) to do. The problem is that studies of medicine in the rest of the world no longer rest on such a narrow methodological base.[26] Their scope has changed rapidly as a result of new analytic tools adapted from history, sociology, anthropology, folklore studies, and other disciplines. Ignoring this larger perspective has isolated East Asian history and made its influence on the history of medicine smaller than it should be.

A few enterprising young scholars of East Asian medicine have already begun the necessary broadening of skills and research questions. They have begun to draw freely on new sources of insight, among them the sociology of knowledge, symbolic anthropology, cultural history, and literary deconstruction. I will not pause over the strengths and weaknesses of subaltern studies, ethnomethodology, discourse analysis, and other methods of approach that they are learning. I will simply call attention to Chinese issues, already mentioned, on which innovative methods cast light. The topics discussed below range from the relations of theory and practice, through therapy as the patient rather than the doctor sees it, to the economics and social organization of medicine.

The Integration of Intellectual and Social History

Benjamin Elman's *From Philosophy to Philology* demonstrated in 1984 that it is possible to overcome the split between intellectual and social history, and how rich the rewards are. It showed that in the Lower Yangtze region from the Sung dynasty onward, official position and commercial wealth tended to run in the same families for many generations, that such families in the Ch'ing dynasty sponsored a system of education that was not aimed at the imperial examinations, and that these schools were at the center of major intellectual transitions. The book paid due attention to astronomy, showing that such a broad approach could throw fresh light on technical history.[27]

As for medicine, Ma Po-ying's 1994 history of medicine in Chinese culture,[28] like Paul Unschuld's earlier history,[29] has raised questions that are neither purely conceptual nor purely social. Ma looks closely and impartially at the role of popular religious practices in the beginnings of medicine, examines the connections of medicine and population growth, and takes up other previously neglected topics. There is still no history of Chinese medicine in any language that draws on current medical anthropology, sociology, and general history, but both Unschuld and Ma have raised important questions that carefully educated young scholars can hope to answer.

Theory and practice

The changing relation between medical theory and practice has been an important theme in the history of Western medicine. Assertions about it regularly appear in studies of China, but they are rarely based on rigorous research. Needham assumes that medicine is a body of abstract knowledge derived directly and unproblematically from empirical findings. Unschuld avers that yin-yang, the Five Phases, and other basic concepts were a collective delusion that distracted physicians from empirically sound results.[30] Both positions are redolent of an earlier generation. Both are philosophically questionable and uninformed about the use of theory in practice.

The anthropologist Judith Farquhar has broken through this impasse with a study based on prolonged and systematic field observation in a school of traditional Chinese medicine and its clinic in Canton. At the same time, the study is informed by Farquhar's familiarity with history. It makes a strong case for the proposition that one cannot speak of theory and practice as separate activities that may or may not be related.[31] Similarly, Joanna Grant has studied the interaction of practice and doctrine in China in the early sixteenth century.[32]

Much of the confusion has arisen because in Europe after the time of Galen, the near collapse of classical culture separated the men of religion, who preserved the medical books but did not use them for practice, from the healers, who had no access to the books. What had previously been a unity, in which concepts arose from therapy and served it, was decisively sundered. It took many centuries to overcome this break.

In China no such break ever took place. Foundational works from the *Inner Canon* onward state clearly their concern with practice. It is remarkable how many authors of very abstract medical books, even philological commentaries, were practitioners, and explicitly addressed the needs of praxis.

I have found it heuristically desirable to avoid using the word "theory" in connection with medicine. One is less likely to confuse the very different European and Chinese experiences if, with respect to China, we speak of the "doctrines" that underlie practice and resist the temptation to trace their history without reference to the latter.[33]

The complexity of this issue has become clear in a new study of the Heat Factors Disorder (*wen-ping* 瘟病) movement, which historians generally describe as the last major new school of theory. Marta Hanson's careful reading of the early writings assigned to this "school" indicates that at the time no one associated them intellectually or institutionally. She has discovered that physicians of the Lower Yangtze region invented this school, putatively based on a new doctrine, in the nineteenth century.[34] This fabrication is not just a medical issue. It was part of a much broader social movement that created local identities for Soochow and other cities in the Lower Yangtze region, and for the region as a whole—a process that was bound to challenge earlier assumptions about the universal scope of classical medicine.

Local Studies

The examples just given are typical of the growing importance of local traditions in research. Anyone who writes on European medicine is aware of the great diversity of that subcontinent. The category Europe often refers to a culture that the elites of many countries, who were educated in Latin, shared. But if we focus on the full diversity of practice and activity up and down the social scale rather than on the learning of a minority, on health care rather than medical doctrine, "Europe" is too large a unit to be of any use.

China, a still larger unit, is even less suitable. G. William Skinner long ago made this point in great detail. He proposed to divide China into nine distinct regional systems, which he called physiographic macroregions. They are defined by the drainage basins of rivers. Each macroregion is environmentally distinct. Each has its own social, cultural, economic, and political resources, which gave it a history more or less independent of the others. Skinner showed that much of what we call Chinese history holds only for the region in which the capital was located. Officials gathered and aggregated some of the data in the standard histories so unreliably that accurate studies must use local records instead.[35]

This is hardly a trivial issue. Evidence from the Sung on indicates that Skinner's Lower Yangtze region (parts of Kiangsu, Anhwei, and Chekiang), and parts of his Middle Yangtze (Kiangsi) and Southeast Coast

(Fukien) regions, have consistently provided leadership in medicine for the past thousand years. It is no doubt pertinent that they have also provided leadership in trade, agriculture, science, technology, art, and, certainly not least, politics. On the other hand, considering the importance of Szechwan as a source of drugs, it is remarkable that no important Szechwanese medical practitioner, aside from legendary ones, is known to have lived before the Sung, and that Szechwanese medical authors do not appear regularly before the Ming.[36]

Wu Yiyi has challenged the looseness with which historians use the word "school." He has reconstructed the lineages of transmission of medical writings that began with the famous Liu Wan-su 劉完素 (1120? to 1200). Wu was able to find biographical information on fifty-three physicians who claimed to be in this line of transmission. He determined the nature of each linkage.[37] Although the textbooks describe this "school" in terms of theoretical tendencies, that is not what held it together. Nor was it united by a single style of practice. In the early phase, what defined it was precisely its locality, Ho-chien 河間, Liu's home town in Hopei province, in or near which all the main figures lived. When, after a century, the center moved decisively to the Lower Yangtze region, its relationships changed just as decisively. It was largely the widespread distribution of printed medical books that again changed those relationships to make personal ties less important than links through textual study.

Local studies have also brought precision for the first time to the history of epidemiology in China. Carol Benedict has used gazetteers and other regional materials to reconstruct in remarkable detail the transmission of bubonic plague from one locality to the next in the nineteenth century.[38] Paul Katz has used a similar technique to document the spreading cult of an epidemic god in nineteenth-century Chekiang.[39] Studies of this kind offer a pattern for many new kinds of investigations.

Explaining Change

The few projects that so far have sought to trace change rigorously have been productive. They point the way to much more comprehensive historical explanations.

For example, it has been clear for some time that the Northern Sung was a major time of transition. Many aspects of medicine changed, including its role in the civil service, the role of government in medical education, the classics people studied, the kinds of medical innovation, special attention to the disorders of women and children, and the economics of the drug trade. In a series of classic studies, Miyasita Saburō has shown that there was a widespread shift in the drugs most often used for particular ailments.[40]

There have been many guesses, ranging from the influence of neo-Confucianism to effective government control, to explain why medicine was so decisively transformed. There has even been some research bearing on such factors as the innovative and flourishing economy centered along the southeastern coast, the growth of medical publishing, and the changing social circumstances of women. Rather than continuing to expand the list of unrelated, unweighted factors, a comprehensive analysis is needed.[41]

Medical Pluralism

Therapy does not begin with doctors. It was normal in China, as in every other society, for people to rely first on themselves for treatment, and then on their families and other people around them. When that did not work, people chose in turn from a great variety of curers, medical, religious, and so on. Anthropologists call this "medical pluralism." They have been exploring the topic in China for much of this century. We find great overlaps with magical and religious curing from the very beginnings of medicine to the present day.[42] My own work in progress on the diversity of Chinese health care in the last thousand years reveals that elite physicians provided only a small part of the health care of the whole population. It shows, not mutually exclusive realms of "scientific" and "superstitious" medicine, but an unceasing flow of methods and understandings up and down the social scale, which were constantly being translated back and forth between the vitalistic and god-centered view of popular medicine and the cosmological and secular assumptions of the various high traditions. Early sources for studying practitioners who did not belong to the elite, although seldom used, are not rare. This work will progress rapidly as more young historians learn the skills of current anthropology.

Gender, Ethnic Group, and Social Class

Medical history has usually been written as though the same therapy were available to everyone in China. This has not been true of any society. The inequality of treatment based on social and ethnic distinctions has not yet been studied, but it needs attention if we are to fully understand the spectrum of health care in China.[43]

In the history of medicine generally, questions of gender have ceased to be simply a feminist theme. They have to do with the most fundamental characteristics of health care. Although the body defined by modern biology is much the same everywhere, people think about their own bodies and those of others, and their ailments, differently in every society and even every subculture. The diseases peculiar to women are not only physiological conceptions, they are also tools of social control, species of deviance, and justifications for low status. Insights about gender cast light on every aspect of medicine, for men as well as for women.[44]

Gender issues illuminate Chinese medicine. Charlotte Furth has presented evidence that from the seventeenth through nineteenth centuries physicians drew the boundaries between genders to emphasize the physical deficiency of women and define their potential almost exclusively as a matter of childbearing and rearing children. She argues that distinct views of female bodies and their disorders emerged in the Sung period. She also takes up the neglected topic of women as practitioners—not only as midwives but as doctors. A number of female physicians were not limited to gynecology, but practiced across the whole range of medicine. At the same time, their seclusion restricted them to treating women and children.[45]

The Experience of Patients

The voice of the patient used to be silent in the history of medicine. In the last decade, however, it has become a central theme in the study of European medicine. The writings of patients offer a wealth of sources. We can now reconstruct the experience of surgery before anesthetics, and understand why patients until late in the nineteenth century endured the purging, bleeding, and other drastic remedies that doctors depended on. We have also learned from patients how inadequately physicians recorded the roles of other healers, especially midwives, in health care.[46]

In China, we do not find the intimate autobiographies and diaries that have been mined so successfully for the West.[47] Still, there are more than enough sources of other kinds to open up the subject. Doctors also have occasionally recorded their own medical experiences among their case records and other writings. They, and articulate laymen such as Yuan Mei 袁枚 (1716–1798), have had a good deal to say on the subject in prefaces and informal writings, but historians have not yet surveyed them for this purpose.[48] Scholars have begun to mine the massive information about a very exceptional class of patient, namely, emperors.[49] On the other hand, for half a century, scholars have been studying the rich depictions of therapy in literature and drama. These depictions are usually written from the patient's point of view and often make the physician a figure of fun.

Negotiation in Medical Encounters

Records in the palace archives make it clear that imperial patients, at least, had a great deal to say about the treatments they received and did not hesitate to say it, whether politely or abusively. Their absolute power made their encounters with their doctors exceptional. Still, there is a parallel to their negotiations in the tug of war between the ordinary patient's economic status and the physician's occupational authority.

Medical textbooks and handbooks routinely give the impression that doctors could count on less exalted patients to do what they were told. But from the informal writings of doctors, from what we can learn directly from patients, and from historical anecdotes, it is clear that therapeutic relationships were negotiated. In the earliest cases for which we have detailed information, from the T'ang dynasty on, we find doctors complaining about patients who ignore their instructions and people in the sickroom who argue with the physician. When patients and their families found that their wishes were not taken seriously, or when they lost confidence in their doctor, they did not hesitate to consult someone else. Because patients chose freely between different types of practitioners, in no set order, this issue is inseparable from that of medical pluralism.[50]

The Economics of Medical Practice

Early primary sources are seldom explicit about the costs of goods and services, with obvious exceptions such as the price of grain. Sinologists have made some progress over the past generation in working out a history of commerce, but we still know very little about the costs of therapy and the incomes of doctors.[51] One reason for this is that elite patients and their physicians preferred to treat therapy, like art, as a matter of give-and-take between gentlemen rather than commerce. The more esteemed the painter or physician, the fewer fees and the more gifts he received. Both careers, in later dynasties, offered exceptional social mobility. Doctors concerned about respectability wanted to be thought of in the same class as officials, not as mercenary artisans or tradesmen.

Patronage was a special social form with complicated but generally understood rules. Historians of Europe have recently shown that it was the major source of support for innovators in science and medicine in the sixteenth and seventeenth centuries. At times, in the upper social reaches of Chinese medicine, it was equally important. The largesse of emperors and of high officials supported celebrated physicians for long periods.[52] From the Sung dynasty on this sort of patronage becomes less visible. Instead, the support of officials and later of local gentry for printing medical books grows in importance. In a number of Ming and Ch'ing dynasty books, we find lists of subscribers with the sums that they contributed.[53]

There were many other forms of patronage. For instance, from 1600 to 1850, the central and local medical academies supported temples to medical deities as a means of "maintaining symbolic control over the provision of medical care." This support, like many other kinds of government subvention for popular religion after the Sung, was justified because only symbolic control was possible.[54]

Publishers not only printed medical books but wrote new ones, compiled popular editions of classics, and invented treatises by combining old ones. Their complex activity will obviously play an important part in clarifying the economics of medicine.[55]

Another area of medical economics that is overdue for exploration has to do with medicines and the growth of what we might call a national drug market, and the shifts in where particular drugs came from. Here too there have been a few useful studies.[56]

Occupational Organization

Sociologists who are dissatisfied with the conventionally vague usage of the term "profession" distinguish the traditional professions from other occupations by the autonomy that society grants them. This autonomy lets them control who enters and leaves their ranks and set their own compensation.[57] By that definition, Chinese medicine was never a profession. At no point in the past can we speak of a single autonomous occupational group.

I know of no organized attempt by elite doctors in premodern China, no matter how much they complained about quackery, to prevent practice by people unlike themselves. The government attempted briefly in the Sung dynasty to set unified standards and to examine physicians for local service.[58] There is no reason to think that this initiative had any lasting effect, and it was not revived. Such a move, had it lasted, might have led to a sense of occupational identity, but hardly, given its origin, to autonomy.

The first associations, in the early part of the twentieth century, could hope for no more than to protect traditional medicine against abolition. They learned to organize lobbies only when the Nationalist government threatened to abolish the legal practice of their art.[59] Since 1949, doctors have been civil servants, until private practice began recently to reemerge on a limited scale with official approval.

If we want to understand the inability of physicians to organize before modern times, the first place to look is guilds (usually called *hang* 行). We know that Chinese guilds were local associations to restrain competition. They were not broad organizations claiming from government or society authority to regulate themselves. Despite a few good studies,[60] we do not know much more than that. We have no idea of how medical guilds differed from those of tradesmen.

The obvious next step is to look at local medical practitioners and their networks. A good deal of the recent scholarship on that topic has to do with "schools" (as usual, a term used so vaguely as to be meaningless), defined by books, not by interactions between people that create permanent institu-

Save over 20% off the newsstand price!

☐ Please enter my one-year subscription (three issues) to *positions: east asia cultures critique* at the low subscription rate of $29.*

Subscribers outside the U.S.: Please add $9 for postage. Canadian subscribers:
Please add 7% GST to the subscription rate, in addition to the outside-U.S. postage.

☐ Enclosed is my check, made payable to Duke University Press.

☐ Please bill me (no issues will be sent until payment is received).

Please charge my   ☐ VISA   ☐ MasterCard   ☐ American Express

_____   _____
Account Number   **Expiration Date**

_____
Signature

_____
Name

_____
Address

_____
City/State/Zip   **PS911**

* Individual subscriptions only. Annual institutional rates: U.S.: $78 Non-U.S.: $87
Send your order to the Journals Fulfillment Department, Duke University Press, Box 90660,
Durham, NC 27708-0660. To place your journal order using a credit card, call toll-free 1-888-DUP-JRNL
(1-888-387-5765). http://www.duke.edu/web/dupress/

Library request for a subscription/examination copy

Please enter my one-year subscription (three issues) to *positions: east asia cultures critique*.
Libraries and institutions: $78 (Add $9 for postage outside the U.S.; Canadian libraries: Please add
7% GST to the subscription rate, in addition to the outside-U.S. postage.)

_____
Institution

_____
Address

_____
                                                                                                 PS911

☐ Purchase order enclosed.
☐ Please bill our agent:

_____

☐ Please send a free examination copy (libraries only).

positions is printed on acid-free paper, as are all journals published by Duke University Press.

Volume 7, 1999 (3 issues); ISSN 1067-9847
Send your order to the Journals Fulfillment Department, Duke University Press, Box 90660,
Durham, NC 27708-0660. To place your journal order using a credit card, call toll-free 1-888-DUP-JRNL
(1-888-387-5765). http://www.duke.edu/web/dupress/

NO POSTAGE
NECESSARY
IF MAILED
IN THE
UNITED STATES

BUSINESS REPLY MAIL

FIRST CLASS MAIL   PERMIT NO. 1000   DURHAM, NC

POSTAGE WILL BE PAID BY ADDRESSEE

Duke University Press
Journals Fulfillment
Box 90660
Durham, NC 27706-9942

NO POSTAGE
NECESSARY
IF MAILED
IN THE
UNITED STATES

BUSINESS REPLY MAIL

FIRST CLASS MAIL   PERMIT NO. 1000   DURHAM, NC

POSTAGE WILL BE PAID BY ADDRESSEE

Duke University Press
Journals Fulfillment
Box 90660
Durham, NC 27706-9942

tions. Still, there are now a few good biographical compilations by province or, in the case of Huichow, by prefecture.[61] They do not analyze their materials for signs of medical organization, but they do facilitate this work. For one thing, it is now possible to trace the movement of physicians in and out of official positions, as they traded in their court status for local eminence. This pattern becomes important in the Ming and Ch'ing periods.

Finally, doctors sometimes mention in their case records other physicians who were consulted at the same time as they, or who had failed to cure the patient earlier. A careful biographical analysis of these data will let us establish local links of cooperation and competition between doctors.

At the same time, the issue of competition will need to be handled subtly. In China, lacking effective organization and government regulation, elite physicians could not hope to monopolize even the care of the gentry. Most collections of case records leave a clear impression that literate doctors were generally not eager to treat their inferiors. The overwhelming majority of the population, in the countryside, were barely involved in the money economy before the 1980s. They could hardly shop for services.

The doctors' frequent complaints about quacks, itinerants, priests of the popular religion, spirit mediums, and Taoist masters were clearly meant to impress prospective patients.[62] These complaints were neither part of an organized campaign nor tools that a cohesive professional group adopted to compete against rival guilds. There was no such group.

I would suggest that individual physicians were trying by this rhetoric not to protect a profession from incompetents, or to drive their competitors out of business, but to assert their personal standing in the company of the Yellow Emperor's successors. No matter what their birth, they wanted to be identified with conventional upper-class medicine, not with the popular therapy that orthodox male patients despised, or the many varieties of practice in the undefined area between the two. The issue, in other words, was social mobility.

Once we look at the Chinese data in the light of recent European studies,[63] we see linked to these social issues a political one. In the late Ming and Ch'ing, profits from business easily bought official status. At the same time, fewer descendants of the gentry than before could hope for good careers. The border between simple respectability and no prospects at all seemed vague and chaotic. Pronouncements about the need for strict stratification of health care *at the same time* expressed nostalgia for a stable society that seemed to be quickly disappearing.

Terra Incognita: The Scientific Value of Therapies

The clinical evaluation of traditional techniques is too important to ignore, but no one has come to grips with it, and so far it appears to be intractable. It is probably impossible to form a view of early medical practice without considering its usefulness in curing medical disorders. Given the limits of curing before the last couple of generations, it might be more apposite to speak of medicine's utility in supporting rather than bringing about the patient's recovery.

It is hard enough to measure the curative power of a broad range of therapies, understood from the purely technical point of view. One must also ask whether their power was in fact purely technical. If it is equally necessary to consider the social and ritual circumstances in which each therapeutic encounter took place, how does one weigh their role? One must then admit that, although medical case records from the Sung on are often detailed and concrete, they are practically never detailed and concrete enough to indicate exactly what the patient's condition was according to modern diagnostic criteria. Any practitioner is aware of how seldom a mature patient presents a simple and classical form of a single disorder. One also encounters claims of cures so clearly at odds with modern knowledge that one has to consider them skeptically, or at least admit that what brought about the result more likely lay in the realms of emotion, ritual, and symbol than in chemistry and physics.[64] But the case records rarely record emotion, ritual, and symbol. These obstacles make the prospect of reasoned evaluation seem unattainable.

Medical historians seldom reflect on this problem. Many in East Asia accept any assertion about efficacy that they find in the sources. Many outside of East Asia refuse to take any such assertions seriously, or even to contemplate them.

Neither of these positions is tenable. The second position falls into one of the most elementary traps of historiography, namely, assuming that the people one studies were less alert and capable of critical reflection than oneself. The first assumes that ancient physicians were able to determine cures and cure rates more precisely than modern doctors can do today. This too is not an informed position. One looks in vain for a clear exposition of how early practitioners defined cure and how they determined when it had taken place.

Blithe claims about curative efficacy also commonly overlook the fact that ancient disease entities do not correspond to those of biomedicine. There was no disease closely equivalent to typhoid, cancer, tuberculosis, or, despite the many recent assertions of entrepreneurs, AIDS. To take the first of these as a single example, *shang han* 傷寒, the modern term for typhoid, has an entirely different meaning in traditional medicine even today. It designates both a particular disorder, Cold Damage, which may correspond to a number of acute infectious febrile diseases, including the common cold, and a large group subsuming it.[65] It is also likely that any classical discussion of the use of acupuncture to treat *shang han* ignores other therapies that were brought to bear—and, as usual, is silent on the most important element, the recuperative powers of the patient. In traditional Chinese medicine, early or contemporary, as in European medicine over most of its history, the conventional wisdom credited the doctor with the cure of every patient who recovered.

But there were unquestionably failures. Christopher Cullen has made the point that, although imperial officials often failed in their duties, this frequently mattered less than whether they said the right thing. The issue was whether orthodox political and ethical convictions backed their actions. In the same way, a physician accomplished his expected task when he set his patient's disorder within the framework of medical cosmology, even if he could not bring about a cure. The same might be said of European physicians in the late eighteenth century, although they quoted Galen rather than the Yellow Emperor.[66]

Conclusion

I believe I have shown that there is a more than adequate basis for students of China to move beyond the methodologies of fifty years ago to reach at least the critical penetration now common in the history of medicine generally. Young researchers can prepare themselves to contribute to this modest but overdue advance by insisting that they be trained at the forefront of both Chinese studies and medical history.

Notes

This essay is extracted and revised from the editor's introduction to *Science and Civilisation in China*, vol. 6, pt. 6, *Medicine* (Cambridge: Cambridge University Press, forthcoming). The author wishes to acknowledge hospitality from the Needham Research Institute and St. John's College, Cambridge, and support from the Needham Research Institute, the National Library of Medicine, and the Research Fund of the University of Pennsylvania.

1 On Greece, see G. E. R. Lloyd, *The Revolutions of Wisdom: Studies in the Claims and Practice of Ancient Greek Science*, Sather Classical Lectures, vol. 52 (Berkeley and Los Angeles: University of California Press, 1987), esp. chap. 5. On the Middle Ages, see, among others, Cornelius O'Boyle, "Surgical Texts and Social Contexts: Physicians and Surgeons in Paris, ca. 1270–1430," in *Practical Medicine from Salerno to the Black Death*, ed. Louis Garcia Ballester et al. (Cambridge: Cambridge University Press, 1994), 156.

2 An important exception to this general shying away from social history is Richard Harrison Shryock, *The Development of Modern Medicine: An Interpretation of the Social and Scientific Factors Involved* (1936; reprint, Madison: University of Wisconsin Press, 1979). Although physician-centered, this book's overview of British, French, German, and American medicine remains unequalled.

3 Some prominent examples are Roy Porter, ed., *Patients and Practitioners: Lay Perceptions of Medicine in Pre-industrial Society*, Cambridge History of Medicine, vol. 9 (Cambridge: Cambridge University Press, 1985); Roy Porter and Dorothy Porter, *In Sickness and in Health: The British Experience, 1650–1850* (London: Fourth Estate, 1988); and, for Japan, William Johnston, *The Modern Epidemic: A History of Tuberculosis in Japan*, Harvard East Asian Monographs, vol. 162 (Cambridge, Mass.: Council on East Asian Studies, Harvard University, 1995).

4 Lloyd, *Revolutions of Wisdom*, 15, 28. See also Michael MacDonald, *Mystical Bedlam: Madness, Anxiety, and Healing in Seventeenth-Century England* (Cambridge: Cambridge University Press, 1981); and Matthew Ramsey, *Professional and Popular Medicine in France, 1770–1830: The Social World of Medical Practice* (Cambridge: Cambridge University Press, 1987).

5 On evidential research, see Benjamin A. Elman, *From Philosophy to Philology: Intellectual and Social Aspects of Change in Late Imperial China*, Harvard East Asian Monographs, vol. 110 (Cambridge, Mass.: Council on East Asian Studies, Harvard University, 1984).

6 By far the best study is Mary Brown Bullock, *An American Transplant: The Rockefeller Foundation and Peking Union Medical College* (Berkeley and Los Angeles: University of California Press, 1980).

7 Nathan Sivin, "Science and Medicine in Imperial China—The State of the Field," *Journal of Asian Studies* 47 (1988): 49–50.

8 On reference books, including those that provide access to other recent publications, see Nathan Sivin, "A Cornucopia of Reference Works for the History of Chinese Medicine," *Chinese Science* 9 (1989): 29–52.

9 See, as an example of official presentation, China Science and Technology Museum and *China Reconstructs, China: Seven Thousand Years of Discovery. China's Ancient Technology*, authorized Beijing ed. (Peking: *China Reconstructs*, 1983).

10 On this point, see Nathan Sivin, "Over the Borders: Technical History, Philosophy, and the Social Sciences," *Chinese Science* 10 (1991): 69–80.

11 Notable examples are Okanishi Tameto 岡西為人, *Sung i-ch'ien i-chi k'ao* 宋以前醫籍考 [Studies of medical books through the Sung period] (Peking: Jen-min Wei-sheng Ch'u-pan-she, 1958); Okanishi, *Chûgoki isho honzô kô* 中國醫書本草考 [Studies of Chinese books on medicine and materia medica] (Ôsaka: Minami Ôsaka Insatsu Sentâ, 1978); Miyashita Saburô, "A Historical Study of Chinese Drugs for the Treatment of Jaundice," *American Journal of Chinese Medicine* 4 (1976): 239–243; Miyashita, "A Historical Analysis of Chinese Formularies and Prescriptions: Three Examples," *Nihon ishigaku zasshi* 日本醫史學雜誌 23 (1977): 283–300; Miyashita, "Malaria (*yao*) in Chinese Medicine during the Chin and Yuan Periods," *Acta Asiatica* 36 (1979): 90–112; Miyashita, "An Historical Analysis of Chinese Drugs in the Treatment of Hormonal Diseases, Goitre, and Diabetes Mellitus," *American Journal of Chinese Medicine* 8 (1980): 17–25; and Akahori Akira 赤堀 昭, "Tô Kôkei to shûshû honzô" 陶弘景と集注本草 [T'ao Hung-ching and the Pharmacopoeia with Collected Annotations], in Yamada Keiji 山田慶兒, *Chûgoku no kagaku to kagakusha* 中國の科學と科學者[Chinese science and scientists] (Kyoto: Jimbun Kagaku Kenkyûsho, 1978), 309–367.

12 An important exception is the work of Yamada Keiji, an original and polymathic scholar who, from time to time, contributes to medical history. See, for example, Yamada, *Yonaku tori: Igaku, Jujutsu, Densetsu* 夜鳴烏。醫學 。咒術。傳説 [The bird that cries at night: Medicine, magic, legend] (Tokyo: Iwanami Shoten, 1990).

13 For previous discussions, see Nathan Sivin, ed., *Science and Technology in East Asia: Selections from Isis* (New York: Science History Publications, 1977), xv–xx; and Sivin, "Science and Medicine," 42–43.

14 Henry Sigerist, cited in Felix Marti-Ibanez, ed., *Henry E. Sigerist on the History of Medicine* (New York: MD Publications, 1960), 25–26. The second quotation is a paraphrase from Judith Walzer Leavitt, "Medicine in Context: A Review Essay of the History of Medicine," *American Historical Review* 95 (1990): 1473.

15 Chang Che-chia analyzes this tension in "The Therapeutic Tug of War: The Imperial
    Patient-Practitioner Relationship in the Era of the Empress Dowager Cixi (1874–1908)"
    (Ph.D. diss., University of Pennsylvania, 1998), chap. 3. For a more general discussion, see Li
    Yun, "Aspects of the Doctor-Patient Relationship in Ancient China," in *Proceedings, Four-
    teenth International Symposium on the Comparative History of Medicine—East and West*
    (Tokyo: Ishiyaku EuroAmerica, 1995).

16 Charles Rosenberg speaks of traditional medicine as "a ritual legitimated . . . by a rationalis-
    tic model of pathology and therapeutic action" (Rosenberg, "The Therapeutic Revolution:
    Medicine, Meaning, and Social Change in Nineteenth-Century America," *Perspectives in
    Biology and Medicine* 20 [1977]: 12). This description also holds for many aspects of modern
    clinical therapy.

17 Charles Rosenberg, "Introduction," *Framing Disease: Studies in Cultural History*, ed. Charles
    Rosenberg and Janet Golden (New Brunswick, N.J.: Rutgers University Press, 1992), xiii.

18 Among the many sources that deal with these issues are MacDonald, *Mystical Bedlam*; Ram-
    sey, *Professional and Popular Medicine*; O'Boyle, "Surgical Texts and Social Contexts"; Irvine
    Loudon, *Medical Care and the General Practitioner, 1750–1850* (Oxford: Clarendon Press,
    1986); and Thomas McKeown, *The Role of Medicine: Dream, Mirage, or Nemesis?*, 2d ed.
    (Princeton, N.J.: Princeton University Press, 1979).

19 For important new discoveries of popular writings, especially about Western science and
    medicine, see Chung Shao-hua 鍾少華, *Jen-lei chih-shih ti hsin kung-chü: Chung-Jih chin-tai
    pai-k'o ch'üan-shu yen-chiu* 人類知識的新工具。中日近代百科全書研究 [New tools for
    human knowledge: Studies of encyclopedias in modern China and Japan] (Peking: Pei-
    ching T'u-shu-kuan, 1996). Charlotte Furth (*A Flourishing Yin: Gender in China's Medical
    History, 960–1665* [Berkeley and Los Angeles: University of California Press, forthcoming])
    studies healers marginal to the elite in Ming and Ch'ing China. Chia-feng Chang ("Aspects
    of Smallpox and Its Significance in Chinese History" [Ph.D. diss., School of Oriental and
    African Studies, University of London, 1996]) discusses what she calls "alternative" practi-
    tioners.

20 Robert P. Hymes, "Not Quite Gentlemen? Doctors in Sung and Yuan," *Chinese Science* 8
    (1987): 57, 65. See also Yamamoto Noriko 山本德子, "Kin-Gen jidai ni okeru shakai to ika
    no chi'i" 金元時代における社會 と醫家の地位 [Chin and Yuan society and the status
    of physicians], *Nihon ishigaku zasshi* 31 (1985): 225–226; and Angela Ki Che Leung, "Orga-
    nized Medicine in Ming-Qing China: State and Private Medical Institutions in the Lower
    Yangtze Region," *Late Imperial China* 8 (1987): 134–166.

21 I have surveyed recent research studies and reference works in Sivin, "Science and Medi-
    cine," and Sivin, "Cornucopia of Reference Works."

22 Michael Loewe, *Early Chinese Texts: A Bibliographical Guide* (Chicago: Society for the Study
    of Early China, 1993) provides a summary of recent studies. See also E. Bruce Brooks and A.
    Taeko Brooks, *The Original Analects: Sayings of Confucius and His Successors* (New York:

Columbia University Press, 1998).

23 See Donald J. Harper, "The Conception of Illness in Early Chinese Medicine, as Docu-
mented in Newly Discovered Third and Second Century B.C. Manuscripts," part 1, *Sudhoffs
Archiv* 74 (1990): 210–235; and Nathan Sivin, "Text and Experience in Classical Chinese
Medicine," in *Knowledge and the Scholarly Medical Traditions*, ed. Don G. Bates (Cambridge:
Cambridge University Press, 1995), 177–204.

24 D. C. Epler Jr., "Blood-letting in Early Chinese Medicine and Its Relation to the Origin of
Acupuncture," *Bulletin of the History of Medicine* 54 (1980): 337–367; and Kuriyama Shige-
hisa, "Interpreting the History of Bloodletting," *Journal of the History of Medicine and Allied
Sciences* 50 (1995): 11–46.

25 See, for example, I Kuang-jui 伊光瑞, *Nei-meng-ku i-hsueh shih lueh* 內蒙古醫學史略 [An
outline history of medicine in Inner Mongolia] (Peking: Chung-i Ku-chi, 1993); Li Keng-
tung 李耕冬, "Liang shan i tsu chi-ping kuan" 涼山彝族疾病觀 [Views of disease among
the I people in the Liang shan I Nationality Autonomous Region], *Chung-hua i-shih tsa-
chih* 中華醫史雜誌 18 (1988): 113–114; Ts'ai Ching-feng 蔡景峰, "Tsang i-hsueh
ho Tsang i-hsueh shih" 藏醫學和藏醫學史 [Tibetan medicine and its history], in Anon.,
Chung-kuo i shih wen-hsien yen-chiu-so chien so lun-wen-chi 中國醫史文獻研究所建所論
文集 [Collected essays for the establishment of the China Research Institute for the History
of Medicine and Medical Literature] (Peking: Chung-kuo Chung-i Yen-chiu-yuan, 1982),
80–81; and Yü Yung-min 于永敏, "Liao-tai Ch'i-tan tsu i-hsueh shih chien-shu" 遼代契丹
族醫學史簡述 [A brief account of the medical history of the Khitan people in the Liao
period], in *Chung-hua i-shih tsa-chih* 17 (1987): 60–63.

26 This is true even of Africa, which has been studied much less than China. See Steven Feier-
man, "Struggles for Control: The Social Roots of Health and Healing in Modern Africa,"
African Studies Review 28 (1985): 73–147; and Gwyn Pryns, "But What Was the Disease?
The Present State of Health and Healing in African Studies," *Past and Present* 124 (1989):
159–179.

27 See Elman, *From Philosophy to Philology*.

28 See Ma Po-ying 馬伯英, *Chung-kuo i-hsueh wen-hua shih* 中國醫學文化史 [A history of
medicine in Chinese culture] (Shanghai: Shang-hai Jen-min Ch'u-pan-she, 1990).

29 See Paul Ulrich Unschuld, *Medicine in China: A History of Ideas* (Berkeley and Los Angeles:
University of California Press, 1985).

30 Joseph Needham, *Clerks and Craftsmen in China and the West: Lectures and Addresses on the
History of Science and Technology* (Cambridge: Cambridge University Press, 1970), 15;
Unschuld, *Medicine in China*, 197. These points of view pervade the writing of both.

31 Judith Farquhar, *Knowing Practice: The Clinical Encounter of Chinese Medicine*, Studies in
the Ethnographic Imagination, vol. 4 (Boulder, Colo.: Westview Press, 1994). See also Farquhar, "Rewriting Traditional Medicine in Post-Maoist China," in Bates, *Knowledge*,
251–276.

32 Joanna Grant, "Wang Ji's *Shishan yi'an*: Aspects of Gender and Culture in Ming Dynasty Medical Case Histories" (Ph.D. diss., School of Oriental and African Studies, University of London, 1997).

33 Historians of Europe also are finding it useful to resist this temptation. See, for instance, Garcia Ballester et al., *Practical Medicine*.

34 Marta Hanson, "Inventing a Tradition in Chinese Medicine: From Universal Canon to Local Medical Knowledge in South China, 17th–19th Century" (Ph.D. diss., University of Pennsylvania, 1997).

35 The most important sources are G. William Skinner's editorial introductions in *The City in Late Imperial China*, Studies in Chinese Society (Stanford, Calif.: Stanford University Press, 1977), 3–31, 253–273, and 521–553 (map, p. 214), and his "Presidential Address: The Structure of Chinese History," *Journal of Asian Studies* 44 (1985); 271–292. On local data, see Skinner, "Sichuan's Population in the Nineteenth Century: Lessons from Disaggregated Data," *Late Imperial China* 8 (1987): 1–79.

36 See Jen Ying-ch'iu 任應秋, "Shu i yuan sou" 蜀醫淵藪 [The aggregation of physicians in Szechwan] in *Jen Ying-ch'iu lun i chi* [Collected essays on medicine by Jen Ying-ch'iu] (Peking: Jen-min Wei-sheng Ch'u-pan-she, 1984), 262–264. See also the data collected in Ch'en Hsien-fu 陳先賦 and Lin Sen-jung 林森榮, *Ssu-ch'uan i-lin jen-wu* 四川醫林人物 [Notable physicians of Szechwan] (Chengtu: Ssu-ch'uan Jen-min Ch'u-pan-she, 1981).

37 Wu Yiyi, "A Medical Line of Many Masters: A Prosopographical Study of Liu Wansu and His Disciples from the Jin to the Early Ming," *Chinese Science* 11 (1993): 36–65.

38 Carol Benedict, *Bubonic Plague in Nineteenth-Century China* (Stanford, Calif.: Stanford University Press, 1996).

39 Paul R. Katz, *Demon Hordes and Burning Boats: The Cult of Marshal Wen in Late Imperial Chekiang* (Albany: State University of New York Press, 1995).

40 Miyashita, "Historical Study of Chinese Drugs"; Miyashita, "Historical Analysis of Chinese Formularies"; Miyashita, "Malaria (*yao*) in Chinese Medicine"; and Miyashita, "Historical Analysis of Chinese Drugs."

41 Such an analysis is Asaf Goldschmidt, "The Transformation of Medicine during the Northern Sung Dynasty" (Ph.D. diss., University of Pennsylvania, forthcoming).

42 See Arthur Kleinman, *Patients and Healers in the Context of Culture: An Exploration of the Borderland between Anthropology, Medicine, and Psychiatry*, Comparative Studies of Health Systems and Medical Care, vol. 3 (Berkeley and Los Angeles: University of California Press, 1980), for an anthropological study of contemporary Taiwan. On early texts, see Donald J. Harper, "Conception of Illness"; and "Warring States Natural Philosophy and Occult Thought," in *The Cambridge History of Ancient China*, ed. M. Loewe and E. Shaughnessy (Cambridge: Cambridge University Press, forthcoming). For occult traditions coexisting with conventional medicine in the late 1980s, see Elisabeth Hsu, "Transmission of Knowledge, Texts, and Treatment in Chinese Medicine" (Ph.D. diss., University of Cambridge,

1992).

43   Although more concerned with perceptions of ethnicity than of race, Frank Dikötter, *The Discourse of Race in Modern China* (London: Hurst, 1992), demonstrates that prejudice existed and was freely expressed in the early twentieth century.

44   The classic anthology on cultural definitions of the body is Michel Feher, ed., *Fragments for a History of the Human Body*, 3 vols. (New York: Zone, 1989). It contains a few essays on China and Japan. See also Catherine Gallagher and Thomas W. Laqueur, eds., *The Making of the Modern Body: Sexuality and Society in the Nineteenth Century* (Berkeley and Los Angeles: University of California Press, 1987); Laqueur, *Making Sex: Body and Gender from the Greeks to Freud* (Cambridge, Mass.: Harvard University Press, 1990); and Angela Zito and Tani E. Barlow, eds., *Body, Subject, and Power in China* (Chicago: University of Chicago Press, 1994). On the dimensions of disease, I paraphrase Rosenberg and Golden, *Framing Disease*, xv–xvi.

45   See Charlotte Furth, "Blood, Body, and Gender: Medical Images of the Female Condition in China, 1600–1850," *Chinese Science* 7 (1986): 43–66; Furth, "Concepts of Pregnancy, Childbirth, and Infancy in Ch'ing Dynasty China," *Journal of Asian Studies* 46 (1987): 7–35; Furth, "Androgynous Males and Deficient Females: Biology and Gender Boundaries in Sixteenth- and Seventeenth-Century China," *Late Imperial China* 9 (1988): 1–31; and Furth, *A Flourishing Yin*. On the last point, see Furth, "Women as Healers in Ming Dynasty China" (paper presented at the Eighth International Conference on the History of Science in East Asia, Seoul, Korea, 26–31 August 1996). An earlier survey is Liu Hai-po 劉海波, "Wo kuo ku-tai nü-i-shih" 我國古代女醫師 [Female physicians in ancient China], *Chung-hua i-shih tsa-chih* 12 (1982): 221. A detailed study of Ming pediatrics is Hsiung Ping-chen 熊秉眞, *Yu-yu: Ch'uan-t'ung Chung-kuo ti ch'iang-pao chih tao* 幼幼。傳統中國的襁褓之道 [Proper care for children: The Tao of infancy in traditional China] (Taipei: Lien Ching, 1995).

46   See Porter, *Patients and Practitioners*; Porter and Porter, *In Sickness and in Health*; Rosenberg, "Therapeutic Revolution"; and Laurel Thrasher Ulrich, *A Midwife's Tale: The Life of Martha Ballard, Based on Her Diary, 1785–1812* (New York: Knopf, 1990).

47   Pei-yi Wu (*The Confucian's Progress: Autobiographical Writings in Traditional China* [Princeton, N.J.: Princeton University Press, 1990]) has shown, however, that Chinese autobiography is a richer genre than previous authors have imagined.

48   Recent reference works greatly ease such work. See Feng Han-yung 馮漢鏞, *T'ang Sung wen-hsien san chien i fang cheng chih chi* 唐宋文獻散見醫方證治集 [Medical formulas, diagnoses, and therapies scattered in T'ang and Sung literature] (Peking: Jen-min Wei-sheng Ch'u-pan-she, 1994); and T'ao Yü-feng 陶御風, Chu Pang-hsien 朱邦賢, and Hung P'i-mo 洪丕謨, *Li-tai pi-chi i shih pieh lu* 歷代筆記醫事別錄 [Record of medical matters in collections of jottings through the ages] (Tientsin: T'ien-chin K'o-hsueh Chi-shu, 1988).

49   For emperors' attitudes toward their physicians, see Ch'en K'o-chi 陳可冀, ed., *Ch'ing kung i-an yen-chiu* 清宮醫案研究 [Studies of medical case records in the Ch'ing imperial palace] (Peking: Chung-i Ku-chi, 1990); Ch'en K'o-chi, Chou Wen-ch'üan 周文泉, and Chiang Yu-

li 江幼李, "T'ai i nan tang: Ts'ung Ch'ing-tai huang-ti yu kuan i-yao te chu-p'i (yü) k'an yü-i" 太醫難當。從清代皇帝有關醫藥的硃批（諭）看御醫 [The difficult lot of the palace physician: The imperial physician as seen from Ch'ing emperors' rescripts pertaining to medicine], *Ku-kung Po-wu-yuan yuan-k'an* 故宮博物院院刊 3 (1982): 14–18; Cheng Wen 鄭文, "Pei Sung Jen-tsung Ying-tsung i-liao an-chien shih-mo" 北宋仁宗英宗醫療案件始末 [The whole story of the incidents involving medical treatment of the emperors Jen-tsung and Ying-tsung in the Northern Sung period], *Chung-hua i-shih tsa-chih* 22 (1992): 244–247; and Chang, "The Therapeutic Tug of War."

50 See Sun Ssu-mo's records of his own illnesses in Nathan Sivin, *Chinese Alchemy: Preliminary Studies*, Harvard Monographs in the History of Science, vol. 1 (Cambridge, Mass.: Harvard University Press, 1968), appendix A. On medical encounters in literature, see Li T'ao 李濤, "Chung-kuo hsi-chü chung ti i-sheng" 中國戲劇中的醫生 [Physicians in Chinese drama], *Chung-hua i-shih tsa-chih* 1, no. 3 (1948): 1–16; Wilt Idema, "Diseases and Doctors, Drugs and Cures: A Very Preliminary List of Passages of Medical Interest in a Number of Traditional Chinese Novels and Related Plays," *Chinese Science* 2 (1977): 37–63; and Christopher Cullen, "Patients and Healers in Late Imperial China: Evidence from the *Jinpingmei*," *History of Science* 31 (1993): 99–150.

51 A large proportion of the best work is Japanese, but for an early example of Western research, see Endymion P. Wilkinson, "Chinese Merchant Manuals and Route Books," *Ch'ing-shih wen-t'i* 2 (1972): 8–34. For an admittedly "crude guess" about the number and average income of "gentry doctors," based on a small collection of biographies from the first half of the nineteenth century, see Chung-li Chang, *The Income of the Chinese Gentry*, Publications on Asia (Seattle: University of Washington Press, 1962), 117–122.

52 See, for instance, Bruce Moran, ed., *Patronage and Institutions: Science, Technology, and Medicine at the European Court, 1500–1750* (Rochester, N.Y.: Boydell Press, 1991), a collection of studies on patronage; and Mario Biagioli, *Galileo, Courtier: The Practice of Science in the Culture of Absolutism*, Science and Its Conceptual Foundations (Chicago: University of Chicago Press, 1993), an innovative study of Galileo. Patronage has been applied to the history of Chinese thought in Nathan Sivin, "Taoism and Science," chap. 7 in *Medicine, Philosophy, and Religion in Ancient China: Researches and Reflections*, Collected Studies Series, CS 512 (Aldershot, Hants.: Variorum, 1995).

53 Marta Hanson ("Inventing a Tradition") has reconstructed the networks of patrons and supporters of Wu Yu-hsing's 吳有性 *Wen i lun* 溫疫論 from the prefaces to over one hundred Ch'ing editions of this canonic book, as well as from related texts.

54 Yuan-ling Chao, "Medicine and Society in Late Imperial China: A Study of Physicians in Suzhou" (Ph.D. diss., University of California, Los Angeles, 1995), 131–140.

55 Among the many interesting Ming and Ch'ing publishers were Hsiung Chün 熊均 (or Hsiung Tsung-li 熊宗立) of Chienyang 建陽, Fukien (fl. 1437–1465), and Wang Ch'i 汪淇 of Hangchow (fl. 1665). Hsiung led the move toward popular editions of the classics, as well as

the popularization of "phase energetics" (*wu yun liu ch'i* 五運六氣), a widely used method of diagnosis. Much information on publishers' concoctions is scattered in Ma Chi-hsing 馬繼興, *Chung-i wen-hsien-hsueh* 中醫文獻學 [The study of Chinese medical literature] (Shanghai: Shang-hai K'o-hsueh Chi-shu, 1990). On Wang Ch'i, see Ellen Widmer, "The Huanduzhai of Hangzhou and Suzhou: A Study in Seventeenth-Century Publishing," *Harvard Journal of Asiatic Studies* 56 (1996): 77–122. On Ming publishing, see Lucille Chia, "Printing for Profit: The Commercial Printers of Jianyang (Fujian), Song-Ming (960–1044)" (Ph.D. diss., Columbia University, 1996).

56 See, for example, Li Ting 李鼎, "Pen-ts'ao ching yao-wu ch'an-ti piao shih" 本草經藥物產地表釋 [Geographic origins of drugs in the Shen-nung materia medica, tabulated and explained], *Chung-hua i-shih tsa-chih* 4 (1952): 167–188; and Wang Yun-mo 王筠默, "Ts'ung *Cheng lei pen-ts' ao* k'an Sung-tai yao-wu ch'an-ti ti fen-pu" 從證類本草看宋代藥物產地的分布 [The distribution of drug production in the Sung period as seen in the materia medica of the Cheng-ho era], *I-hsueh-shih yü pao-chien tsu-chih* 醫學史與保健組織, no. 2 (1958): 114–119. *Chung-hua i-shih tsa-chih* used the latter title in 1957–1958, interrupting the series of volume numbers.

57 Eliot Friedson (*Profession of Medicine: A Study of the Sociology of Applied Knowledge* [New York: Dodd, Mead, 1970]) provides the best critical discussion for historical purposes. Yuanling Chao ("Medicine and Society") makes professionalization a focus of her study of Soochow physicians in the Ch'ing. She tends to use "profession" as a synonym for "livelihood."

58 See Needham, *Clerks and Craftsmen*, chap. 18. A revision of this work is forthcoming in Needham, *Science and Civilisation*.

59 See Chao Hung-chün 赵洪钧, *Chin-tai Chung-hsi-i lun-cheng shih* 近代中西醫論爭史 [A history of the polemics between Chinese and western medicine in modern times] (Hefei: Anhui K'o-hsueh Chi-shu, 1989). Chao's work is summarized in Zhao Hongjun, "Chinese versus Western Medicine: A History of Their Relations in the Twentieth Century," *Chinese Science* 10 (1991): 21–37. See also Bridie J. Andrews, "The Making of Modern Chinese Medicine" (Ph.D. diss., University of Cambridge, 1996).

60 See, for example, Niida Noboru, "The Industrial and Commercial Guilds of Peking and Religion and Fellow Countrymanship as Elements of Their Coherence," *Folklore Studies* 9 (1950): 179–206; and Katô Shigeshi 加藤敏, *Shina keizaishi koshô* 支那經濟史考證 [Studies in Chinese economic history], 2 vols. (Tokyo: Tôyô Bunkô, 1953).

61 See, for example, on Kiangsu Province, Ch'en Tao-chin 陳道瑾 and Hsueh Wei-t'ao 薛渭濤, *Chiang-su li-tai i jen chih* 江蘇歷代醫人志 [Physicians of Kiangsu through history] (Nanking: Chiang-su K'o-hsueh Chi-shu, 1985). On Huichow, see Li Chi-jen 李濟仁, *Hsin-an ming i k'ao* 新安名醫考 [Famous physicians of Hui prefecture] (Huichow: An-hui K'o-hsueh Chi-shu, 1990).

62 The gentry and their physicians called doctors of whom they did not approve *yung-i* 庸醫 and lumped together the last three categories as *wu* 巫. Neither of these terms stands for a

social category; both were epithets.

63   For example, see Ramsey, *Professional and Popular Medicine*.

64   See William C. Cooper and Nathan Sivin, "Man as a Medicine: Pharmacological and Ritual Aspects of Drugs Derived from the Human Body," in Shigeru Nakayama and Sivin, *Chinese Science: Explorations of an Ancient Tradition*, MIT East Asian Science Series, no. 2 (Cambridge, Mass.: MIT Press, 1973), 203–272.

65   Nathan Sivin, *Traditional Medicine in Contemporary China: A Partial Translation of* Revised Outline of Chinese Medicine *(1972) with an Introductory Study on Change in Present-Day and Early Medicine* (Ann Arbor: Center for Chinese Studies, University of Michigan, 1987).

66   Cullen, "Patients and Healers," 121–122.

Contributors

Warwick Anderson is director of the Centre for the Study of Health and Society, University of Melbourne. His article "'The Trespass Speaks': White Masculinity and Colonial Breakdown" appeared in the *American Historical Review* (1997).

Michael Bourdaghs teaches in the East Asian languages and cultures department of the University of California, Los Angeles. His current research focuses on ideologies of national identity in Japanese popular culture.

Judith Farquhar is associate professor of anthropology at the University of North Carolina, Chapel Hill, and the author of *Knowing Practice: The Clinical Encounter of Chinese Medicine* (1994).

Marta Hanson is assistant professor of History at the University of California, San Diego. Her research centers on indigenous Chinese medical conceptions of human difference.

Thomas Lamarre is associate professor of East Asian studies, McGill University. His book *The Order of the Senses: Poetry, Calligraphy, and Cosmology in Heian Japan* is forthcoming.

Philippa Levine teaches history at the University of Southern California. Her most recent book is *Feminist Lives in Victorian England: Private Roles and Public Commitment* (1990).

She is completing a study of venereal disease and prostitution legislation in the British colonies.

Hugh Shapiro is assistant professor of history at the University of Nevada, Reno. His article in this issue is part of his ongoing research on disease in early twentieth-century China.

Nathan Sivin is Professor of Chinese Culture and of the History of Science at the University of Pennsylvania and Honorary Professor of the Chinese Academy of Sciences. He is now on research leave for a year, with support from the Chiang Ching-kuo Foundation for Scholarly Exchange, to complete a book with Sir Geoffrey Lloyd that compares the formation of early Greek and Chinese natural philosophy, science, and medicine.

Art from *Contentious Traditions*

The Death of Authentic Primitive Art and Other Tales of Progress
SHELLY ERRINGTON

In this lucid, witty, and forceful book, Errington argues that Primitive Art was invented as a new type of art object at the beginning of the 20th century but that now, at the century's end, it has died a double but contradictory death. She explores an eclectic collection of "artifacts" including public sites in Indonesia and Mexico.

$48.00 cloth, $19.95 paper, illustrated

Contentious Traditions
THE DEBATE ON *SATI* IN COLONIAL INDIA
LATA MANI

"An important and disturbing book. Lata Mani has reopened the archives on widow burning in colonial India. Her meticulous reading of contemporary texts … is exemplary for its conceptual sophistication."
—Ranajit Guha, founding editor, *Subaltern Studies*

"[A] brilliant and persuasive analysis."
—Dipesh Chakrabarty, University of Chicago

$47.00 cloth, $18.00 paper, illustrated

Hiroshima Traces
TIME, SPACE, AND THE DIALECTICS OF MEMORY
LISA YONEYAMA

Remembering Hiroshima has been a complicated and intensely politicized process, as we learn from Lisa Yoneyama's sensitive investigation of the "dialectics of memory." She explores unconventional texts and dimensions of culture involved in constituting Hiroshima memories.

Twentieth-Century Japan: The Emergence of a World Power
$45.00 cloth, $17.95 paper

A Flourishing Yin
GENDER IN CHINA'S MEDICAL HISTORY, 960–1665
CHARLOTTE FURTH

"Highly original, and sophisticatedly and convincingly argued. This book is one of the best studies in any language of how Chinese medicine evolved intellectually and socially in the course of the imperial period."
—Francesca Bray, author of *Technology and Gender*

A Philip E. Lilienthal Book
$45.00 cloth, $17.95 paper, illustrated

Other Modernities
GENDERED YEARNINGS IN CHINA AFTER SOCIALISM
LISA ROFEL

"Cogent, evocative, and theoretically rigorous. I know of no one else who has so artfully delineated the complex, heterogeneous effects of political mobilization on the formation of collective and individual subjectivities."
—Dorinne Kondo, author of *Crafting Selves*

$40.00 cloth, $16.95 paper, illustrated